Instructor's Manual

for

Laboratory Manual for General Biology
For Starr's Biology Texts
Fifth Edition

Kamau W. Mbuthia
Bowling Green State University

Loretta A. Johnson
*Pennsylvania State University –
Altoona College*

Joy B. Perry
*University of Wisconsin –
Fox Valley*

James W. Perry
*University of Wisconsin –
Fox Valley*

David Morton
Frostburg State University

THOMSON
™
BROOKS/COLE

Australia • Brazil • Canada • Mexico • Singapore • Spain • United Kingdom • United States

Thomson Higher Education
10 Davis Drive
Belmont, CA 94002-3098
USA

Printed in the United States of America

1 2 3 4 5 6 7   10 09 08 07 06

Printer: Thomson/West

ISBN-13: 978-0-534-40325-6
ISBN-10: 0-534-40325-5

For more information about our products,
contact us at:
Thomson Learning Academic Resource Center
1-800-423-0563

For permission to use material from this text or
product, submit a request online at
http://www.thomsonrights.com.
Any additional questions about permissions can be
submitted by email to **thomsonrights@thomson.com.**

CONTENTS

PREFACE

This *Instructor's Manual* accompanies Perry and Morton's *Laboratory Manual* for Starr and Taggart's *Biology: The Unity and Diversity of Life* and Starr's *Biology: Concepts and Applications*. Generating maximum student interest and educational benefit requires organization and timely planning. This manual will help achieve this goal and make the tasks of the instructor and laboratory technicians less complicated.

The instructor in charge of the course should select and schedule the exercises for the term. Laboratory exercises are presented in sections so that instructors may elect to do portions as desired. Likewise, materials and their preparation appear by section.

The lab technician should read each of the exercises, as well as the preparation notes in this guide. Then, with a calendar at hand, produce a precise schedule for the term by consulting the *Schedule for Materials Preparation* and *Materials and Equipment* needed for the various exercises. We find it most convenient to actually list daily tasks on the calendar.

Special note should be made of living materials that must be ordered and the dates they must be ordered by for timely arrival. It's less worrisome to obtain the material a few days in advance.

Periods given for culture incubation or growing living materials are approximate. Living organisms often do not follow human-devised schedules; start more cultures or plant more seeds than you actually anticipate needing. Start your materials at two or three different times until you become familiar with their performance under your particular conditions.

Preparation notes for each exercise are organized as follows:

1. *Materials and Equipment* for each section of an exercise by quantity needed (that is, under headings such as "Per student," "Per student group (4)," or "Per laboratory room"). Your course budget may dictate that students share expensive materials in larger groups than we have indicated.

2. *Preparation of Materials and Equipment* where directions for assembly of any specialized apparatus are given, as well as culturing methods and directions for making all required solutions and media.

3. *Notes* presenting special tips to help the exercise go smoothly.

4. *Ordering Information,* including vendor catalog numbers, for all materials and equipment needed for the exercise. The items listed are those that work well, though item and vendor substitutions are often possible. Occasionally a listed vendor is the only known source. Prepared microscope slides listed are those that show the specific details referred to in the exercise. The materials are given in quantities for 24 students per laboratory section.

Pre-lab Questions are supplied so that they may be duplicated and distributed as quizzes. Please note that these questions are **scrambled in order** from those in the students' lab manuals to prevent memorization of answer order.

Answers to Pre- and Post-lab Questions are summarized in their own section of this guide. Answers are supplied for *Pre-Lab Questions*, both in the order in which they appear in the lab manual and in the scrambled order in this instructor's manual.

Sources of Materials and Supplies provides addresses for each supplier listed in the ordering information.

When practical, provide more material than is required for all activities. In addition, you may wish to show a whole specimen of a living organism even when only a portion is used in an exercise. This gives the students a greater perspective of how the material they are examining relates to the whole. Additional photos, micrographs, and/or preserved materials of related organisms also add to students' understanding of the unity of biological principles and the diversity of life forms.

Always perform each new exercise well beforehand, testing reagents and any modifications. Keep detailed notes of any changes you have made; don't rely on memory. Finally, we encourage you to communicate to us any suggestions or comments on these exercises. Our goal is to provide an instructive and stimulating biology laboratory experience for the student.

SCHEDULE FOR MATERIALS PREPARATION

Exercise	Materials	Time to Be Started Prior to Use
6	bacterial plate cultures	3 days
	Oscillatoria class cultures	5 days
	Physarum stock culture	5 days
	Physarum class cultures	2 days
9	geranium leaf masking	7 days
	masked geranium light treatment	2 days
10	germinating pea seeds	3 days
11	*Allium* or *Narcissus* root tips	7 days minimum
14	*Halobacterium* class cultures	2 weeks
	E. coli stock cultures	2 days
	E. coli class cultures	1 day
	E. coli mating mixture	12 hours
15	*E. coli* class cultures	2 days
17	dandelion seedlings	2-3 months
19	*Oscillatoria* class cultures	5 days
	Saprolegnia class cultures	10 days
	Achyla class cultures	13, 8, 6 days
	Phytophthora cactorum class cultures	15 to 20 days
	Physarum stock culture	5 days
	Physarum class cultures	2 days
	Physarum sclerotium	5 days
	Physarum sporangia	5 days
	Congo red–yeast mixture	12 to 24 hours
21	*Rhizopus* vegetative class cultures	5 days
	Rhizopus sexual stage demonstration cultures	10 days
	Eurotium chevelieri class cultures	10 to 14 days
	Penicillium class cultures	5 days
	Alternaria alternata class cultures	14 to 28 days
22	moss protonemata culture	4 to 6 weeks
23	fern gametophytes	6 weeks
24	*Pinus edulis* seedlings	12, 36 weeks
	soaked bean seeds	12 hours
	germinating bean seeds	6 days
	bean seedlings	10 days
32	bean and corn plants	21 days
	radish seedlings	5 days
42	induction of leopard frog ovulation	1 to 3 days

beakers, 100 mL, Kimax—Fisher 02-539H
beakers, 1L, Kimax—Fisher 02-539P
beakers, 1L, with handle—Fisher 02-591-9A
beakers, 20 mL, Kimax—Fisher 02-539-1
beakers, 250 mL Kimax—Fisher 02-555-20A
beakers, 400 mL, Kimax—Fisher 02-539L
beakers, 50 mL, Kimax—Fisher S30730-3
beakers, 600 mL, Kimax—Fisher 02-539M
blunt probe—Carolina 62-7400
boiling chips—Carolina 84-8278
bottle, 8 oz.—Fisher 02-8935D
bottle, dropping—Fisher 02-992A
bottle, stock, 8 oz. (237 mL), clear Boston round,
    with polyseal screw cap—Fisher 02-911-785
Buchner funnel—Fisher 10-365D
calculator, solar powered—local stationery store
carboy, Nalgene, 5 gal., with spigot—Fisher 02-963B
carboy, Nalgene, with spigot, 20 L—
    Fisher 02-963BB
Carolina Protozoa and Invertebrates Manual—
    Carolina 45-3904
china marker—Fisher 13-380-15A
colored pencils—Carolina 64-4285
cotton applicator stick, 6 in.—Fisher 14-959-92B
coverslips, 22 mm.—Fisher 12-540B
culture dish, 2 1/2 in. diam.—Carolina 74-1000
culture dish, 3 1/2 in. diam.—Carolina 74-1002
culture dish, 4 1/2 in. diam.—Carolina 74-1004
culture dish, 8 in. diam.—Carolina 74-1006
depression slide—Fisher S175201
disposable transfer pipet—Fisher 13-711-5A
dissecting needle—Fisher 08-965A
dissecting pins, 2 in.—Carolina 62-9122
dissecting scalpel—Carolina 62-6031
dissecting scissors, sharp—Carolina 62-1692
dissecting tray with vinyl pad—Carolina 62-9004
thermometer, dual scale—Carolina 74-5000
electronic balance—Fisher 01-913-258
Erlenmeyer flask, 1L—Fisher 10-039K
Erlenmeyer flask, 250-mL—Fisher 10-039F
ethanol, 95%—Carolina 86-1281
filter paper, Whatman No. 1—Fisher 09-805D
fine-line marking pens—Fisher 13-383
fine-pointed water-resistant marker—Fisher 13-379-4
flint lighter—Carolina 70-6630
Flint, renewal—Carolina 70-6632
forceps 4.5 in.—Carolina 62-4084
forceps, 10 in.—Carolina 62-4335
funnel—Fisher 10-322F
gloves, disposable, large—Carolina 70-6347
gloves, disposable, medium—Carolina 70-6346
gloves, disposable, small—Carolina 70-6345
graduated cylinder, 10 mL—Fisher 08-570-21A

graduated cylinder, 25 mL—Fisher S318871
graduated pipet, Mohr, 4 mL—Fisher 13-665K
hand lens—Carolina 60-2116
heat resistant glove—Carolina 70-1640
hot plate—Fisher S50412A
ice bucket—Fisher 11-676-35
immersion oil, Cargille, Type B—Fisher 12-369A
laboratory Burner—Fisher 03-917
lens cleaning solution—Fisher 11-999-30
lint free cloth, Kimwipe—Carolina 63-3950
Micropipettes—Call Fisher
microscope slides—Fisher 12-549
Pasteur pipet—Fisher 13-678-6A
penlight—Carolina 69-4650
petri dish, polystyrene 100 x 15mm—
    Fisher 08-757-12
petri dish, 100 x 15mm, corning—Fisher 08-747C
petri dish, pyrex 20 x 150 mm—Carolina 74-1164
petri dish, 60 x 15mm, disposable—
    Fisher 08-757-100B
pipet, 5 mL, graduated—Carolina 73-6982
pipet, 5 mL, nonplugged—Fisher 13-678-31H
Pipette pump, 10 mL—Fisher 13-683C
Pipette pump, 2 mL—Fisher 13-683B
Pi-pump, up to 10 mL—Fisher 13-683-1C
plastic tray—purchase locally
Protoslo Quieting Solution—Carolina 88-5141
Razor blade, single edged, Carolina—62-6940
rubber bulbs—Fisher 14-065B
rubber stopper, 1 hole, size 4—Fisher 14-135F
rubber stopper, 1-hole, size 7—Fisher 14-135L
rubber stopper, 2 hole, size 12—Fisher 14-140P
rubber stopper, solid, size 6—Carolina 71-2408
ruler meter stick—Fisher 12-096
ruler metric, 6"—Carolina 70-2603
ruler dual scale 30cm—Fisher 12-090
safety bulb—Fisher 13-681-50
safety goggles—Fisher S47619B
scalpel—Carolina 62-6031
scissors—local supply
single-edged razor blade—Carolina 62-6931
stirring rod, 125 mm—Fisher S63447
support stand—Fisher 14-050B
test tube clamp—Fisher 05-840
test tube rack—Fisher S47844-1H
test tube rack, poxy grid—Fisher 14-792-11
test tube rack—Fisher 14-792-12
test tubes, 10 x 75 mm—Fisher 14-961-25
test tubes, 13 x 100 mm—Fisher 14-925E
test tubes, 13 x 100 mm, screw-cap—
    Fisher 14-930AA
test tubes, 16 x 125 mm—Fisher 14-961-30

test tubes, 16 x 125 mm with screw caps—Fisher—14-932A

test tubes, 16 x 150 mm—Fisher 14-958H

test tubes, 20 x 150 mm, Pyrex—Fisher 14-955G

thermometer, Celsius—Fisher S63348

thermometer holder—Carolina 74-5500

tissue paper, Kimwipes—Fisher 06-666A

tripod—Carolina 70-6955

volumetric flask, 1000 mL—Fisher 10-199H

volumetric flask, 1000 mL, Kimax—Fisher 10-212F

vortex mixer, 115V—Fisher 12-811R

vortex mixer, 230V—Fisher 12-810-1

wash bottle, 125 mL—Fisher 03-409-10AA

wash bottle, 500 mL—Fisher 03-409-10E

wash bottle, 500 mL fine stream—Fisher 03-409-22C

wire gauze square with ceramic fiber center—Fisher S50322

trowel—local garden supply

EXERCISE 1

THE SCIENTIFIC METHOD

Materials and Equipment

1.1 Modern Scientific Method

Per lab room
- four or five liquid crystal thermometers
- plastic beakers with an inside diameter of about 8 cm stuffed with cotton wool
- blindfold

1.2 Research Article

Per lab student
- copy of a typical biological research article
- copy of research article from *Science*

1.3 Bioassay

Per lab student
- fine-pointed water-resistant marker
- four microcentrifuge tubes with caps
- 35-mm film canister with four holes in lid
- 15-cm plastic ruler
- forceps
- four paper towel wicks
- disposable pipet and bulb

Per student group (6)
- solution of test substance (see *Notes*)
- distilled water (dH$_2$O) in dropping bottle

Preparation of Materials and Equipment

1.1 Modern Scientific Method

None required.

1.2 Research Article

None required.

1.3 Bioassay

Preparation of film canister: Many film processing outlets or camera stores discard great numbers of empty film canisters. Ask them to save the film containers for you. Punch four 7-mm diameter holes in lid of 35-mm film canister with a drill press. Alternatively, heat a small Pyrex test tube and melt holes in lid.

Wicks: Cut wicks from white household paper towels or rough filter paper. Wicks should be triangular, approximately 3.5 cm in length, and 1 cm across base.

Seeds: RCBr (rapid-cycling *Brassica rapa*) seeds are extremely small. Supply adhesive tape to your students and direct them to attach the seeds to the tape to prevent seed loss.

Extra seeds may be stored for a few years if refrigerated in a sealed container with a small amount of silica gel desiccant or powdered milk to absorb moisture.

Test solutions: Many different test substances can be used. Paint thinner (use only with adequate ventilation), household cleaner, perfume, coffee, vinegar, liquid detergent, orange juice, salt solution, pH buffered solutions, and plant fertilizer are only a few possibilities.

Students' bioassay canisters should be placed where they will be undisturbed and where temperatures can be maintained between 21°C and 27°C for optimal germination within 24 hours. Germination will not occur if temperature is below 15°C.

Ordering Information

See General Laboratory Supplies list on page vii for basic items

1.1 Modern Scientific Method

Liquid crystal thermometer—purchase from local pharmacy

1.2 Research Article

None required.

1.3 Bioassay

microcentrifuge tubes with caps	Carolina	19-9684
RCBr (Wisconsin Fast Plants™) seeds (200)	Carolina	15-8805
35-mm film canister	local film processing outlet or camera store	

Answers to In-text Questions

1.1 Modern Scientific Method

TABLE 1-1 Some Observations About the Human Body

V. E.g., Skin is sensitive to touch / Is the skin's sensitivity to touch the same everywhere? / Different areas of the skin have different sensitivities to touch / If the hypothesis is correct, then a two-point discrimination test will result in a shorter distance on the fingertips compared to the back of the neck.

Step 5. Experiment or Pertinent Observations

INSTRUCTIONS. Members of groups testing predictions in rows I, II, and IV of Table 1-1 read items 1, 2, or 3, respectively. Then all groups describe in item 4 an experiment or a pertinent observation to test their prediction.

4. Describe your experiment or pertinent observation:

To test prediction for observation I (Table 1-1):
Locate a vein segment that shows through the skin of each of as many of your group members as possible. Follow the procedure outlined in section 1 above in the lab manual. Specify Table 1-2 as follows.

Subject	Blood flows back into segment after it is squeezed out toward the heart. (yes or no)	Blood flows back into segment after it is squeezed out away from the heart. (yes or no)
1		
2		
3		
4		
5		
Frequency		

To test prediction for observation II (Table 1-1):

Subjects sit about 5 ft. away from and directly in front of the student making the high pitched sound. Students take turns being the subject. Each subject blocks the same ear. Follow the procedure given in section 2 above in the lab manual. Specify Table 1-2 as follows.

Subject	Angle of Error (0–180°) with Ear Unblocked	Angle of Error (0–180°) with Ear Blocked
1		
2		
3		
4		
5		
Average		

To test prediction for observation III (Table 1-1):

Students take turns being the subject. Each subject stops breathing after a normal inhalation and measures the time in seconds that they can hold their breath. This procedure is repeated after running in place for three minutes. Specify Table 1-2 as follows.

Subject	Time of Breath Holding after Rest (sec.)	Time of Breath Holding after Rest (sec.)
1		
2		
3		
4		
5		
Average		

To test prediction for observation IV (Table 1-1):

Each group member measures the surface temperature of the forehead, back of neck, and anterior surface of forearm with a liquid crystal thermometer. Specify Table 1-2 as follows.

Subject	Temperature of Forehead	Temperature of Back of Neck	Temperature of Forearm
1			
2			
3			
4			
5			
Average			

To test prediction for observation V (Table 1-1):

Each group member uses a pair of calipers to determine the two-point discrimination distance or maximal distance that two simultaneous touches are felt as two touches. Measure the distance in centimeters with a small plastic ruler. Specify Table 1-2 as follows.

Subject	Two-Point Discrimination Distance (cm).		
	Back of the Neck	Anterior Forearm	Fingertip
1			
2			
3			
4			
5			
Average			

5. Describe the variables involved with testing the prediction your group chose from Table 1-1.

Prediction	Independent Variable	Dependent variable	Controlled Variables
I	direction in which blood is squeezed out of vein segment (away vs. toward the heart)	whether blood flows back into vein segment after it is squeezed out	standard body position for subjects, all subjects start at the same level of restful activity, etc.
II	both ears unblocked vs. one ear blocked	angle of error	standard experimental setup, all subjects have excellent hearing, same background noise level, etc.
III	during rest vs. after exercise	duration of breath holding	all subjects start at the same level of restful activity, use same timekeeping device, etc.
IV	body location	temperature	all subjects start at the same level of restful activity, use same brand of liquid crystal thermometers, etc.
V. E.g.	**body location**	**two-point discrimination distance**	**use same brand of calipers, etc.**

6. After your instructor's approval, perform the procedure you outlined in item 4 and record your results in Table 1-2. You may not need all of the rows and columns to accommodate your data.

See tables in 4 above.

7. Describe or present your results in one of the bar charts shown on the next page.

Prediction I - Use a written description. Blood should not flow back into vein segments after it is squeezed out in a direction toward the heart. Occasionally, blood will flow back into the vein segment, usually because there is a joining vein that cannot be seen. Conversely, blood will flow back into vein segments after it is squeezed out away from the heart.

Prediction II - Use the bar chart provided in the lab manual. There should be a minimal angle of error with unblocked ears. Blocking one ear means the sound will be louder in the remaining unblocked ear. The subject's perception is that the source of the sound is closer to the unblocked ear. Therefore, the angle of error should increase to that side.

Prediction III - Use the bar chart provided in the lab manual. Because of lower tissue CO_2 levels, subjects can hold their breath for a longer time during rest compared to just after exercise.

Prediction IV - Use the bar chart provided in the lab manual. Body temperature on the surface of the neck or forearm is lower than that of the forehead. This is because the scalp is one of the more vascularized areas of the skin.

Prediction V - e.g., Modify the bar chart provided for skin temperature in the lab manual. Change the dependant variables to back of neck, forearm, and fingertip and the independent variable to distance (cm). Change the scale of the independent variable to 0, 2, 4, 6, 8, and 10. The two-point discrimination distance should decrease from back of neck to forearm to fingertip due to an increasing number of skin receptors and decreasing convergence of the neural pathways.

Step 6. Conclusion.

For all the predictions listed in Table 1-1, the prediction should be conditionally accepted and the associated hypothesis supported.

1.2 Research Article

1   (a) Example: Abstract-summary of paper
      (b) Introduction
      (c) Methods or Materials and Methods
      (d) Results
      (e) Discussion
      (f) Literature Cited or References

Note: The above are standard for a typical research paper in biology but other variations are possible. For example, sometimes the introduction section does not have a heading. Also, there can be other sections such as Acknowledgments.

2.   **(a) Results**
      (b) Methods or Materials and Methods
      (c) Introduction
      (d) Discussion

3. The steps of the scientific method are contained in the narrative. Pertinent observations are given; questions are frequently asked; hypotheses are often formulated; predictions are often made; the results of experiments or observations are given, and conclusions are made.

1.3 Bioassay

2. Write the name of your test substance. **See section on preparation of materials and equipment above.**

10. Independent variable—**concentration of test substance.**
      Dependent variable—**germination of seeds (growth of shoots and roots of germinated seeds).**
      Controlled variables—**standard test apparatus and environmental conditions for germination and growth.**

TABLE 1-3 Effect of _____ on Germination of RCBr Seeds

Prediction: If my substance affects germination in (and/or growth of shoots and roots of) RCBr seeds, the effects will increase with concentration.

14. If germination occurred in the lower concentrations but not the higher ones, what effective dose prevents germination? Alternatively, could you have defined any other effective doses? **If you define the ED as the LD_{100}, it is the dose where none of the seeds germinate. Other effects may be noted (e.g., enhanced growth) and an ED definition constructed to include them.**

15. Considering your germination results, estimate or make a statement about the LD_{50} for your test substance. If negative effects on germination were observed, describe how you could modify the procedure to better determine the LD_{50}. **If the test substance negatively affects germination, it is the dose of the test substance where half the seeds (LD_{50}) germinate. Repeating the experiment with concentrations of the test substance that are more closely grouped around the effected dose should result in a better estimate of this value.**

16. Make a conclusion regarding the effect of the test substance on germination of RCBr seeds. **The test substance affects germination in (and/or shoot and root growth of) RCBr seeds.**

17. Does your conclusion allow you to accept or reject your prediction? Is the hypothesis supported or falsified? Explain your answer. **If the predicted effects are observed, the prediction is accepted and the hypothesis supported.**

THE SCIENTIFIC METHOD

Pre-lab Questions

1. In an experiment the subjects or items being investigated are divided into the experimental group and:
    a. the non experimental group; b. the control group; c. the statistics group; d. none of these choices.

2. The results of an experiment: a. don't have to be repeatable; b. should be repeatable by the investigator;
    c. should be repeatable by other investigators; d. must be both b and c.

3. Bioassays can be used to: a. test new drugs; b. determine the effectiveness of new fertilizers and herbicides;
    c. measure the effects their waste discharges have on aquatic organisms; d. do all of these choices.

4. The first step of the scientific method is to: a. ask a question; b. construct a hypothesis; c. observe carefully;
    d. formulate a prediction.

5. Which series of letters lists the four steps of the scientific method (see question 4) in the correct order?
    a. a, b, c, d
    b. a, b, d, c
    c. c, a, b, d
    d. d, c, a, b

6. The variables that investigators try to keep the same for both the experimental and the control groups are:
    a. independent; b. controlled; c. dependent; d. a and c.

7. The natural philosophy of Aristotle and his colleagues was: a. mechanistic; b. vitalistic; c. teleological;
    d. a and c.

8. Variables that are *always* different between the experimental and the control groups are: a. independent;
    b. controlled; c. dependent; d. a and c.

9. The detailed report of an experiment is usually published in a: a. newspaper; b. book; c. scientific journal;
    d. magazine.

10. A person who believes that the universe is at least partially controlled by supernatural powers can best be
    described as a(n): a. teleologist; b. vitalist; c. empiricist; d. mechanist.

THE SCIENTIFIC METHOD

Answers to Pre-lab Questions in Lab Manual Order

1.	d	6.	b
2.	b	7.	a
3.	c	8.	d
4.	c	9.	c
5.	b	10.	d

Answers to Pre-lab Questions in Instructor's Manual Order

1.	b	6.	b
2.	d	7.	d
3.	d	8.	a
4.	c	9.	c
5.	c	10.	b

Answers to Post-lab Questions

1. How does the modern scientific method differ from the natural philosophy of the ancient Greeks? **Modern scientific method rejects the idea of absolute truth, which the natural philosophy of the ancient Greeks accepted. One major flaw in the natural philosophy of the Greeks was a difficulty in discarding or modifying a principle after it had been generated. The modern scientific method encourages the continued testing of hypotheses, theories, and principles.**

2. List the six steps of one full cycle of the scientific method. **a. Observe carefully; b. Ask a question; c. Make a research hypothesis; d. Formulate a prediction; e. Perform an experiment or make pertinent observations; f. Make a conclusion.**

3. What is tested by an experiment? **The prediction made from the research hypothesis.**

4. Within the framework of an experiment, describe the:
    a. independent variable—**the variable that the experimenter purposely changes in hopes of producing an observable result in the experimental group when compared to the control group.**
    b. dependent variable—**the variable that may change in the experimental group compared to the control group because of the independent variable.**
    c. controlled variables—**the variables that the experimenter attempts to keep constant for both the experimental and the control groups.**

5. Is the statement "In the majority of biology experiments, the relationship between the independent and the dependent variable can best be described as cause and effect" true or false? **False.** Explain your answer. **In scientific experiments, cause and effect is rarely proven even if the results are repeatable. Rather, it is usually more accurate to say that the independent and dependent variables are correlated.**

6. Is a scientific principle taken as absolutely true? **Never.** Explain your answer. **Like hypotheses and theories, principles may be modified or even discarded in the light of new knowledge. If scientific knowledge was accepted as absolute truth, there would be no way to correct errors.**

7. What is the function of research articles in scientific journals? **Research articles are published accounts of the scientific method. They are one way that scientists share knowledge. Their narrative should provide the information necessary to enable the experiment or pertinent observation to be repeated by other scientists.**

8. Define the design and structure of a bioassay. **Bioassays are experiments—with one or more experimental and control groups—designed to test the effects of man-made substances (e.g., new drugs, new fertilizers, and new herbicides and human designed protocols (e.g., waste discharges) on humans in general and on other aspects of the environment. They often establish the quantity of a substance that results in a particular effect. One example is the LD_{50} of toxic substances (the lethal dose causing the death of 50% of exposed organisms).**

9. Describe how you have applied or could apply the scientific method to an everyday problem. **My son recently purchased a new CD burner. Burned audio CDs sounded fine on his home and auto stereo system but the high frequencies were distorted on mine. Even though commercial CDs played on my system without distortion, he hypothesized that my 10-year old system was the problem. He predicted that if he played his burned CDs on other old and new systems a similar pattern would emerge. He tested his prediction by playing his burned CDs on ten other systems of known age. A similar pattern did emerge and I had to acknowledge that my system and not his CD burner was the likely source of the problem.**

10. Do you think the differences between the nature of religious and scientific knowledge make it difficult to debate points of perceived conflict between them? Explain your answer. **There is no one right answer to this question. It is the author's opinion that, although it is often stimulating and intellectually interesting to debate such issues as the existence of a god or of evolution, the differences in the nature of religious and scientific knowledge makes this difficult at best. Religious knowledge is largely a function of faith and cannot be tested in the scientific sense. Scientific knowledge cannot be absolute truth and must be open to further testing.**

MEASUREMENT

Materials and Equipment

2.1 Metric System

Per student pair

- dual scale 30-cm ruler
- 1-qt. bottle or jar marked with fill line
- 250-mL Erlenmeyer flask
- graduated cylinders, 10 mL
- graduated cylinders, 25 mL
- 1-gal. milk jug
- metric tape measure
- hot plate
- one-piece, plastic dropping pipet (not graduated) **or** Pasteur pipet and bulb
- graduated pipet and safety bulb or filling device(optional)

- ceramic coffee cup
- 1-lb. "brick" of coffee
- 1-L measuring cup
- 250-mL beakers
- graduated cylinders, 100-mL
- thermometer holder
- dual scale thermometer (non-mercury)
- three boiling chips

Per student group (table)

- triple beam balance

Per lab room

- dH$_2$O carboy or tap
- metric bathroom scale

- source of ice

2.2 Micromeasurement

Per student group

- small test tube in rack
- source of distilled water
- electronic balance-capable of weighing 0.001 g, readability of 0.001 g, repeatability of ±0.001 g, linearity of 0.002 g
- micropipets with matching tips, to measure 10 μL, 50μL, and 100μL volumes

- scientific calculator
- weighing dish

Preparation of Materials and Equipment

None required.

Notes

2.2 Micromeasurement

The student lab manual does not give specific instructions on the use of micropipets and tips. The instructor should familiarize the students with the various stops on the micropipets for filling and dispensing accurately, as well as how to eject the tips.

Ordering Information

See General Laboratory Supplies list on page vii for basic items

2.1 Metric System

dual scale 1-L measuring cup, Pyrex	Local hardware or housewares store	
Graduated pipet—serological, 5 mL	Fisher	13-675K
metric bathroom scale	Fisher	S40051
metric tape measure	Fisher	S79375
triple beam balance, Ohaus, Model 710	Fisher	02-032

2.2 Micromeasurement

electronic balance	Fisher	S65232
weighing dishes	Fisher	02-202B
micropipets, set of adjustable pipettors	Fisher	21-377-250

individual pipets can also be purchased, see catalog/supplier for more information
tips will need to purchase specific tips for micropipets that are purchased, see catalog/supplier
for accurate information.

Answers to In-text Questions

2.2 Metric System

A. Length

1. For example, if you want to convert 1.7 km to centimeters, your first step is to determine how many centimeters
there are in 1 km. Remember, like units may be cancelled.
Using the method most comfortable for you, calculate how many millimeters there are in 4.8 m? **4,800 or
4.8 x 10³ mm**
Calculate how many kilometers there are in 16 cm. **0.00016 or 1.6 x 10⁻⁴ km**

2. Precisely measure the length of this page in centimeters to the nearest tenth of a centimeter with the metric edge
of a ruler. Note that nine lines divide the space between each centimeter into 10 mm.
The page is **27.6 or 2.76 x 10 cm long**.
Calculate the length of this page in millimeters, meters and kilometers.
276 or 2.76 x 10² mm   0.276 or 2.76 x 10⁻¹ m   0.000276 or 2.76 x 10⁻⁴ km

Now repeat the above measurement using the American Standard edge of the ruler. Measure the length of this
page in inches to the nearest eighth of an inch. **10.87 in**
Convert your answer to feet and yards. **0.906 ft   0.302 yd**
Explain why it is much easier to convert units of length in the metric system than in the American Standard system.
**The unit conversions in the metric system can be done in our heads by either shifting decimal points or
adding exponents. Even if you use a calculator, it is easier to work with units that are multiples or divisibles
of 10. Also, in the American Standard system, it is more difficult to convert the actual measurement to a
decimal.**

B. Volume

1. How many milliliters are there in 1.7 L? **1,700 or 1.7 x 10³ mL**
How many liters are there in 1.7 mL? **0.0017 or 1.7 x 10⁻³ L**

3. Pour some water into a 100-mL graduated cylinder and observe the boundary between fluid and air: the
meniscus. Surface tension makes the meniscus curved, not flat. The high surface tension of water is due to its
cohesive and adhesive or "sticky" properties. Draw the meniscus in the plain cylinder outlined in Figure 2-3. The
correct reading of the volume is at the *lowest* point of the meniscus.

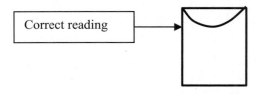

4. Using the 100-mL graduated cylinder, pour water into a 1-qt. jar or bottle. About how many milliliters of water are needed to fill the vessel up to the line? **947 mL**

5. (d) Repeat steps b and c two more times and calculate the average for your results in Table 2-2.

TABLE 2-2 Estimate of the Number of Drops in 1 mL	
Trial	**Drops/mL**
1	14
2	12
3	13
Total	39
Average	13

This is an example, drops/mL will vary.

(e) Explain why the average of three trials is more accurate than if you only do the procedure once.
As the number of samples increase, the consistency of the estimate increases or the sample mean is a better estimate of the population mean.

C. Mass

1. How many milligrams are there in 1 g? **1000 or 10^3 mg**
Convert 1.7 g to milligrams and kilograms. **1700 or 1.7×10^3 mg**   **0.0017 or 1.7×10^{-3} kg**

2. A 1-cc cube, if filled with 1 mL of water, has a mass of 1 g (Figure 2-1). The mass of other materials depends on their **density** (water is defined as having a density of 1). The density of any substance is its mass divided by its volume.

Approximately how many liters are present in 1 cubic meter (m^3) of water? As each of the sides of 1 m^3 are 100 cm in length, it's easy to calculate the number of cubic centimeters (that is, 100 cm x 100 cm x 100 cm = 1,000,000 cc). Now just change cubic centimeters to milliliters and convert 1,000,000 mL to liters. **1000 L**
What is its mass in kilograms? **1000 kg**

3.

TABLE 2-3 Weighing an Unknown Quantity of Water with a Triple Beam Balance	
Objects	**Mass (g)**
Beaker and water	204.4 g
Beaker	108.2 g
Water	96.2 g

This is an example, weights will vary.

(h) Now measure the volume of the water in milliliters with a graduated cylinder.
What is the volume? **108.2 mL**
4. Using the triple beam balance, determine the mass of (that is, weigh) a pound of coffee in grams.
454 g

D. Estimating Length, Volume, and Mass

1. Estimate the length of your index finger in centimeters. **e.g., 6 cm**
2. Estimate your lab partner's height in meters. **e.g., 2 m**
3. How many milliliters will it take to fill a ceramic coffee mug? **e.g., 250 mL**
4. How many liters will it take to fill a 1-gallon milk bottle? **e.g., 4 L**
5. Estimate the weight of some small personal item (for example, loose change) in grams. **e.g., 8 g**
6. Estimate your or your lab partner's weight in kilograms. **e.g., 90 kg**

TABLE 2-4 Differences Between Estimates and Measurements

Number	Estimate	Measurement	Estimate - Measurement
1	6 cm	9 cm	- 3 cm
2	2 m	1.83 m	0.17m
3	250 mL	240 mL	10 mL
4	4 L	3.8 L	0.2 L
5	9 g	11.4 g	-2.4 g
6	90 kg	85.5 kg	4.5 kg

This is an example, measurements will vary.

E. Temperature

2.

TABLE 2-5 Comparison of Celsius and Fahrenheit Temperatures

Location	^{0}C	^{0}F
Room	21	70
Cold running tap water	18	64
Hot running tap water	51	124
Ice water	0	32
Boiling water	100	212

This is an example, temperatures will vary.

4. To convert Celsius degrees to Fahrenheit degrees, multiply by 9/5 and add 32. Is 4°C the temperature of a hot or cool day? **Cold.** What temperature is this in degrees Fahrenheit? **39.2 °F**

5. To convert Fahrenheit degrees to Celsius degrees, subtract 32 and multiply by 5/9. What is body temperature 98.6°F in degrees Celsius? **37 °C**

2.2 Micromeasurement

1. Remember that in section 2-1 we established a relationship between the volume and mass of water. If the mass of 1 mL of water is 1 g (Figure 2-1), how much does 1 µL weigh? **0.001** or **10^{-3} g** or **1 mg**

TABLE 2-6 Comparison of Volumes of Water with Their Masses

Prediction: If 1 µL weighs 1 mg, then 100 µL, 50 µL, and 10 µL weighs respectively 100 mg, 50 mg, and 10 mg.

Note: Results will give a mean close to 100 mg for 100 µL, 50 mg for 50 µL, and 10 mg for 10 µL with small standard deviations.

Conclusion: The prediction is accepted.

MEASUREMENT

Pre-lab Questions

1.   If your mass were 70 kilograms on the earth, how much would your mass be on the moon? a. less than 70 kg; b. more than 70 kg; c. 70 kg; d. none of the above.

2.   A thermometer measures: a. the degree of hot or cold; b. temperature; c. a and b; d. none of the above.

3.   Length is the measurement of: a. a line extending from one point to another; b. the space an object occupies; c. the quantity of matter present in an object; d. the degree of hot or cold of an object.

4.   Mass is the measurement of: a. a line extending from one point to another; b. the space an object occupies; c. the quantity of matter present in an object; d. the degree of hot or cold of an object.

5.   Volume is the measurement of: a. a line extending from one point to another; b. the space a given object occupies; c. the quantity of matter present in a object; d. the degree of hot or cold of an object.

6.   The metric system is the measurement system of choice for: a. science educators; b. science researchers; c. the citizens of most countries in the world; d. all of the above.

7.   If 1 cc of a substance has a mass of 1.5 g, its density is: a. 0.67; b. 1.0; c. 1.5; d. 2.5.

8.   A millicurie, a unit of radioactivity, is: a. a tenth of a curie; b. a hundredth of a curie; c. a thousandth of a curie; d. a millionth of a curie.

9.   A kilowatt, a unit of electrical power is: a. ten watts; b. a hundred watts; c. a thousand watts; d. a million watts.

10.   Above zero degrees, the actual number of degrees Celsius for any given temperature is _____ the degrees Fahrenheit. a. higher than; b. lower than; c. the same as; d. a or b.

MEASUREMENT

1. d	6. c	1. c	6. d
2. c	7. c	2. c	7. c
3. c	8. c	3. a	8. c
4. a	9. b	4. c	9. c
5. b	10. c	5. b	10. b

Answers to Post-lab Questions

1. What is the importance of measurement to science? **Science relies on collection of numerical data so that it can be quantified and the results repeated and verified by independent researchers.**

2. Convert 1.24 m to millimeters, centimeters, and kilometers. **1,240 mm   124 cm   00124 km**

3. Observe the following carefully and read the volume. **154 mL**

4. Construct a conversion table for mass. Construct it so that if you wish to convert a measurement from one unit to another, you multiply it by the number at the intersection of the original unit and the new unit.

	New Unit		
Original Units	**mg**	**G**	**kg**
mg	1	**0.001**	**0.000001**
g	**1000**	1	**0.001**
kg	**1000000**	**1000**	1

5. How is it possible for objects of the same volume to have a different mass? **Volume is the quantity of space an object occupies and mass is the quantity of matter it contains. Two objects of the same volume but different masses contain different amounts of matter. This will be reflected in their densities with the heaviest object having the highest density of matter and vice versa.**

6. Today, many packaged items have the volume or weight listed in both American Standard and metric units. Before your next lab period, find and list 10 such items. **Answers will vary depending on items found.**

7. Each °F is **smaller** (larger, smaller) than each °C.

8. Describe what it means to tare or zero an electronic balance. What purpose does this function serve? **Pressing the zero or tare key of the balance resets the digital display to read zero. This action means a new reading includes only the mass of new matter added to the pan or weighing dish.**

9. How are length, area, and volume related in terms of the three dimensions of space? **Length is one-dimensional, area two-dimensional and volume three-dimensional.**

10. If you were to choose between the metric and American Standard systems of measurement for future generations, which one would you choose? Set aside your familiarity with the American Standard system and consider their ease of use and degree of standardization with the rest of the world. **The metric system because conversion from a unit with one prefix to another is simply a matter of multiplying or dividing by a unit of 10. A majority of nations recognize the metric system. Uniformity of measurements among nations means that communication, particularly in terms of commerce, would be facilitated.**

EXERCISE 3

MICROSCOPY

Materials and Equipment

3.1 Compound Light Microscope

Per student

- compound light microscope
- lens paper, 4 x 6 in. packet
- prepared slide with mounted letter "e"
- unlabeled diagram of the compound light microscope used in this course (optional)
- prepared slide with Wright stained smear of mammalian blood
- prepared slide with a whole mount of stained diatoms
- prepared slide with crossed colored threads coded for thread order

- lint free cloth (optional)
- prepared slide with unstained fibers
- index card

Per student group (4)

- bottle of lens cleaning solution (optional)
- dropper bottle of immersion oil (optional, see *Notes*)

Per lab room

- labeled chart of a compound light microscope

3.2 How to Make a Wet Mount

Per student

- compound microscope
- dissecting needle
- cork
- glass microscope slide
- bottle of lens-cleaning solution (optional)

- lens paper
- lint-free cloth (optional)
- razor blade
- glass coverslip

Per student group (4)

- dropper bottle of dH$_2$O

3.3 Microscopic Observations

Per student

- compound microscope
- bottle of lens-cleaning solution (optional)
- glass microscope slide

- lens paper
- lint-free cloth (optional)
- glass coverslip

Per student group (4)

- dropper bottle of Protoslo®
- pond water or some mixed culture in a container with dropping pipet

Per lab room:

- reference books for identification of microorganisms

3.4 Dissecting Microscope

Per student group

- dissecting microscope

- viewing specimens (see Note)

3.5 Other Microscopes

Per student group
- Photographs of TEM micrographs or digital images
- Photographs of SEM negatives or digital images

Preparation of Materials and Equipment

3.1 Compound Light Microscope

Calibration and use of ocular micrometers: Precise measurements may be made with an ocular micrometer. This must be calibrated, using a stage micrometer for each combination of lenses.

The ocular contains a glass disk micrometer bearing a scale of arbitrary length divided into 100 parts, which fits into the eyepiece. This scale is superimposed on the image of any specimen in focus on the stage. Remember that the apparent distance between two divisions on the ocular micrometer will depend on the magnification of the lenses in use.

Place a micrometer slide on the microscope stage. It bears a scale 2 mm long that is divided into 200 small divisions of 10 μm each.

Focus on the micrometer slide. Move the slide and/or rotate the eyepiece until the zero end of the two scales are superimposed. (If the eyepiece scale is out of focus, it has probably been inserted upside down.) Count the number of ocular divisions until you find the first one that matches *precisely* with one of the lines on the stage micrometer. List the number of mm this represents: _____. Now, divide the distance by the number of ocular micrometer divisions to obtain the distance represented by *one* ocular micrometer division. Students should repeat this process and record the calibration for the eyepiece and all objectives.

Sample calculation: Suppose 30 eyepiece divisions correspond to 0.5 mm. Thus, one eyepiece division corresponds to about 17 μm (0.5 mm/30). If a cell is two eyepiece divisions wide, then the cell is about 34 μm wide.

Notes

3.1 Compound Light Microscope

Purchase only Cargille immersion oil. Many older types of immersion oil contain PCBs and present a health hazard. Dispose of PCB-containing oils according to your institution's guidelines.

Further discussion of optical properties of light microscopes may be found in APPENDIX B, Basic Optics for Microscopy, which may be photocopied for your students.

3.4 Dissecting Microscope

Many items are suitable three-dimensional specimens for viewing with a dissecting microscope. Pinned insects mounted on small blocks of styrofoam or on corks are excellent specimens, as are bread molds or other sporulating fungal cultures in petri dishes and small flowers.

Ordering Information

See General Laboratory Supplies list on page vii for basic items

3.1 Compound Light Microscope

labeled chart of compound light microscope	Carolina	57-2002
prepared slide with mounted letter "e"	Triarch	GZ1-1
prepared slide, cotton fibers	Triarch	GZ2-1
prepared slide, crossed colored threads	Triarch	GZ1-2
prepared slide, diatoms, mixed freshwater species with stained protoplasts, w.m.	Triarch	2-20
prepared slide, human blood smear, Wright stain	Triarch	HC1-40
unlabeled diagram of the compound light microscope used in your course	check with microscope manufacturer	

3.2 How to Make a Wet Mount

See General Laboratory Supplies list on page vii for basic items

3.3 Microscopic Observations

mixed algae culture	Carolina	15-1216
pond water culture	Carolina	13-2060
pond water culture	can be collected locally	

3.4 Dissecting Microscope

None required.

3.5 Other Microscopes

None required.

Answers to In-text Questions

3.1 Compound Light Microscope

PROCEDURE
Figure 3-2 Compound light microscope.
From the top to the bottom leaders, the sequence of answers are ocular, arm, nosepiece, stage clip, stage, condenser, lever for iris diaphragm of condenser, coarse adjustment knob, fine adjustment knob, illuminator, and base.

TABLE 3-2 Characteristics of My Microscope		
Characteristic	**Description**	**Function**
Code	####	Identification of my microscope
Light Source	**built-in illuminator with an on off switch and rheostat**	**source of light to illuminate specimen**
Condenser	**condenser with iris diaphragm, lever, focus knob, and disk holder**	**focus light on specimen**
Stage	**mechanical stage with vernier scales**	**hold and position specimen**
Focusing Knobs	**coarse and fine focusing knobs**	**focus the specimen**
Objective	**4X, 10X, 40X, 100X**	**projects image of specimen**
Ocular	**10X binocular/along with your eye lens**	**projects objective image on retina of eye**

Note: answers will differ depending on the microscope used. The answers below are for a microscope with all the "bells and whistles."

B. Parts of the Compound Light Microscope

See Figure 3-2 and Table 3-2 above.

4. *Focusing knobs* (Figure 3-1).
a) Toward or away

TABLE 3-3 Objectives Present On My Compound Light Microscope			
Objective	**Objective Magnifying Power (ObMP)**	**Total Magnifying Power (ObMP X OcMP= ___X)**	**Numerical Aperture (NA)**
Low-power	**4X**	**40X**	**e.g., 0.1**
Medium-power	**10X**	**100X**	**e.g., 0.25**
High-dry	**40X**	**400X**	**e.g., 0.65**
Oil-immersion	**100X**	**1000X**	**e.g., 1.25**

6. Ocular.
(a) See Table 3-3 above; usually 10X

(d) monocular or binocular

E. Orientation of the Image Compared to the Specimen

1. The "e" is flipped vertically and horizontally.
   Figure 3-7 Drawing of the letter *e* as seen through the ocular (**e.g., 4X**).
2. Right side up or upside down compared to the specimen? **Upside down; yes**
3. Left
4. Down

F. Depth of Field

1. (a) low-power objective? **3**; medium-power objective? **2**; high-dry objective? **1**
   (b) With which objective is it easiest to focus a specimen? **Low-power.**
   (c) At which magnification is it most difficult to focus a specimen? **Highest.**
2. (a) TABLE 3-4 Order of Threads (**Assumes you obtained slides from source suggested in Instructor's Manual.**) Closest to slide – **yellow**; middle – **blue**; closest to coverslip – **red.**
   (b) Did you move the knob away from or toward you? **Away from or toward.**
4. (a) The shape of renal corpuscles is **round**. The shape of nephron tubules is **a tube.**

G. Using the Iris Diaphragm to Improve Contrast

2. Does this procedure increase or decrease contrast? **Increase.**

H. Units of Measurement

1000 µm = 1 mm 1000 nm = 1 µm. How many nanometers are there in 1 mm? **1,000,000 nm**. How many millimeters are there in 1 nm? **0.000001 mm**

I. Determining the Diameter of the Field of View

1. What is the total magnification? **40X**
2. Place a transparent 15 cm ruler on the stage.
3. What is the diameter of the field of view? **About 4.5 mm**
4. Repeat step 3 with the medium-power objective in the light path. The total magnification is **100X**
   The diameter of the field of view is **about 2.0 mm**
5. 0.45 mm is the diameter of the field of view when high-dry objective is in the light path. Once you've calculated this value, convert it to micrometers: **450 µm**
6. Complete Table 3-5.

TABLE 3-5 Diameter of Field of View		
Objective	**Magnifying Power**	**Diameter of Field of View**
Low-power	**40X**	**4.5 mm**
Medium-power	**100X**	**2.0 mm**
High-dry	**400X**	**0.45 mm or 450 µm**
Oil-immersion	**1000X**	**0.18 mm or 180 µm**

7. 1.0 mm

3.4 Dissecting Microscope

PROCEDURE

1. e.g., **8X** to **50X**

2. Is the image of the specimen inverted as in the compound light microscope? (yes or no) **No.**

3. Describe the type of illumination used by your dissecting microscope. Is there a choice?
e.g., reflected, transmitted, or both

3.5 Other Microscopes

PROCEDURE

3.

TABLE 3-7 Microscope Use	
Specimen	**Microscope**
Living surface of the finger	**dissecting**
Dye-stained slide of a section of the finger	**compound light**
Gold-coated bacteria on a single cell of the finger	**SEM**
Unstained section of a biopsy from the finger	**Phase contrast**
Heavy metal–stained, very thin section of the finger	**TEM**

MICROSCOPY

Pre-lab Questions

1. Magnification: a. is the amount that an object's image is enlarged; b. is the extent to which detail in an image is preserved during the magnifying process; c. is the degree to which image details stand out against their background; d. focuses radiation emanating from an object to produce an image.

2. The distance through which a microscopic specimen can be moved and still have it remain in focus is called the: a. field of view; b. working distance; c. depth of focus; d. magnification.

3. Electron microscopes differ from light microscopes in that: a. electrons are used instead of light; b. magnetic lenses replace glass lenses; c. the electron path has to be maintained in a high vacuum; d. a, b, and c are all true.

4. If the magnification of the two image-forming lenses are both 10X, the total magnification of the image will be: a. 1X; b. 10X; c. 100X; d. 1,000X.

5. The maximum useful magnification for a light microscope is about: a. 100X; b. 1,000X; c. 10,000X; d. 100,000X.

6. Resolving power: a. is the amount that an object's image is enlarged; b. is the extent to which detail in an image is preserved during the magnifying process; c. is the degree to which image details stand out against their background; d. focuses radiation emanating from an object to produce an image.

7. The two image-forming lenses of a compound light microscope are: a. the condenser and objective; b. the condenser and ocular; c. the objective and ocular; d. none of these choices.

8. A lens: a. is the amount that an object's image is enlarged; b. is the extent to which detail in an image is preserved during the magnifying process; c. is the degree to which image details stand out against their background; d. focuses radiation emanating from an object to produce an image.

9. Contrast: a. is the amount that an object's image is enlarged; b. is the extent to which detail in an image is preserved during the magnifying process; c. is the degree to which image details stand out against their background; d. focuses radiation emanating from an object to produce an image.

10. Dyes are usually added to sections of biological specimens to increase: a. resolving power; b. magnification; c. contrast; d. all of the above.

EXERCISE 3

MICROSCOPY

Answers to Post-lab Questions

1. What is the function of each of the following parts of a compound light microscope?
   a. condenser lens—**focuses the light on the specimen so that each of its points is evenly illuminated.**
   b. iris diaphragm—**limits the cone of light reaching the back of the objective lens; effectively controls contrast.**
   c. objective—**projects an image of the specimen to a point just beneath the ocular.**
   d. ocular—**magnifies the image produced by the objective, and, in conjunction with the eye lens, projects an image onto the retina.**

2. In order, list the lenses in the light path between a specimen viewed with the compound light microscope and its image on the retina of the eye. **Objective, ocular, lens of eye.**

3. What happens to contrast and resolving power when the aperture of the condenser (that is, the size of the hole through which light passes before it reaches the specimen) of a compound light microscope is decreased? **Contrast increases, resolving power (quality of image) decreases.**

4. What happens to the field of view in a compound light microscope when the total magnification is increased? **The field of view decreases.**

5. Describe the importance of the following concepts to microscopy.
   a. magnification—**the lenses of the compound light microscope project a magnified image of the specimen to a position where the eye lens can focus this image onto the retina. Magnification of this image results in a specimen detail covering a larger proportion of the retina than it would otherwise cover.**
   b. resolving power—**magnification is useful only when adjacent points in a specimen are seen as separate. Magnification without adequate resolving power would be "empty" in that specimen details would not be preserved.**
   c. contrast—**contrast is necessary to see a specimen detail against the background of the image. That is, there must be sufficient intensity or color difference, or both, between a detail and the surrounding specimen for the detail to be seen.**

6. Which photomicrograph of unstained cotton fibers was taken with the iris diaphragm closed? **Photomicrograph a, which has the greatest contrast.**

7. Describe how you would care for and put away your compound light microscope at the end of lab. **Turn off light source. Rotate objective so that lowest power objective is in light path. Remove slide from stage. Clean all lenses with lens tissue. Fold power cord onto itself and secure with rubber band or plastic strap. If supplied, place dust cover over microscope. Return to cabinet, holding onto the microscope arm with one hand while supporting the microscope base with the other.**

8.   Describe how to make a wet mount.   **Place a transparent specimen or a very thin shaving on a glass microscope slide. Gently add a drop of distilled water. Then position one end of a glass coverslip next to the specimen so that the rest of the slip is held at a 45° angle over the specimen. Slowly lower the coverslip with a dissecting needle so as not to trap air bubbles.**

9.   A camera mounted on a **SEM** microscope took this photo of a cut piece of cork.

10.   Why were humans unaware of microorganisms for most of their history? **Most microorganisms are too small to be resolved with the naked eye. Until microscopes were invented, there was no way to see them. Even now microbiologists suspect most species still are unknown as their specific culture requirements are unknown.**

HOMEOSTASIS

Materials and Equipment

4.1 Homeostatic Mechanisms

Per student
- human biology textbook

4.2 Regulation of pH

Per student group (4)
- plastic tray
- 1-mL pipet and safety bulb
- wide-range pH test paper and dispenser
- five 100-mL beakers, labeled: W, M, OJ, D, V
- glass stirring rod
- pencil

Per lab room:
- cartons of milk
- source of distilled water
- 500-mL container of non-phosphate detergent solution (1/4 teaspoon/500 mL)
- orange juice
- 500-mL bottle of white vinegar

4.3 Simulation of Homeostatic Mechanisms Regulating Body Fluid Volume

Per student group (4)
- vertically stacked double-buret system
- 1-L Erlenmeyer flask of water
- 1-L container of alkaline buffer solution, containing phenol red
- empty 1-L Erlenmeyer flask
- 1-L container of acid buffer solution

4.4 Blood Pressure

Per student pair
- sphygmomanometer
- stethoscope

Preparation of Materials and Equipment

4.3 Simulation of Homeostatic Mechanisms Regulating Body Fluid Volume

Alkaline (pH 10) and acidic (pH 6) buffer solutions (1 L each):
Purchase in prepackaged dry form (see *Ordering Information*) or prepare as follows:

Mix Solution A and Solution B according to the directions below to prepare 1 L of a buffer solution of the desired pH.

Solution A: Dissolve 12.37 g anhydrous boric acid (H_3BO_3) and 10.51 g citric acid ($H_3C_6H_5O_7 \cdot H_2O$) in distilled water and dilute to 1 L in a volumetric flask.

Solution B: Dissolve 38.01 g $Na_3PO_4 \cdot 12H_2O$ in distilled water and dilute to 1 L in a volumetric flask.

For pH 6.0 buffer, mix 590 mL Solution A with 410 mL Solution B.

For pH 10.0 buffer, mix 270 mL Solution A with 730 mL Solution B.

| *Alkaline buffer with phenol red (1 L):* | phenol red | 0.4 g |
| | Buffer solution | 1000 mL |

Double buret system: Refer to figure 4-5 in the laboratory manual for assembly of this apparatus. Use buret clamps to hold upper buret directly over lower buret. Half-fill lower buret with alkaline buffer with phenol red, fill about 3/4 of the reservoir of the upper buret with water. Lower buret should be positioned to drip into a 1-L flask of acid buffer solution.

Notes

4.3 Simulation of Homeostatic Mechanisms Regulating Body Fluid Volume

You may be able to customize this apparatus to accommodate the specific labware available to you. Important features include an upper buret with a reservoir, as in the recommended buret (see *Ordering Information*). A reservoir is an enlarged portion of the buret tube above a narrow bore section directly above the stopcock and tip. This is necessary to maintain a constant drip rate regardless of the mass of water above the tip.

Additionally, the lower buret must be of large enough inside diameter that the tip of the upper buret will fit into it and water can drip cleanly into the lower buret.

This demonstration is designed so that the alkaline buffer with phenol red will appear red to simulate blood, and the acidic buffer will appear yellow after dripping the phenol red solution into it and will so simulate the appearance of urine.

4.4 Blood Pressure

The recommended sphygmomanometer displays blood pressure as mm Hg on a mercury column similar to a thermometer. In our experience, students are apt to understand blood pressure with this kind of visual display. However, the more common aneroid sphygmomanometer with a dial read-out is also adequate.

Similarly, the recommended stethoscope has a diaphragm type chest piece, but a bell-type stethoscope is also adequate.

Ordering Information

See General Laboratory Supplies list on page vii for basic items

4.2 Regulation of pH

cartons of milk, orange juice and vinegar	can be purchased locally
non-phosphate detergent	can be purchased locally
plastic tray	can be purchased locally
wide-range pH test paper and dispenser	Fisher 14-850-1

4.3 Simulation of Homeostatic Mechanisms Regulating Body Fluid Volume

anhydrous boric acid	Fisher	A74-500
buffer, Chemvelope - pH 10.00	Carolina	84-9410
buffer, Chemvelope - pH 6.00	Carolina	84-9370
buret clamp	Carolina	F6-70-7362
buret, 100 mL (for lower buret)	Fisher	03-700D
citric acid, monohydrate	Fisher	A104-500
dispensing buret, 250 mL (for upper buret)	Fisher	03-790A
phenol red	Fisher	P74-10
sodium phosphate, tribasic	Fisher	S377-500
support stand, extra large	Carolina	F6-70-7196

4.4 Blood Pressure

Bowles stethoscope	Carolina	69-1634
Mercurial sphygmomanometer	Carolina	69-1470

Answers to In-text Questions

4.1 Homeostatic Mechanisms

PROCEDURE

B. Regulation of Body Temperature

TABLE 4-2 Organ Systems of Mammals	
Systems	**Vital Functions**
Integumentary	e.g., protection, thermoregulation (sweating), reception of stimuli from external environment
Nervous	point to point (neuronal) control of body functions, integration of body activities, perception of sensations
Endocrine	hormonal control of body functions
Skeletal	support of body, protection of internal organs, skeletal muscle attachment sites, blood cell production, mineral storage and release
Muscular	moves body and its parts, posture, heat generation
Circulatory	rapid transport of materials throughout body, maintenance of stability of internal environment
Lymphatic	immunity, return of tissue fluid to blood
Respiratory	gas exchange between external environment and blood, short term regulation of acid-base balance
Digestive	ingestion of food molecules and water, digestion, absorption, defecation
Urinary	urine production, maintenance of stability of internal environment, long term control of acid-base balance
Reproductive	production of eggs and sperm, sex, gestation and birth (female)

1. From your own experience and Figure 4-2, describe the effector that is activated when the body temperature gets too hot - and its response to cool the body down.
(a) Effector - **sweat glands**
(b) Response - **sweating**
(c) Name the involved organ system - **integumentary**

2. From your own experience and Figure 4-2, describe the effector that is activated when the temperature gets too cold—and its response to warm the body up.
(a) Effector - **skeletal muscles**
(b) Response - **shivering**
(c) Name the involved organ system- **muscular system**

4.2 Regulation of pH

PROCEDURE

TABLE 4-3 pH Values of Common Fluids				
		pH After Addition of		
Fluid	**pH**	**Addition of 1 mL Vinegar**	**2 mL Vinegar**	**3 mL Vinegar**
Water	e.g., 6.2	3.1	3.1	
Milk	6.6	5.1	4.6	
Orange juice	4			
Detergent	10.5			
Vinegar	3.1			

13. Which fluid is more likely to contain buffers (water or milk)? **Milk.**

26

14. Explain any differences that you observe between the slopes of the two lines in Figure 4-4. **The slope of the line for milk is less steep than that for water because buffering molecules in milk bind to the H$^+$ ions added in the vinegar and thus minimize the decrease in pH.**

4.3 Simulation of Homeostatic Mechanisms Regulating Body Fluid Volume

PROCEDURE

4. … **"fill in number"** This number represents the normal value for body fluid volume.

9. Match each body part with its function in the homeostatic feedback loop. Use each answer only once.

Body Part		**Homeostatic Feedback Loop**
b	Hands	a. Integration center
c	Eyes	b. Effector
a	Brain	c. Sensor

4.4 Blood Pressure

PROCEDURE

7. Record your lab partner's blood pressure: **"fill in number"** mm Hg

8. Have your lab partner measure your blood pressure: **"fill in number"** mm Hg

Name _____

Section No. _____

HOMEOSTASIS

Pre-lab Questions

1. All the body fluid located outside of cells is: a. interstitial fluid; b. plasma; c. intracellular fluid; d. extracellular fluid.

2. In the case of temperature regulation, the integrating center is(are): a. the receptors in the hypothalamus; b. a center in the hypothalamus; c. muscles or glands; d. none of the above.

3. Normal blood pressure for an eight-year-old male is 100/67 mm Hg. The systolic blood pressure is: a. 33 mm Hg; b. 100 mm Hg; c. 67 mm Hg; d. 167 mm Hg.

4. When measuring blood pressure the sounds of Korotkoff are heard: a. below the diastolic pressure; b. above the diastolic pressure; c. above the systolic pressure; d. between the diastolic and systolic pressures.

5. The instrument used to measure blood pressure is called: a. a sphygmomanometer; b. a hemocytometer; c. a hematocrit centrifuge; d. none of the above.

6. The portion of the body fluid contained in cells is: a. interstitial fluid; b. plasma; c. intracellular fluid; d. extracellular fluid.

7. In the case of temperature regulation, the effector is(are): a. receptors in the hypothalamus; b. a center in the hypothalamus; c. muscles or glands; d. none of the above.

8. Extracellular fluid includes: a. interstitial fluid; b. plasma; c. intracellular fluid; d. both a and b.

9. A neutral solution has a pH of: a. 3; b. 4; c. 5; d. 7.

10. In the case of temperature regulation, the sensor is(are): a. receptors in the hypothalamus; b. a center in the hypothalamus; c. muscles or glands; d. none of the above.

EXERCISE 4

HOMEOSTASIS

Answers to Post-lab Questions

1. Define *homeostasis*. **Homeostasis refers to the body's ability to maintain stable internal operating conditions. Homeostatic mechanisms function throughout the body to maintain chemical and physical properties of the body fluids within physiological limits.**

2. List and describe the various body fluid components. **Body fluids are divided into two major components: intracellular and extracellular. Intracellular fluid is the fluid component of cytoplasm, while extracellular fluids consist of interstitial fluid and plasma. Interstitial fluid is the fluid between the cells and the blood vessels and plasma is the fluid portion of the blood.**

3. Which organ systems are involved with the acquisition of oxygen and its delivery to the cells of the body? **Respiratory and circulatory systems.**

4. Explain the pH scale. How many hydrogen ions are present in a solution at pH 5 compared to a solution at pH 6? **The pH scales measures the concentration of hydrogen ions (H^+) in solution. A neutral pH is pH 7. Because the scale is logarithmic, each unit is 10 times more or less than the next unit. A solution at pH 5 will have 10 times more H^+ than a solution at pH 6.**

5. Describe how neutral, alkaline, and acidic solutions differ from each other. **Neutral solutions contain an equal concentration of H^+ and hydroxyl ions (OH^-). When there are less H^+ than OH^- ions the solution is alkaline. Conversely, when H^+ outnumber OH^- ions, the solution is acidic.**

6. List the components of a homeostatic feedback loop. Use the regulation of fluid volume to illustrate your answer. **Feedback loops consist of sensors, integrating centers, and effectors. Many examples are possible. Refer to textbook p. 81 for several.**

7. A normal blood pressure for a man in his late forties is 130/82 mm Hg. Why are there two numbers? **Blood pressure changes quickly over time with the contractions of the heart, producing the diastolic and systolic pressures.**

8. Furred animals like cats and dogs cannot sweat. Describe any pet behaviors you have observed that suggest the presence of other homeostatic mechanisms for lowering body temperature. **Dogs decrease activity, increase saliva flow, and pant in response to their bodies overheating. Cats do likewise but don't pant; rather they spread saliva over the surfaces of their bodies with their tongues and paws.**

9. The lowest body pH is found in the fluid of the working stomach. How does a pH of about 3 in this particular location benefit the body as a whole? **It creates a perfect environment for the acid hydrolysis of food. Enzymes secreted by the stomach work best at this pH and further contribute to digestion, especially of protein. The low pH also kills many potential pathogens (disease causing microorganisms) that may be present in ingested materials.**

10. What is hypertension? **Hypertension is high blood pressure.** List some possible causes for this condition. **Hypertension arises through a gradual increase in resistance to blood flow through the small arteries. Heredity may be a factor, as is diet. High sodium levels resulting from excessive salt intake or poor ion balance, is a factor as is obesity.**

EXERCISE 5

MACROMOLECULES AND YOU: FOOD AND DIET ANALYSIS

Materials and Equipment

5.1 Identification of Macromolecules

A.1 Carbohydrates: Test for Sugars Using Benedict's Solution

Per student group (4)
- china marker
- eleven 13 X 100 mm test tubes in rack
- test tube clamp
- stock bottle with Benedict's solution*
- stock bottle with distilled water (dH$_2$O)*
- stock bottle with 6% glucose solution*
- 250- or 400-mL beaker with boiling chips
- hot plate *or* ring stand with wire gauze support and Bunsen burner
- vortex mixer (optional)

- stock bottle with 6% maltose solution*
- stock bottle with 6% lactose solution*
- stock bottle with 6% sucrose solution*
- stock bottle with 6% fructose solution *
- stock bottle with 6% starch solution*
- stock bottle with lemon juice*
- stock bottle with unsweetened orange juice*
- stock bottle with colorless non-diet soda*
- stock bottle with colorless diet soda*

*each stock bottle should be fitted with a 5-mL pipet with a Pi-pump

A.2 Carbohydrates: Test for Starch Using Lugol's Solution

Per student group (4)
- china marker
- seven 13 X 100 mm test tubes in rack
- dropper bottle with Lugol's solution
- stock bottle with distilled water (dH$_2$O)*
- stock bottle with 6% glucose solution*
- stock bottle with 6% maltose solution*

- stock bottle with 6% lactose solution*
- stock bottle with 6% sucrose solution*
- stock bottle with 6% starch solution*
- stock bottle with cream*
- vortex mixer (optional)

*each stock bottle should be fitted with a 5-mL pipet with a Pi-pump

B.1 and B.2 Lipids: Uncoated Paper Test and Sudan IV Test

Per student group (4)
- china marker
- dropper bottle with dH$_2$O
- dropper bottle with vegetable oil
- six 13 X 100 mm test tubes in rack
- stock bottle with dH$_2$O
- stock bottle with vegetable oil
- stock bottle with hamburger juice*

- stock bottle with onion juice*
- stock bottle with colorless non-diet soft drink*
- stock bottle with cream*
- dropper bottle of Sudan IV
- vortex mixer (optional)
- piece of uncoated paper (grocery bag)

*each stock bottle should be fitted with a 5-mL pipet with a Pi-pump

C.1 Proteins: Biuret Test for Proteins with Biuret Reagent

Per student group (4)

- china marker
- five 13 X 100 mm test tubes in rack
- dropper and stock bottle with Biuret reagent*
- stock bottle with dH$_2$O*
- vortex mixer (optional)

- stock bottle with 6% starch solution*
- stock bottle with egg albumin*
- stock bottle with 6% glucose solution*
- stock bottle with colorless soft drink*

*each stock bottle should be fitted with a 5-mL pipet with a Pi-pump

D. Testing Unknown Food Substances

Per lab room

Provide the students with sample food substances to test for macromolecules.

5.2 The Food Pyramid and Diet Analysis

Per student group (4)

glue or tape   colored paper squares
Diet analysis books or computers with diet analysis software

Preparation of Materials and Equipment

5.1 Identification of Macromolecules

A. Carbohydrates: Test for Sugars Using Benedict's Solution

Benedict's solution: Purchase (see *Ordering Information*) or prepare as follows:

copper sulfate (CuSO$_4$)	17.3 g
sodium or potassium citrate	173.0 g
sodium carbonate (Na$_2$CO$_3$)	100.0 g
distilled water to make	1 L

Dissolve citrate and sodium carbonate in 800 mL of warm water. Filter and pour into a graduated cylinder and add distilled water up to 850 mL. Dissolve copper sulfate in 100 mL dH$_2$O. Pour the carbonate-citrate solution into a large beaker and slowly add the copper sulfate while stirring constantly. Add dH$_2$O to 1 L.

Yield: 1 L of Benedict's solution is adequate for many student groups to perform this exercise.
Shelf life: Benedict's solution is stable and long lasting at room temperature.

6% sugar solutions [glucose (dextrose), lactose, fructose, maltose, sucrose (table sugar); 1 L each]:

Sugar	60 g
distilled water to make	1000 mL

Add appropriate sugar to water while stirring. Heat gently as needed to dissolve sugar. Store in refrigerator.
Yield: 1 L of sugar solution is adequate for approximately 200 student groups to perform Parts A.1 and A.2 of this exercise.
Shelf life: up to 2 to 3 weeks under refrigeration. Cloudiness indicates microorganism contamination and growth.

6% starch solution: (1 L):

starch (soluble, potato or arrowroot)	60 g
distilled water	1000 mL

Make a thin paste by combining the starch and a small amount of water. Heat the remainder of the water to boiling. Remove boiling water from burner and add starch paste while stirring constantly until smooth and homogeneous. Cool.

Yield: 1 L is adequate for approximately 180 student groups to perform all portions of this exercise.
Shelf life: weeks, if refrigerated.

A.2 Carbohydrates: Test for Starch Using Lugol's Solution

Lugols's solution (300 mL): Purchase (see *Ordering Information*) or prepare as follows:

iodine	1 g
potassium iodide	2 g
distilled water	300 mL

Dissolve the potassium iodide in the water, then add the iodine and stir until dissolved. Store in darkened glass bottle. Pour into dropper bottles for classroom use.
    Yield: 300 mL Lugol's solution is adequate for approximately 100 student groups.
    Shelf life: months, if stored in darkened bottle.

6% sugar solutions (glucose, maltose, lactose, sucrose): See above.

6% starch solution: See above.

B.1 and B.2 Lipids: Uncoated Paper Test and Sudan IV Test

hamburger juice: Crumble fatty hamburger into a 250-mL beaker to approximately 1/4 full. Add 150 mL dH_2O. Bring to a boil. Boil for 5 minutes and allow meat to settle to bottom of beaker. Use supernatant only; discard hamburger pieces. Keep refrigerated if prepared in advance. For class use, keep hamburger lipid/water mix warm; shake to emulsify lipids.

onion juice: Peel and dice one medium onion and place in a blender. Add 100 to 200 mL dH_2O to cover. Blend the mixture and then strain through cheesecloth. Decant supernatant into dropper bottles.
    Yield: each 100 mL onion juice is adequate for approximately 30 student groups.

Sudan IV (100 mL): Purchase (see *Ordering Information*) or make as follows:

Sudan IV	0.2 g
95% ethyl alcohol to make	100 mL

C.1 Proteins: Biuret Test for Proteins with Biuret Reagent

Biuret reagent (approx. 100 mL): Purchase (see *Ordering Information*) or prepare as follows:
    1. Prepare 0.01M solution of copper sulfate:

copper sulfate	.25 g
distilled water	100 mL

    2. Prepare 10M sodium hydroxide solution as follows:

sodium hydroxide (NaOH)	44 g
dH_2O	100 mL

In fume hood, dissolve NaOH in small amount of water (*CAUTION),* then add water to make 100 mL.

    3. To prepare Biuret reagent, add 2.5 mL copper sulfate solution to 100 mL of hydroxide solution. Dispense into stock bottles.
    Yield: 100 mL Biuret reagent is adequate for approximately 45 student groups.

6% glucose solution: See above.
6% starch solution: See above.

1% egg albumin solution: (100 mL):	powdered egg albumin	1 g
	distilled water to make	100 mL

Add albumin to small amount of water and stir carefully and slowly *to avoid foaming*. Bring volume to 100 mL. Dispense into stock bottles. Store in refrigerator.

Yield: 100 mL should be adequate for approximately 90 student groups.

Notes

General

Be sure to label each stock bottle appropriately as well as the corresponding pipette. If available, use color-coded tapes to distinguish the labels of various solutions.

Remind students of the need to *thoroughly* wash and rinse the test tubes so that test results are not ruined by contamination.

5.1.B. Lipids

When several drops of Sudan IV are added to a test tube, a red droplet will appear where a lipid layer is present. Otherwise the red color disperses throughout the solution.

Sudan IV is very messy. Students must use hot, soapy water to clean the test tubes after completion of this portion of the exercise.

Ordering Information

See General Laboratory Supplies list on page vii for basic items

5.1 Identification of Macromolecules

A.1 Carbohydrates: Test for Sugars Using Benedict's Solution

Benedict's solution, 500 mL	Carolina	84-7111
copper (cupric) sulfate, anhydrous	Carolina	85-6550
fructose (levulose)	Carolina	87-2340
glucose (dextrose)	Sigma	G8270
glucose (dextrose)	Carolina	85-7430
lactose	Carolina	87-1750
maltose	Carolina	87-3750
sodium citrate, granular	Carolina	88-9050
sodium carbonate, granular	Carolina	88-8760
starch, soluble (potato)	Fisher	S71202
sucrose—purchase from grocery store or	Carolina	89-2860
Potassium citrate	Fisher	P218-500

A.2 Carbohydrates: Test for Starch Using Lugol's Solution

glucose (dextrose)	Sigma	G8270
iodine, I_2	Fisher	I37-100
lactose	Carolina	87-1750
Lugol's solution, 100 mL	Carolina	87-2793
maltose	Carolina	87-3750
potassium iodide, KI	Fisher	P410-100
starch, soluble (potato)	Fisher	S71202
sucrose—purchase from grocery store or	Carolina	89-2860

B.1 and B.2 Lipids

Sudan IV	Carolina	89-2980
Sudan IV stain, 120 mL	Carolina	89-2993

C.1 Proteins: Biuret Test for Proteins with Biuret Reagent

albumin, powdered	Carolina	84-2250
Biuret reagent, 120 mL	Carolina	84-8211
copper (cupric) sulfate, anhydrous	Carolina	85-6550
glucose (dextrose)	Sigma	G8270
sodium hydroxide pellets	Fisher	S318-100
starch, soluble, potato	Fisher	S71202

Answers to In-text questions

5.1 Identification of Macromolecules

A.1 Carbohydrates: Test for Sugars Using Benedict's Solution

TABLE 5-1 Benedict's Test for Sugars

Tube	Contents	Initial Color	Color After Heating	Conclusion
1	Distilled water	Blue	Blue	No simple sugars
2	Glucose	Blue	Orange	Has simple sugars that react with Benedict's
3	Maltose	Blue	Orange	Has simple sugars that react with Benedict's
4	Lactose	Blue	Orange	Has simple sugars that react with Benedict's
5	Sucrose	Blue	Blue	No simple sugars
6	Starch	Blue	Blue	No simple sugars
7	Fructose	Blue	Orange-brown	Has simple sugars that react with Benedict's
8	Lemon Juice	Blue	Orange	Has simple sugars that react with Benedict's
9	Orange Juice	Blue	Orange	Has simple sugars that react with Benedict's
10	Non-diet soda	Blue	Orange	Has simple sugars that react with Benedict's
11	Diet soda	Blue	Blue	No simple sugars

A.2 Carbohydrates: Test for Starch Using Lugol's Solution

TABLE 5-2 Lugol's Test for Starch

Tube	Contents	Initial Color	Color After Adding Lugol's	Conclusion
1	Distilled water	Clear, colorless	Amber	No starch
2	Glucose	Clear, colorless	Amber	No starch
3	Maltose	Clear, colorless	Amber	No starch
4	Lactose	Clear, colorless	Amber	No starch
5	Sucrose	Clear, colorless	Amber	No starch
6	Starch	Clear, slightly cloudy	Black	Starch present
7	Cream	White, opaque	Yellow	No starch

5. Hypothesize about why you got the results you did with the Benedict's test for each substance. **Answers will vary, but should indicate an understanding that the Benedict's test is a presence/absence test for certain kinds of simple sugars.**

B. Lipids

B.1 Uncoated Paper Test

2. After 10 minutes, describe the appearance of each spot on the paper.
distilled water—**wet**
vegetable oil—**translucent spot**

4. After 10 minutes, describe the appearance of each spot on the paper.
hamburger juice—**translucent spot**
onion juice—**wet, slight translucence around edges**
colorless non-diet soft drink—**wet**
cream—**wet**

5. What can you infer about the lipid content of each substance?
Hamburger juice contains lipids. Onion juice *may* contain lipids (inconclusive), and soft drinks and cream don't contain significant amounts of lipids.

B.2 Sudan IV Test

Tube	Contents	Observations After Addition of Sudan IV	Conclusion
TABLE 5-3 Test for Lipids with Sudan IV			
1	Distilled water	**Uniform light pink**	**No lipids**
2	Vegetable oil	**Red layer on top of pink**	**Lipids present**
3	Hamburger juice	**Red layer on top of pink**	**Lipids present**
4	Onion juice	**Small red layer**	**Some lipids present**
5	Soft drink	**Uniform light pink**	**No lipids**
6	Cream	**Globules of red within light pink**	**Globules of lipids present**

1. Answers may vary depending on concentration and student perceptions, but generally the Sudan IV test is more sensitive.
2. Foods are mixtures of many compounds and macromolecules generally. Low concentrations of lipids may be difficult to distinguish.

C. Proteins

C.1 Biuret Test for Proteins with Biuret Reagent

Tube	Contents	Color Reaction	Conclusion
TABLE 5-4 Test for Protein with Biuret Reagent			
1	Distilled water	**Blue**	**No proteins**
2	Starch	**Blue**	**No proteins**
3	Egg albumin	**Purple**	**Proteins present**
4	Glucose	**Blue**	**No proteins**
5	Soft drink	**Blue**	**No proteins**

D. Testing Unknown Food Substances

TABLE 5-5 Tests for Unknown Food Substances
Variable answers.

5.2 The Food Pyramid and Diet Analysis

A. Food Diary

Variable for each student.

B. In-Class Food Diary Analysis

6. (a) What is your typical level of physical activity (sedentary, moderate, active)? **Answers will vary.**

(b) What is your approximate daily calorie requirement? **Answers will vary.**

(c) How does your caloric intake compare with the recommendations for your gender and activity level? **Answers will vary but should refer to following: "In general, less active women require about 1600 calories per day to maintain body mass; children, teen girls, active women, and less active men require about 2200 calories, and teen boys and active men require about 2800."**

(d) What food groups are you getting too much of? What kinds of nutrients are you thus overconsuming? What are the potential consequences of this excess for your health? **If grain group is too high then students may overconsume starchy polysaccharides, and therefore, calories. (Consequences: risk of obesity, diabetes, and complications.) If fruit/vegetable groups are overconsumed, then students may likewise overconsume fiber (consequence diarrhea). If dairy and soy group or meat and bean group are overconsumed, students may also overconsume protein and fat. (Consequence: risk of obesity, diabetes, heart disease, some cancers.) If overconsuming vegetable oils or discretionary calories, the consequences are a risk of obesity, diabetes, heart disease, some cancers and a lack of other essential nutrients.)**

(e) What food groups are you not eating enough of? What kinds of specific nutrient molecules are thus underrepresented in your diet? What are the potential consequences of this deficiency for your health? **If grain group is underconsumed, polysaccharides are lacking. (The consequence is likely to be too few calories, low energy levels and a compromised immune system.) If fruits/vegetables are underconsumed, there is likely to be a lack of vitamins, minerals, and phytochemicals, low energy levels, poor immune function and general negative health impacts. If dairy products are lacking, calcium levels will also be low, which will increase the risk of osteoporosis. If meat and beans are too low, then proteins will also be lacking. If vegetable oils are underrepresented, levels of essential fatty acids will also lower.**

(f) What proportion of your grain servings included whole grains? **Answers will vary.**
How many different *kinds* of vegetables and fruits did you consume? **Answers will vary.**
How many food items contained saturated or trans fats? **Answers will vary.**

(g) Given all the above information, describe two *reasonable* changes you could make to improve your diet and your health. **Answers will vary. Note: "reasonable" changes would include such goals as incorporating more whole grains into diet, more vegetables and fruits, fewer foods and drinks with added sugars, etc. It would be unreasonable to suggest radical dietary changes, such as a confirmed meat-eater thinking that they will become vegan immediately.**

Personal Food Pyramid
Varies for each student.

MACROMOLECULES AND YOU: FOOD AND DIET ANALYSIS

Pre-lab Questions

1. To test for starch one would use: a. Benedict's solution; b. uncoated paper; c. Sudan IV; d. Lugol's solution.

2. Rich sources of stored energy that are dissolvable in organic solvents are: a. carbohydrates; b. proteins; c. glucose; d. lipids.

3. Proteins consist of: a. monosaccharides linked in chains; b. amino acid units; c. polysaccharide units; d. condensed fatty acids.

4. The largest number of food servings in your daily diet should be from: a. meats and beans; b. dairy products; c. vegetable and fruits; d. vegetable oils.

5. Rubbing a substance on uncoated paper should reveal if it is a: a. lipid; b. carbohydrate; c. protein; d. sugar.

6. A carbohydrate consists of: a. amino acid units; b. one or more sugar units; c. lipid droplets; d. glycerol.

7. A protein is made up of: a. amino acid units; b. one or more sugar units; c. lipid droplets; d. Biuret solution.

8. Glycogen is: a. a polysaccharide; b. a storage carbohydrate; c. found in human tissues; d. all of the above.

9. Benedict's solution is commonly used to test for: a. proteins; b. certain carbohydrates; c. nucleic acids; d. lipids.

10. Biuret reagent will indicate the presence of: a. peptide bonds; b. proteins; c. amino acid units linked together; d. all of the above.

MACROMOLECULES AND YOU: FOOD AND DIET ANALYSIS

Answers to Pre-Lab Questions
  in Lab Manual Order

1.	b	6.	d
2.	a	7.	a
3.	b	8.	b
4.	d	9.	d
5.	d	10.	c

Answers to Pre-lab Questions
  in Instructor's Manual Order

1.	d	6.	b
2.	d	7.	a
3.	b	8.	d
4.	c	9.	b
5.	a	10.	d

Answers to Post-lab Questions

1. Let's suppose you are teaching science in a part of the world without ready access to a doctor and you're worried that you may have developed diabetes. (Diabetics are unable to regulate blood glucose levels, and glucose accumulates in blood and urine.) What could you do to gain an indication of whether or not you have diabetes? **You could collect some urine, find some Benedict's solution and perform a Benedict's test. As in class, a reddish-orange precipitate would indicate the presence of high urine glucose levels.**

2. The test tubes in the photograph contain Benedict's solution and two unknown substances that have been heated. What do the results indicate? **The substance in the right hand test tube is a carbohydrate with carbonyl groups that reacted with the Benedict's solution to produce a positive test. The left hand test tube shows a negative Benedict's test, so the substance in that test tube is NOT a carbohydrate with carbonyl groups.**

3. How could you verify that a soft drink can contained diet soda rather than soda sweetened with fructose? **Test the two liquids with a Benedict's test. Soda sweetened with fructose will test positive (form a reddish-brown precipitate), while diet soda will give a negative test and the Benedict's solution will remain blue in color.**

4. Observe the photomicrograph accompanying this question. This section of a potato tuber has been stained with Lugol's iodine solution. When you eat French fries, the potato material is broken down in your small intestine into what small subunits? **Glucose.**

5. The test tube in the photograph contains water at the bottom and another substance that has been stained with Sudan IV at the top. What is the macromolecular composition of this stained substance? **Lipid.**

6. You are given a sample of an unknown food. Describe how you would test it for the presence of lipids. **Obtain an extract of the food by blending or mashing it. Spot test the extract on uncoated paper as you did in lab, or conduct a Sudan IV test as described on pages 59 and 60 of the lab manual.**

7. You wish to test the same unknown food for the presence of sugars. Describe how you would do so. **Obtain an extract of the food by blending or mashing it. Conduct the test for sugars using Benedict's Solution as described on page 57 of the lab manual.**

8. What is the purpose of the distilled water sample in each of the chemical tests in this exercise? **The distilled water sample serves as a control to give a negative result to each of the chemical tests.**

9. Many health food stores carry enzyme preparations that are intended to be ingested orally (by mouth) to supplement existing enzymes in various organs like the liver, heart, and muscle. Explain why these preparations are unlikely to be effective as advertised. **Ingested proteins are digested to small peptide fragments and amino acids. Amino acids are absorbed in the small intestine. Enzyme activity depends on the intact three-dimensional structure of proteins. Digested enzymes would no longer have their three-dimensional protein structure and therefore would not function as enzymes.**

10. A young child grows rapidly, with high levels of cell division and high energy requirements. If you were planning the child's diet, which food groups would you emphasize, and why? Which food groups would you de-emphasize, and why? **You would want to emphasize protein for building cellular and tissue structures, and fruits and vegetables for vitamin and mineral content, as well as energy sources. Young children also need a proper balance of lipids for building membranes and, again, energy sources. You would de-emphasize calorie-dense, but low quality sweets and fats without crucial nutrients. Such a diet would also help establish healthy eating habits.**

EXERCISE 6

STRUCTURE AND FUNCTION OF LIVING CELLS

Materials and Equipment

6.1 Prokaryotic Cells

Per student
- dissecting needle
- compound microscope
- microscope slide
- coverslip

Per student pair
- distilled water (dH$_2$O) in dropping bottle

Per student group (table)
- culture of a cyanobacterium (either *Anabaena* or *Oscillatoria*)

Per lab room
- three bacterium-containing nutrient agar plates—set as a demonstration
- three slides of bacteria (coccus, bacillus, spirillum)—set as a demonstration

6.2 Eukaryotic Cells

Per student
- toothpick
- microscope slide and coverslip
- Forceps and dissecting needle
- culture of *Physarum polycephalum*
- compound microscope
- textbook

Per student pair
- distilled water (dH$_2$O) in dropping bottle
- methylene blue in dropping bottle

Per student group (table)
- onion bulb
- *Elodea* in water-containing culture dish
- alcohol-containing disposal jar
- paper towel

Per lab room
- model of plant cell
- model of animal cell

6.2.B. Experiment: Cytoplasmic Streaming

Per experimental group
- culture of *Physarum polycephalum*
- refrigerator or container with ice
- timer or watch with second hand
- compound microscope
- Celsius thermometer

Preparation of Materials and Equipment

6.1 Prokaryotic Cells

Nutrient agar (1 L):

beef extract	3 g
peptone	5 g
agar	15 g
distilled water	1000 mL

Mix and heat to boiling to dissolve. Dispense into bottles and sterilize in autoclave for 15 minutes at 15 pounds pressure and 121°C. Pour while hot into sterilized petri dishes, approximately 20 mL per plate.

Nutrient agar powder may also be purchased (see *Ordering Information*). Mix 23 g Difco nutrient agar with 1000 mL dH$_2$O and follow above directions.

Store sterilized agar in refrigerator.

Yield: 1000 mL nutrient agar is sufficient for approximately 50 petri dishes.

Oscillatoria: Oscillatoria cultures may be purchased or collected and cultured for future use. This cyanobacterium is commonly found in most greenhouses, growing on the surface of wet soil or flowerpots, especially those kept standing in water.

Culture *Oscillatoria* on the surface of plaster blocks kept constantly moist. Place a 2-cm square chunk of the cyanobacterium in the center of the plaster block and set the culture in a petri dish containing enough water to keep the block moist. Cover the dish, illuminate and check daily to ensure an adequate water level to prevent drying. The *Oscillatoria* should begin to spread out on the plaster block surface within two days.

Small clumps of *Oscillatoria* may also be placed on culture dishes of water agar. The cyanobacterium will spread out over the agar surface within two days.

To prepare water agar, follow directions for nutrient agar, omitting the beef extract and peptone.

Yield: Luxurious cyanobacterial growth on six bricks or flowerpots from a greenhouse should be sufficient for several laboratory sections. Four plaster blocks should be sufficient for approximately 20 students.

Plaster blocks: Prepare quick-setting plaster of Paris according to package directions. Pour it into small cartons (yogurt, milk, etc.) to a depth of about 7 mm. After the plaster has hardened, peel off the carton.

6.2 Eukaryotic Cells

Physarum polycephalum:

Stock culture preparation: Place the lid or bottom of a 15 x 100 mm petri dish—surface side up—in an 8 in. diameter culture dish. Place a 170 mm circle of filter paper on top of the petri dish. Add enough tap water so that the filter paper overhanging the edges of the petri dish serves as a wick.

Place a piece of filter paper covered with *Physarum* sclerotia (purchased or prepared as described below) at one edge of the filter paper in the culture dish. Sprinkle rolled oats on the surface of the filter paper adjacent to the sclerotia. Cover the dish with glass and *place the culture in the dark.* The plasmodium will cover the surface of the filter paper and the oat flakes in 4 or 5 days. Replace the water in the culture daily and add more rolled oats 2 days after the initial inoculation. The culture *must* remain in darkness throughout growth; light induces sporangial formation within 24 to 36 hours after illumination.

Sclerotium preparation: Prepare a plasmodial culture like the stock culture described above. Decant the excess water and replace the glass cover with brown wrapping paper. Incubate the culture below 25°C in darkness. After 7 to 10 days of gradual drying, the plasmodium should aggregate into a thick, spongy mass. Test viability by cutting off a small portion and placing it on moistened filter paper or water agar. If viable, place the sclerotium in an envelope and store it in a refrigerator.

Class cultures: Pour water agar into 15 x 60 mm petri dishes to a depth of about 1 cm. Place a small amount of plasmodium from stock culture into each petri dish. Place 1 or 2 oat flakes adjacent to the plasmodium. Incubate the covered dishes at room temperature in darkness for 1 to 2 days before needed in class.

| *Water agar*, 1% (1000 mL): | Agar | 10 g |
| | dH$_2$O | 1000 mL |

Suspend agar in water and heat to boiling to dissolve. Dispense into bottles or stoppered flasks and autoclave for 15 minutes at 121°C and 15 pounds pressure.

Yield: 1000 mL agar is sufficient for approximately 50 15 x 100 mm petri dishes, or approximately 80-90 15 x 60 mm petri dishes.

Methylene blue (100 mL): Mix 0.01 g methylene blue crystals with 100 mL absolute (100%) ethanol. Alternatively, dilute methylene blue stain (1:20,000) may be purchased (see *Ordering Information*).

| *70% ethanol* (950 mL): | 95% ethanol | 700 mL |
| | dH$_2$O | 250 mL |

6.2.B. Experiment: Cytoplasmic Streaming

Physarum polycephalum cultures: See above.

Notes

6.1 Prokaryotic Cells

Maintain stock cultures of bacteria on slants of nutrient agar. Transfer about every 6 months to maintain viability. Refrigerate after growth appears.

Incubate inoculated agar plates in an inverted position. Bacterial growth rates generally increase with increasing temperature to 30°C. Bacterial plates may be stored in a refrigerator. Seal plates with Parafilm strips or place them in plastic bags to prevent desiccation.

6.2 Eukaryotic Cells

Use healthy, actively growing *Elodea* plants. Clean the plants by gently swishing them in clean water before class use. *Elodea* may be grown in an illuminated, aerated aquarium or purchased (see *Ordering Information*).

Ordering Information

See General Laboratory Supplies list on page vii for basic items

6.1 Prokaryotic Cells

E. coli, live culture	Carolina	15-5065
Anabaena, live culture	Carolina	15-1710
Oscillatoria, live culture	Carolina	15-1865
bacteria, prepared slide, three forms mixed	Triarch	4-100SP
beef extract	VWR	90000-718
peptone	Fisher	S71604
agar	VWR	90000-760
Difco nutrient agar	VWR	DF00001-02

6.2 Eukaryotic Cells

absolute (100%) ethanol	Fisher	S739852
agar	VWR	90000-760
animal cell model	Carolina	56-3960
Elodea (purchase from aquarium shop or)	Carolina	16-2100
ethanol, 95%	Carolina	86-1281
methylene blue, crystals	Carolina	87-5684
methylene blue, prepared, 1:20,000	Carolina	87-5915
Physarum polycephalum plasmodium	Carolina	15-6192
Physarum polycephalum, sclerotium	Carolina	15-6190
plant cell model	Carolina	56-8050

6.2.B. Experiment: Cytoplasmic Streaming

Physarum polycephalum, sclerotium	Carolina	15-6190
Physarum polycephalum, plasmodium	Carolina	15-6192
agar	VWR	90000-760

Answers to In-text Questions

6.1 Prokaryotic Cells

1. Observe the culture plate with bacteria growing on the surface of a nutrient medium. Can you see the individual cells with your naked eye? **No.**

2. Observe the microscopic preparations of bacteria on *demonstration* next to the culture plate. The three slides represent the three different shapes of bacteria. Which objective lenses are being used to view the bacteria? **High dry and/or oil immersion.**

Would you say bacteria are large or small organisms? **Small.** Can you discern any detail within the cytoplasm? **No.**

10. Look at the captions for Figures 6-3 and 6-5. Judging by the magnification of each electron micrograph, which cell is larger: the bacterium *E. coli* or the cyanobacterium *Anabaena*? **The cyanobacterium *Anabaena***

6.2 Eukaryotic Cells

B. Experiment: Cytoplasmic Streaming

TABLE 6-2, Prediction. Answers will vary but here's a possibility: **There will be an inverse relationship between temperature and cytoplasmic streaming.**

D. Animal Cells as Observed with the Electron Microscope

3. Figure 6-10 is an electron micrograph (EM) of an animal cell (kingdom Animalia). Study the electron micrograph and, with the aid of Figure 6-9 and any electron micrographs in your textbook, label each structure listed.
Figure 6-10, Labels (from top to bottom):
    Plasma membrane
    Cytoplasm
    Nuclear envelope
    Golgi body
    Nuclear pore within membrane (provided)
    Nucleus (provided)
    Chromatin
    Mitochondrion
    Smooth ER
    Rough ER

5. Using your textbook as a reference, list the function for the following cellular components:

(a) plasma membrane: **boundary between external environment and cytoplasm; mediates movement of materials into and out of cytoplasm; recognition phenomena.**

(b) cytoplasm: **living substance of the cell; contains various organelles.**

(c) nucleus (the plural is *nuclei*): **location of genetic material, DNA.**

(d) nuclear envelope: **boundary between nucleus and cytoplasm.**

(e) nuclear pores: **openings in nuclear envelope that allow passage of messenger RNA from nucleus to cytoplasm.**

(f) chromatin: **the substance of chromosomes consisting of DNA and proteins.**

(g) nucleolus (the plural is *nucleoli*): **body within the nucleus consisting largely of RNA and site of ribosome synthesis.**

(h) rough endoplasmic reticulum (RER): **protein transport within the cytoplasm; possesses protein-producing ribosomes on external membrane surface.**

(i) smooth endoplasmic reticulum (SER): **lipid transport within the cytoplasm.**

(j) Golgi body: **lipid secretion; produces vesicles that migrate within the cytoplasm to the plasma membrane where the contents are used for membrane construction.**

(k) mitochondrion (the plural is *mitochondria*): **site of cellular respiration resulting in the formation of cellular energy in the form of ATP.**

E. Plant Cells Seen with the Light Microscope

E.1 Elodea leaf cells

11. Describe the three-dimensional shape of the *Elodea* leaf cell. **Each cell is like a rectangular shoe box.**

12. What are the shapes of the chloroplasts and nucleus? **The chloroplasts are blimp shaped and the nucleus is a sphere.**

15. Compare the size of the mitochondria to chloroplasts: **Mitochondria are smaller than chloroplasts.**

E.2 Onion scale cells

6. You may see numerous **oil droplets** within the cytoplasm, visible in the form of granule like bodies.
These oil droplets are a form of stored food material. You may be surprised to learn that onion scales are actually leaves! Which cellular components present in *Elodea* leaf cells are absent in onion leaf cells? **Chloroplasts are absent in the onion leaf cells.**

F. Plant Cells as Seen with the Electron Microscope

3. Now, examine Figure 6-16, a transmission electron micrograph from a corn leaf. Label all the structures labeled.

Figure 6-16, Labels (from top to bottom):

> **Cell wall**
> **Plasma membrane**
> **Endoplasmic reticulum**
> **Vacuole**
> **Vacuolar membrane**
> **Chromatin**
> **Nuclear envelope**
> **Nucleolus**
> **Nucleus (provided)**
> **Mitochondrion**
> **Chloroplast**

4. With the help of Figure 6-15 and any transmission electron micrographs and text in your textbook, list the function of the following structures.

(a) cell wall: **contains plasma membrane and cytoplasm.**

(b) chloroplast: **site of photosynthesis resulting in the production of sugars used for cellular respiration and starch for storage.**

(c) vacuole: **contains mostly water, but may also contain various water-soluble pigments, crystals, enzymes or various waste products; active in cellular enlargement.**

(d) vacuolar membrane: **semi-permeable membrane creating the boundary between the vacuolar contents and the cytoplasm.**

(e) Plasma membrane: **boundary between external environment and cytoplasm; mediates movement of materials into and out of cytoplasm; recognition phenomena.**

(f) cytoplasm: **living substance of the cell; contains various organelles.**

(g) nucleus: **location of genetic material, DNA.**

(h) nuclear envelope: **boundary between nucleus and cytoplasm.**

(i) nuclear pores: **openings in nuclear envelope that allow passage of messenger RNA from nucleus to cytoplasm.**

(j) chromatin: **the substance of chromosomes consisting of DNA and proteins.**

(k) nucleolus: **body within the nucleus consisting largely of RNA and site of ribosome synthesis.**

(l) rough endoplasmic reticulum (RER): **protein transport within the cytoplasm; possesses protein-producing ribosomes on external membrane surface**

(m) smooth endoplasmic reticulum (SER): **lipid transport within the cytoplasm.**

(n) Golgi body: **lipid secretion; produces vesicles that migrate within the cytoplasm to the plasma membrane where the contents are used for membrane construction and cell wall synthesis.**

(o) mitochondrion: **site of cellular respiration resulting in the formation of cellular energy in the form of ATP.**

Name _____

Section No. _____

STRUCTURE AND FUNCTION OF LIVING CELLS

Pre-lab Questions

1.   A bacterium is an example of a(an): a. prokaryotic cell; b. eukaryotic cell; c. plant cell; d. all of the above.

2.   All cells contain: a. a nucleus, plasma membrane, and cytoplasm; b. a cell wall, nucleus, and cytoplasm; c. DNA, plasma membrane, and cytoplasm; d. mitochondria, plasma membrane, and cytoplasm.

3.   Prokaryotic cells *lack*: a. DNA; b. a true nucleus; c. a cell wall; d. none of the above.

4.   The person responsible for first using the term *cell* was: a. Darwin; b. Leeuwenhoek; c. Hooke; d. Watson.

5.   The word *eukaryotic* refers specifically to a cell containing: a. photosynthetic membranes; b. a true nucleus; c. a cell wall; d. none of the above.

6.   An envelope: a. surrounds the nucleus; b. surrounds mitochondria; c. consists of two membranes; d. does all of the above.

7.   The intercellular spaces between plant cells: a. contain air; b. are responsible for cytoplasmic streaming; c. are nonexistent; d. contain chloroplasts.

8.   A central vacuole: a. is found only in plant cells; b. may take up between 50% and 90% of the cell's interior; c. both of the above; d. none of the above.

9.   Methylene blue: a. is used to kill cells that are moving too quickly to observe; b. renders cells non-toxic; c. is a portion of the electromagnetic spectrum used by green plant cells; d. is a biological stain used to increase contrast of cellular constituents.

10.   Components typical of plant cells but not of animal cells are: a. nuclei; b. cell walls; c. mitochondria; d. ribosomes.

EXERCISE 6

STRUCTURE AND FUNCTION OF LIVING CELLS

*Answers to Pre-lab Questions
in Lab Manual Order*

1. c   6. d
2. c   7. b
3. b   8. c
4. b   9. a
5. a   10. d

*Answers to Pre-lab Questions
in Instructor's Manual Order*

1. a   6. d
2. c   7. a
3. b   8. c
4. c   9. d
5. b   10. b

Answers to Post-lab Questions

1. Did all living cells that you saw in lab contain mitochondria? **Yes.**

2. Below is a high-magnification photomicrograph of an organism you observed in this exercise. Each rectangular box is a single cell. What organelle is absent from each cell that makes it "prokaryotic"? **They do not contain a membrane bound nucleus.**

3. Is it possible for a cell to contain more than one nucleus? **Yes.** Explain. **More than one nucleus can occur in the cytoplasm of certain cells. For example, *Physarum polycephalum* is a multinucleate organism.**

4. When students are asked to distinguish between an animal cell and a plant cell, they typically answer that plant cells contain chloroplasts and animal cells do not. If you were the professor reading that answer, what sort of credit would you give and why? **Only partial credit could be given for that answer since there are other distinctions between plant cells and animal cells, such as cell walls and vacuoles.**

5. Describe a major distinction between plant and animal cells. **Plant cells may have cell walls and chloroplasts present in contrast to animal cells.**

6. Observe the electron micrograph above. Is the cell prokaryotic or eukaryotic? **Eukaryotic.** Identify the labeled structures. **A. vacuole B. nucleus C. chloroplast**

7. Look at the photomicrograph below taken with a technique that gives a three-dimensional impression. Identify the structures labeled A, B, and C. **A. chloroplast B. nucleus C. cell wall.**

8. Is this electron micrograph of a plant or an animal cell? **Animal cell.** Identify structures labeled A and B. **A. mitochondrion B. nucleus.**

9. What are the numerous "wavy lines" within the cell (labeled 'c')? **Endoplasmic reticulum.**

10. What structure(s) found in plant cells is (are) primarily responsible for cellular support? **Cell walls and vacuoles.**

11. What structural differences did you observe between prokaryotic and eukaryotic cells? **See Table 6-1 for characteristics that you should be able to observe.**

12. Are the cells in the electron micrograph below prokaryotic or eukaryotic? **Prokaryotic.** How do you know? **There are no membrane bound nuclei present or other membrane bound organelles.**

EXERCISE 7

DIFFUSION, OSMOSIS, AND THE FUNCTIONAL SIGNIFICANCE OF BIOLOGICAL MEMBRANES

Materials and Equipment

7.1 Experiment: Rate of Diffusion of Solutes

Per student
- 15-cm metric ruler

Per student group (table)
- three screw-cap 13 x 100 mm test tubes of 5% gelatin labeled "5°C" with the following dyes
  - potassium dichromate, 1 mL
  - aniline blue, 1 mL
  - Janus green, 1 mL
- three screw-cap test tubes as above but labeled "Room Temperature"
- test tube rack

Per lab room
- 5°C refrigerator

7.2 Experiment: Osmosis

Per student group (4)
- Funnel
- eight 10-cm pieces string
- Support stand and ring , 3 in. diameter
- 25-mL graduated cylinder
- four 15-cm lengths dialysis tubing soaking in dH_2O
- four 400-mL beakers
- four small string tags
- china marker

Per student group (table)
- dishpan half-filled with dH_2O
- balance
- paper toweling

Per lab room
- carboys of dH_2O at each sink
- bottle of 15% sucrose
- bottle of 30% sucrose
- scissors at each sink

7.3 Experiment: Selective Permeability of Membranes

Per student group (4)
- funnel and scissors
- two 10-cm pieces string
- 25-cm length of dialysis tubing, soaking in dH_2O
- Support stand
- support ring, 3 in. diameter
- 1% albumin in 1% sodium chloride (NaCl)
- 2% barium chloride ($BaCl_2$) in dropping bottle
- 2% silver nitrate ($AgNO_3$) in dropping bottle
- 1% soluble starch in 1% sodium sulfate (Na_2SO_4)
- graduated 400-mL beaker
- dishpan half-filled with dH_2O
- eight test tubes, 16 x 150 mm
- test tube rack
- china marker
- 25-mL graduated cylinder
- iodine (I_2KI) solution in dropping bottle
- biuret reagent in dropping bottle
- albustix reagent strips (optional)

Per lab room
- 400-mL beaker (for soaking dialysis tubing)
- scissors at each sink
- demonstration series composed of four 16 x 150 mm test tubes in rack showing positive tests for starch, sulfate ion, chloride ion and protein
- dH$_2$O

7.4 Experiment: Plasmolysis in Plant Cells

Per student
- forceps
- compound microscope
- two microscope slides, 1 x 3 in.
- two coverslips, 22 mm sq.

Per student group (table)
- *Elodea* in tap water
- two dropping bottles of dH$_2$O
- two dropping bottles of 20% NaCl

7.5 Experiment: Osmotic Changes in Red Blood Cells

Per student
- compound microscope

Per student group (4)
- three screw-cap test tubes, 13 x 100 mm
- test tube rack
- 15-cm metric ruler
- china marker
- bottle of 0.9% sodium chloride (NaCl)
- bottle of 10% sodium chloride (NaCl)
- bottle of dH$_2$O
- three disposable plastic pipets
- three clean microscope slides, 1 x 3 in.
- three coverslips, 22 mm sq.

Per group (table)
- bottle of defibrinated sheep blood
- ice bucket with ice

Per lab room
- carboy or other source of dH$_2$O

7.6 Experiment: Determining the Concentration of Solutes in Cells

Per student group (4)
- five 250-mL beakers
- china marker
- 15-cm metric ruler
- large potato tuber
- single-edge razor blades **or** paring knife
- potato peeler

Per table
- metric balance
- bottles containing solutions of 0.15 M, 0.20 M, 0.25 M, 0.30 M and 0.35 M sucrose
- paper toweling

Preparation of Materials and Equipment

7.1 Experiment: Rate of Diffusion of Solutes

| *5% gelatin* (100 mL): | gelatin (Knox or other granulated) | 5 g |
| | dH$_2$O to make | 100 mL |

Sprinkle gelatin over surface of 50 mL cold water. Dissolve by bringing to boil with constant stirring; remove from heat and bring up to 100 mL with dH$_2$O. Dispense into screw-cap test tubes, approximately 15 mL per tube.

Shelf life: dry gelatin, indefinite; colloidal suspension, several weeks in refrigeration, especially if screw-caps are tightly closed.
  Yield: 100 mL is generally adequate for 8 test tubes.

Potassium dichromate, 0.02 M (100 mL):	potassium dichromate (K$_2$Cr$_2$O$_7$) (MW = 294.21)	0.588 g
	dH$_2$O to make	100 mL
Aniline blue, 0.02 M (100 mL):	aniline blue WS (C$_{32}$H$_{25}$N$_3$O$_9$S$_3$Na$_2$) (MW = 737.742)	1.475 g
	dH$_2$O to make	100 mL
Janus green, 0.02 M (100 mL):	Janus green B (C$_{30}$H$_{31}$ClN$_6$) (MW = 511.09)	1.022 g
	dH$_2$O to make	100 mL

Solute diffusion set-up: 8 to 12 hours before class time, pipet 1 mL of dye solution atop solidified gelatin in appropriately labeled tubes. Place one set of tubes (labeled "4°C") with dyes into 4°C refrigerator; other set (labeled "Room Temperature") should remain at room temperature.
  Tubes labeled "4°C" should remain in refrigerator except when actually being used in laboratory class. Return tubes to refrigerator immediately after student observation of this part is finished.

7.2 Experiment: Osmosis

Sucrose, 15% and 30% (100 mL): Prepare 30% sucrose and then dilute portions of it to make 15% sucrose.

| | sucrose (C$_{12}$H$_{22}$O$_{11}$) | 300 g |
| | dH$_2$O | 1000 mL |

Mix 1 part dH$_2$O with 1 part 30% sucrose to make 15% sucrose.
Yield: 1000 mL 30% sucrose is sufficient for 4 student groups. 100 mL 15% sucrose is sufficient for at least 7 student groups. To conserve materials, students may be able to reuse the 30% sucrose from beaker 4 through several laboratory sections.

7.3 Experiment: Selective Permeability of Membranes

1% soluble starch in 1% Na$_2$SO$_4$ (1 L):	Soluble starch (potato)	10 g
	Na$_2$SO$_4$	10 g
	dH$_2$O	1000 mL

Make a thin paste of the starch and a small amount of the water. Bring the remaining water to a boil and, with constant stirring, add the starch paste. Allow to cool, then add the Na$_2$SO$_4$.
  Yield: 1 L starch-Na$_2$SO$_4$ solution is generally adequate for 35 groups.

1% albumin in 1% NaCl (1 L):	albumin, soluble	10 g
	NaCl	10 g
	dH$_2$O	1000 mL

Yield: 1 L is generally sufficient for 5 student groups.

Iodine (I₂KI) solution (100 mL):	potassium iodide (KI)	7 g
	iodine (I₂)	1 g
	dH₂O	100 mL

Dissolve the potassium iodide in the water, then add the iodine and stir until dissolved.
Shelf life: months, if stored in darkened glass bottle.

| *2% barium chloride* (100 mL): | barium chloride (BaCl₂) | 2 g |
| | dH₂O | 100 mL |

| *2% silver nitrate* (100 mL): | silver nitrate (AgNO₃) | 2 g |
| | dH₂O | 100 mL |

*Preparation of positive test **demonstration** tubes:* Label 4 test tubes as follows: Tube 1, "starch"; Tube 2, "sulfate"; Tube 3, "chloride"; Tube 4, "protein." Half-fill the tubes as follows:

Tubes 1 and 2—1% soluble starch in 1% Na_2SO_4
Tubes 3 and 4—1% albumin in 1% NaCl

Add several drops of the solution indicated below to the appropriate tubes:

Tube 1—iodine (I₂KI) solution
Tube 2—2% barium chloride (BaCl₂)
Tube 3—2% silver nitrate (AgNO₃)
Tube 4—biuret reagent

The appropriate reactions described in the laboratory manual should be visible. Display these **demonstration** tubes in a rack in the laboratory.

7.4 Experiment: Plasmolysis in Plant Cells

| *20% NaCl* (100 mL): | sodium chloride (NaCl) | 20 g |
| | dH₂O | 100 mL |

7.5 Experiment: Osmotic Changes in Red Blood Cells

0.9% sodium chloride (physiological saline) (100 mL):		
	sodium chloride (NaCl)	0.9 g
	dH₂O	100 mL

| *10% sodium chloride* (100 mL): | sodium chloride (NaCl) | 10 g |
| | dH₂O | 100 mL |

7.6 Experiment: Determining the Concentration of Solutes in Cells

| *0.15M sucrose* (1 l): | sucrose | 51.3 g |
| | dH₂O to make | 1000 mL |

| *0.20M sucrose* (1 l) | sucrose | 68.5 g |
| | dH₂O to make | 1000 mL |

| *0.25M sucrose* (1 l): | sucrose | 85.6 g |
| | dH₂O to make | 1000 mL |

| *0.30M sucrose* (1 l): | sucrose | 102.7 g |
| | dH₂O to make | 1000 mL |

| *0.35M sucrose* (1 l): | sucrose | 119.8 g |
| | dH₂O to make | 1000 mL |

Yield: 1 L of each of these solutions should be adequate for approximately 10 student groups.

Notes

7.2 Experiment: Osmosis

Students often need much time to set up this portion of the exercise. The instructor may wish to prepare some materials beforehand (e.g.,dialysis tubing bags) in order to have sufficient time for the rest of the exercise.

One 100-foot roll of dialysis tubing should be adequate for 200 15-cm strips. Cut a roll on a band saw to quickly provide strips approximately 15 cm long. Special dialysis membrane closures are available (Fisher 08-670-11A), but are expensive.

7.3 Experiment: Selective Permeability of Membranes

Special dialysis membrane closures are available (Fisher 08-670-11A), but are expensive.

7.4 Experiment: Plasmolysis in Plant Cells

Elodea should be rinsed in clean water before using. Hold it in a bowl of tap water for class use. It is important that only young leaves be used for microscopic observation since these are only a few cell layers thick. Older leaves are thicker, making observation of a single cell difficult.

Ordering Information

See General Laboratory Supplies list on page vii for basic items

7.1 Experiment: Rate of Diffusion of Solutes

aniline blue, water soluble	Fisher	A967-25
gelatin	local grocery store	
Janus green B	Carolina	86-9573
potassium dichromate	Fisher	P188-500

7.2 Experiment: Osmosis

dialysis tubing, 1 in. wide, 100 ft. roll	Carolina	68-4216
string tags	local office supply	

7.3 Experiment: Selective Permeability of Membranes

albumin	Fisher	A388-500
albustix reagent strips (optional)	Fisher	AM2870
barium chloride	Fisher	B34-500
biuret reagent	Fisher	S93405
dialysis tubing, 1 in. wide, 100 ft. roll	Carolina	68-4216
iodine (I_2)	Fisher	I37-100
potassium iodide	Fisher	P410-100
silver nitrate	Fisher	S181-25
sodium chloride	Fisher	S271-500
sodium sulfate	Fisher	S419-500
starch, soluble (potato)	Fisher	S71202

7.4 Experiment: Plasmolysis in Plant Cells

sodium chloride (NaCl)	Fisher	S271-500
Elodea	Carolina	15-7350

Elodea can often be purchased from aquarium supply shops

7.5 Experiment: Osmotic Changes in Red Blood Cells

sheep blood, defibrinated	Carolina	82-8890
sodium chloride	Fisher	S271-500

7.6 Experiment: Determining the Concentration of Solutes in Cells

sucrose	Fisher	S5-500

Answers to In-text Questions

7.1 Experiment: Rate of Diffusion of Solutes

Two sets of three screw-cap test tubes have been half-filled with 5% gelatin; and 1 mL of a dye has been added to each test tube. Set 1 is in a 5°C refrigerator; set 2 is at room temperature. Record the time at which your instructor tells you the experiment was started: **(variable answer)**

TABLE 7-1 Effect of Temperature on Diffusion Rates of Various Solutes				
	Set 1 (5°C)		**Set 2 (Room Temp.)**	
Solute (dye)	**Distance (mm)**	**Rate**	**Distance (mm)**	**Rate**
Potassium dichromate (MW = 294)	**fastest**		**Fastest**	
Janus green (MW = 511)	**intermediate**		**intermediate**	
Aniline blue (MW = 738)	**slowest**		**Slowest**	

Which of the solutes diffused the slowest (regardless of temperature)? **Aniline blue.**
Which diffused the fastest? **Potassium dichromate.**
What effect did temperature have on the rate of diffusion? **Lowering the temperature slowed the rate of diffusion.**

Make a conclusion about the diffusion of a solute in a gel, relating the rate of diffusion to the molecular weight of the solute and to temperature. **The rate of diffusion of a solute in a gel is inversely proportional to the solute's molecular weight and directly proportional to the temperature to which the solute/gel is subjected.**

7.2 Experiment: Osmosis

(Results shown are from experiments performed by a sample class)

TABLE 7-2 Change in Weight as a Consequence of Osmosis								
			Bag Weight (g)					
Bag	**Bag contents**	**Beaker Contents**	**0 min.**	**15 min.**	**30 min.**	**45 min.**	**60 min.**	**Weight Change (g)**
1	dH$_2$O	dH$_2$O						**+0.65 g**
2	15% sucrose	dH$_2$O						**+2.4 g**
3	30% sucrose	dH$_2$O						**+3.74 g**
4	dH$_2$O	30% sucrose						**-3.49 g**

*These are the averages for one class' results. Your results will vary slightly.

Make a *qualitative* statement about what you have observed. **The bag that contained the sucrose solution became more "plump," indicating that the net movement of water took place from the beaker into the bags. By contrast, the bag that was filled with distilled water and soaked in the sucrose solution shrank, indicating that some of the water from the bag moved into the sucrose solution. There was no change in the bag containing distilled water that was soaked in distilled water .**

Was the direction of *net* movement of water in bags 2–4 into or out of the bags? **Into the bags.**

Which bag gained the most weight? Why? **The bag containing 30% sucrose soaked in distilled water gained the most weight because the high sucrose concentration (low water concentration) in the bag resulted in greater net movement of water into the bag.**

7.3 Experiment: Selective Permeability of Membranes

18. Record your results of this series of tests in Table 7-4

To which substances was the dialysis tubing permeable? **Sulfate and chloride ions.**

What physical property of the dialysis tubing might explain its differential permeability? **The size of pores in the bag.**

TABLE 7-3 Results of Tests for Substances in Beaker [a]

	At Start of Experiment	After 75 min
Starch	-	-
Sulfate ion	-	+
Chloride ion	+	+
Albumin	+	+

[a] Contents of beaker:(+) = presence, (-) = absence

TABLE 7-4 Results of Tests for Substances in Dialysis Bag [a]

	At Start of Experiment	After 75 min
Starch	+	+
Sulfate ion	+	+
Chloride ion	-	+
Albumin	-	-

[a] Contents of dialysis bag:(+) = presence, (-) = absence

7.4 Experiment: Plasmolysis in Plant Cells

5. Label the photomicrograph of turgid cells (Figure 7-3) **Labels from left to right: cell wall, nucleus (provided), chloroplasts in cytoplasm, central vacuole.**

6. Now observe the leaf mounted in 20% NaCl solution. After several minutes, the cell will have lost water, causing it to become **plasmolyzed.** (This process is called **plasmolysis.**) Label the plasmolyzed cells shown in Figure 7-4. **Figure 7.4, Labels (from left to right): plasma membrane, cell wall, chloroplasts in cytoplasm, space (between cell wall and plasma membrane).**

Were the contents of the vacuole in the *Elodea* leaf in distilled water hypotonic, isotonic, or hypertonic compared to the dH_2O? **Hypertonic.**
Was the 20% NaCl solution hypertonic, isotonic, or relative to the cytoplasm? **Hypertonic.**

If a hypotonic and a hypertonic solution are separated by a selectively permeable membrane, which direction will the water move? **Net movement of water will take place from the hypotonic solution into the hypertonic solution.**

Name two selectively permeable membranes that are present within the *Elodea* cells and that were involved in the plasmolysis process. **1. Plasma membrane 2. Vacuolar membrane**

7.5 Experiment: Osmotic Changes in Red Blood Cells

16. Record the relative tonicity of the sodium chloride solutions you added to the test tubes in Table 7-5. Why do red blood cells burst when put in a hypotonic solution whereas *Elodea* leaf cells do not? **Blood cells lack a cell wall to keep the contents inside. The plasma membrane of the plant cell pushes against the cell wall but the pressure exerted by the cell wall prevents enough water from entering the cytoplasm to call the cell to burst**.

TABLE 7-5 Effect of Salt Solutions on Red Blood Cells

Tube	Contents	Print Visible?	Microscopic Appearance of Cells	Tonicity of External Solution[a]
1	**0.9% NaCl + blood**	No	**Normal (bi-concave discs)**	Isotonic
2	**10% NaCl + blood**	Yes	**Crenate**	Hypertonic
3	**0.9% NaCl + dH₂O+ blood**	Yes	**Absent**	Hypotonic

[a]With respect to that inside the red blood cells at the start of experiment.

7.6 Experiment: Determining the Concentration of Solutes in Cells

(Results shown are from experiments performed by a sample class)

TABLE 7-6 Determining the Solute Concentration in Potato Tuber Cells

Solution	Weight Initial	Final	Change	Percent Change
0.15 M				+5.6%*
0.20 M				+3.2%
0.25 M				+1.9%
0.30 M				+0.8%
0.35 M				-1.1%

*These are the averages for one class' results. Results will vary slightly depending on tuber quality.

What was the approximate concentration of solute in the potato tuber? **0.32 M**

Which concentration resulted in the *greatest* percentage change? **0.15 M**

Make a statement that relates the amount of water loss or gain to the concentration of the solute. **More water will be gained by the tuber placed in a solution that is most different from the naturally occurring tuber solute concentration**.

Name _____

Section No. _____

DIFFUSION, OSMOSIS, AND THE FUNCTIONAL SIGNIFICANCE OF BIOLOGICAL MEMBRANES

Pre-lab Questions

1. Which of the following reagents does not fit with the substance being tested for? a. biuret reagent protein; b. $BaCl_2$ starch; c. $AgNO_3$ chloride ion; d. albustix protein

2. A solvent is: a. the substance in which solutes are dissolved; b. a salt or sugar; c. one component of a biological membrane; d. selectively permeable.

3. Specifically, osmosis: a. requires the expenditure of celluler energy; b. is diffusion of water from one region to another; c. is diffusion of water across a selectively permeable membrane; d. none of the above.

4. An example of a solute would be: a. Janus green B; b. water; c. sucrose; d. both a and c.

5. If one solution contains 10% NaCl and another contains 30% NaCl, the 30% solution is a. isotonic; b. hypotonic; c. hypertonic; d. plasmolyzed.

6. Dialysis membrane is: a. selectively permeable; b. used in these experiments to simulate cellular membranes; c. permeable to water but not to sucrose; d. all of the above.

7. If one were to identify a single most important compound for sustenance of life, it would probably be: a. salt; b. $BaCl_2$; c. water; d. I_2KI.

8. Cellular membranes: a. consist of a phospholipid bilayer containing embedded proteins; b. control the movement of substances into and out of cells; c. are selectively permeable; d. are all of the above.

9. When the cytoplasm of a plant cell is pressed against the cell wall, the cell is said to be: a. turgid; b. plasmolyzed; c. hemolyzed; d. crenate.

10. Diffusion: a. is a process requiring cellular energy; b. is the movement of molecules from a region of higher concentration to one of lower concentration; c. occurs only across selectively permeable membranes; d. is none of the above.

EXERCISE 7

DIFFUSION, OSMOSIS, AND THE FUNCTIONAL SIGNIFICANCE OF BIOLOGICAL MEMBRANES

Answers to Pre-lab Questions in Lab Manual Order

1. c	6. d		
2. a	7. c		
3. b	8. b		
4. d	9. a		
5. d	10. c		

Answers to Pre-lab Questions in Instructor's Manual Order

1. b	6. d		
2. a	7. c		
3. c	8. d		
4. d	9. a		
5. c	10. b		

Answers to Post-lab Questions

1. You want to dissolve a solute in water. Without shaking or swirling the solution, what might you do to increase the rate at which the solute would go into solution? Relate your answer to your method's effect on the motion of the molecules. **Heat the water. This increases the number of collisions between molecules.**

2. If a 10% sugar solution is separated from a 20% sugar solution by a differentially permeable membrane, in which direction will there be a net movement of water? **10% sucrose is 90% water while 20% sucrose is 80% water. Therefore, water moves from the 10% sucrose to the 20% sucrose.**

3. Based upon your observations in this exercise, would you expect dialysis membrane to be permeable to sucrose? Why? **No. Since sucrose is a fairly large molecule, it would be too large to cross the pores.**

4. Suppose you are having a party and you plan to serve celery, but your celery has become limp and stores are closed. What might you do to make the celery crisp (turgid) again? **Put the celery in water. This will cause the cells that have lost water to regain it and become turgid again.**

5. Why don't plant cells undergo osmotic lysis? **Because they have a rigid cell wall surrounding the plasma membrane.**

6. This drawing represents a plant cell that has been placed in a solution. a. What *process* is taking place in the direction of the arrows? **Plasmolysis.** What is happening at the cellular level when a wilted plant is watered and begins to recover from the wilt? **The cells are taking in water and are becoming turgid.** b. Is the solution in which the cells have been placed hypotonic, isotonic, or hypertonic relative to the cytoplasm? **Hypertonic.**

7. A human lost at sea without fresh drinking water is effectively lost in an osmotic desert. Why would drinking salt water be harmful? **Same reasoning as question 5. Salt water is high in sodium chloride (salt). As a salt solution moves through the intestinal and excretory system, water would be drawn from the cells, resulting in dehydration.**

8. How does diffusion differ from osmosis? **Diffusion is the movement of solute molecules from a region of high to lower concentration. Osmosis is the movement of water across a differentially permeable membrane from a region of high to lower concentration.**

9. Plant fertilizer consists of numerous different solutes. A small dose of fertilizer may enhance plant growth, but overfertilization can kill the plant. Why might overfertilization have this effect? **Fertilizer is made up of numerous solute molecules. If the soil around a plant becomes loaded with solutes, water will move *out* of the cells of the root because of osmosis, rather than in.**

10. What does the word *lysis* mean? **To break.**

EXERCISE 8

ENZYMES: CATALYSTS OF LIFE

Materials and Equipment

8.1 Using a Spectronic 20 (Spec 20) to Determine Color Changes

Per student
- disposable plastic gloves

Per student group (4)
- 1-mL pipet and bulb
- 5-mL pipet and bulb
- Spec 20 spectrophotometer
- wash bottle of potato extract containing catechol oxidase
- bottle of dH_2O
- china marker

8.2 Formation and Detection of Benzoquinone

Per student
- disposable plastic gloves

Per student group (4)
- three test tubes, 16 x 125 mm
- test tube rack
- metric ruler
- wash bottle containing potato extract with catechol oxidase
- china marker
- ice bucket and ice
- bottle of dH_2O
- wash bottle containing 1% catechol solution

Per lab room
- 40°C waterbath plus test tube racks
- spectrophotometer (optional)
- vortex mixer (optional)

8.3 Experiment: Enzyme Specificity

Per student group (4)
- three test tubes, 16 x 125 mm
- test tube rack
- metric ruler
- wash bottle containing 1% catechol solution
- wash bottle containing 1% hydroxyquinone
- wash bottle containing potato extract with catechol oxidase
- china marker
- ice bucket and ice
- bottle of dH_2O

Per lab room
- 40°C waterbath plus test tube racks
- spectrophotometer (optional)
- vortex mixer (optional)
- box of disposable polyethylene gloves

8.4 Experiment: Effect of Temperature on Enzyme Activity

Per student group (4)
- six test tubes, 16 x 125 mm
- test tube rack
- metric ruler
- three 400-mL graduated beakers
- wash bottle containing 1% catechol solution
- wash bottle containing potato extract with catechol oxidase
- china marker
- ice bucket and ice
- bottle of dH_2O
- heat resistant glove
- Celsius thermometer

Per group (table)
- two hot plates **or** tripod
- boiling chips
- wire gauze square
- flint lighter
- laboratory burner
- spectrophotometer (optional)

Per lab room
- 40°C waterbath plus test tube racks
- 60°C waterbath plus test tube racks
- 80°C waterbath plus test tube racks
- vortex mixer (optional)
- carboy of room temperature water

8.5 Experiment: Effect of pH on Enzyme Activity

Per student group (4)
- seven test tubes, 16 x 125 mm
- test tube rack
- metric ruler
- wash bottle containing 1% catechol solution
- wash bottle containing potato extract with catechol oxidase
- china marker
- ice bucket and ice
- bottle of dH_2O

Per lab room
- 40°C waterbath plus test tube racks
- spectrophotometer (optional)
- buffer series, pH 2–12 (pH 2, 4, 6, 7, 8, 10, 12) in wash bottles
- vortex mixer (optional)
- box of disposable polyethylene gloves

8.6 Experiment: Necessity of Cofactors for Enzyme Activity

Per student pair
- two 16 x 125 mm test tubes in a rack
- scoopula (small spoon)
- metric ruler
- phenylthiourea crystals in small screw-cap bottle
- wash bottle containing 1% catechol solution
- wash bottle containing potato extract with catechol oxidase
- china marker
- ice bucket and ice
- bottle of dH_2O

Per lab room
- 40°C waterbath plus test tube racks
- spectrophotometer (optional)
- bottle of 95% ethanol (at each sink)
- vortex mixer (optional)
- box of disposable polyethylene gloves
- tissues (at each sink)

Preparation of Materials and Equipment

8.2 Formation and Detection of Benzoquinone

Potato extract with catechol oxidase (approx. 450 mL): Peel mature potato tubers (approximately 200 grams) and dice or slice thinly. Place in blender and add 500 mL dH_2O. Blend at high speed for two minutes. Strain solution through four layers of cheesecloth into beaker. Immediately pour into wash bottles, tightly close the bottles and place in icewater bath. Prepare this solution immediately before each laboratory session, as oxygen allows the enzymatic reaction to proceed. Unpredictable results may occur in class if the solution has aged. Use the smallest wash bottles possible so that the potato extract has minimal contact with atmospheric oxygen.

    Shelf life: short; prepare fresh when needed.

    Yield: 450 mL extract should be sufficient for 3 or 4 student groups to perform all 5 parts of this exercise.

1% catechol (100 mL):	Catechol	1 g
	distilled water	100 mL

    Yield: 100 mL 1% catechol should be sufficient for two student groups to perform all five parts of this exercise.

8.3 Experiment: Enzyme Specificity

Potato extract with catechol oxidase: See above.
1% catechol: See above.

1% hydroquinone (100 mL):	Hydroquinone	1 g
	distilled water	100 mL

    Yield: 100 mL 1% hydroquinone should be sufficient for 50 student groups.

8.4 Experiment: Effect of Temperature on Enzyme Activity

Potato extract with catechol oxidase: See above.
1% catechol: See above.

8.5 Experiment: Effect of pH on Enzyme Activity

Potato extract with catechol oxidase: See above.
1% catechol: See above.

pH 2–12 buffer series: Mix Solution A and Solution B according to the chart below to prepare 1 L of a buffer solution of the desired pH. *Yield:* 1 L of each buffer is generally adequate for 240 student groups.

    Solution A: Dissolve 12.37 g anhydrous boric acid (H_3BO_3) and 10.51 g citric acid ($H_3C_6H_5O_7 \cdot H_2O$) in distilled water and dilute to 1 L in a volumetric flask.

    Solution B: Dissolve 38.01 g $Na_3PO_4 \cdot 12H_2O$ in dH_2O and dilute to 1 L in a volumetric flask.

Desired pH	Solution A, mL	Solution B, mL
2.0	975	25
4.0	775	225
6.0	590	410
7.0	495	505
8.0	425	575
10.0	270	730
12.0	85	915

8.6 Experiment: Necessity of Cofactors for Enzyme Activity

Potato extract with catechol oxidase: See above.
1% catechol: See above.

Notes

This exercise consists of five parts that, taken together, require a minimum of two hours of intense lab activity. If the instructor must provide an introduction and/or quiz at the start of the laboratory session, each student group will not be able to complete all parts in two hours. A possible solution is to assign different parts to each student group. (Note: not all groups should do part 8.2, however.) A representative of each group should then describe the experiment and results to the entire class.

8.2 Formation and Detection of Benzoquinone

Students tend not to understand that the catechol oxidase is a component of the potato extract. We suggest labeling the bottles "Potato extract containing catechol oxidase" to avoid confusion.

Results: reaction proceeds in Tube I_1, containing both substrate and enzyme, only.

8.3 Experiment: Enzyme Specificity

Results: reaction proceeds in Tube II_1 rapidly, in Tube II_2 more slowly, since hydroquinone does not "fit" the active site as well as catechol.

8.4 Experiment: Effect of Temperature on Enzyme Activity

Results: enzyme activity occurs at $0^{\circ}C$ through $80^{\circ}C$, with optimum near $40^{\circ}C$. Activity is low at $0^{\circ}C$, slightly impaired at $60^{\circ}C$, highly impaired at $80^{\circ}C$. No activity at $100^{\circ}C$.

8.5 Experiment: Effect of pH on Enzyme Activity

Buffers may be ordered in prepackaged dry form if desired (see *Ordering Information*). Each "Chemvelope" is dissolved in dH_2O to make 500 mL buffer with 5 Chemvelopes per carton unit.

Buffers of the highest and lowest extremes of pH may, when combined with potato extract, be lightly tinted in various colors. Students may believe this to be a positive indication of benzoquinone, but should be reminded to compare their tubes with the color standard they produced in part I.

Results: expect minimal activity at pH 2, low activity at pH 4, strong activity at pH 6-10, and minimal at pH 12.

8.6 Experiment: Necessity of Cofactors for Enzyme Activity

Results: no activity in tube V_1 (with PTU) because copper is a necessary cofactor for catechol oxidase.

Ordering Information

See General Laboratory Supplies list on page vii for basic items

8.1 Using a Spectronic 20 (Spec 20) to Determine Color Changes

Spectronic 20	Fisher	14-385-445

8.2 Formation and Detection of Benzoquinone

catechol	Fisher	P370-500

8.3 Experiment: Enzyme Specificity

catechol	Fisher	P370-500
hydroquinone	Carolina	86-8230
polyethylene gloves, disposable	Fisher	11-394-100B

8.4 Experiment: Effect of Temperature on Enzyme Activity

catechol	Fisher	P370-500

8.5 Experiment: Effect of pH on Enzyme Activity

buffer, "Chemvelope"— pH 2.0	Carolina	84-9330
buffer, "Chemvelope"— pH 4.0	Carolina	84-9350
buffer, "Chemvelope"— pH 6.0	Carolina	84-9370
buffer, "Chemvelope"— pH 7.0	Carolina	84-9380
buffer, "Chemvelope"— pH 8.0	Carolina	84-9390
buffer, "Chemvelope"— pH 10.0	Carolina	84-9410
buffer, "Chemvelope"— pH 12.0	Carolina	84-9430
anhydrous boric acid	Fisher	A74-500
sodium phosphate, tribasic	Fisher	S377-500
catechol	Fisher	P370-500
citric acid, monohydrate	Fisher	A104-500

8.6 Experiment: Necessity of Cofactors for Enzyme Activity

catechol	Fisher	P370-500
phenylthiourea	Carolina	88-1218
microspoon	Carolina	70-2706
ethanol, 95%	Carolina	86-1281

Answers to In-text Questions

Note: Potato extract after filtration is light brown due to formation of benzoquinone resulting from the reaction of catechol and oxygen. Potato extract should be kept in ice bath to minimize the formation of benzoquinone.

8.2 Formation and Detection of Benzoquinone

TABLE 8-1 Formation and Detection of Benzoquinone: Record Color			
Time	**Tube 2$_A$: Potato Extract and Catechol**	**Tube 2$_B$: Potato Extract and Water**	**Tube 2$_C$: Catechol and Water**
0 min	pale pink	pale pink	colorless
10 min	red-brown	pale pink	colorless

What is the brown-colored substance that appeared in tube 2$_A$? **Benzoquinone**
What is the substrate for the reaction that occurred in tube 2$_A$? **Catechol**
What is the product of the reaction in tube 2$_A$? **Benzoquinone**
What substances do tubes 2$_B$ and 2$_C$ lack that account for the absence of the brown-colored substance?
2$_B$ **catechol;** 2$_C$ **catechol oxidase**
What is the purpose of tubes 2$_B$ and 2$_C$? **These are controls.**

TABLE 8-2 Color Intensity Scale or Absorbance		
Intensity/Absorbance	**Tube**	**Color of Product**
0/0	2$_C$	colorless
0/0.62	2$_B$	pale pink
5/1.2	2$_A$	red-brown

8.3 Experiment: Enzyme Specificity

11. Upon which substrate does catechol oxidase work best, forming the most benzoquinone in the shortest amount of time? **Catechol**
12. Based on your knowledge of the structures of the two substrates, what apparently determines the specificity of catechol oxidase? **The location of the hydroxyl (-OH) group on the ring.**
13. Why was tube 3C included in this experiment? **This is a control for the experiment.**

TABLE 8-3 Specificity of Catechol Oxidase for Different Substrates

Prediction: (variable student answers)

Time	Relative Color Intensity or Absorbance		
	Tube 3$_A$: Catechol	Tube 3$_B$: Hydroquinone	Tube 3$_C$: dH$_2$0
0 min.	0	0	0
10 min.	5 /0.61	3/0.37	0/0
Conclusion			

(Absorbance figures are from one run. Your results may vary.)

8.4 Experiment: Effect of Temperature on Enzyme Activity

7. (f) Temperature of boiling water: **100°C**

14. *Color-intensity method:* Record the color intensity (scale 0-5) of each tube's content in Table 8-4.

TABLE 8-4 Effect of Temperature on Enzyme Activity

Prediction: (variable student answers)

Time	Relative Color Intensity or Absorbance					
	Tube 4$_A$	Tube 4$_B$	Tube 4$_C$	Tube 4$_D$	Tube 4$_E$	Tube 4$_F$
0 min						
10 min.	3	4	5	2.5	1	1
Conclusion: (variable student answers)						

Table represents expected color intensity trend on a scale of 0-5.

16. Plot the data from table 8-4 for the 10 minute reading in figure 8-5.

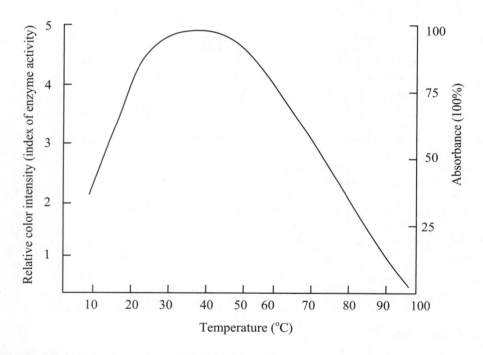

Figure 8-5 Effect of temperature on catechol oxidase activity.

17. Over what temperature *range* is catechol oxidase active? **0-60C**

18. What is the *optimum* temperature for activity of this enzyme? **40C**

19. What happens to enzyme activity at very high temperatures? **With this enzyme, it ceases to function (due to becoming denatured).**

8.5 Experiment: Effect of pH on Enzyme Activity

11. *Color-intensity method:* Record the color intensity (scale 0-5) of each tubes content in Table 8-5.

	Relative color intensity or Absorbance						
Time	**Tube 5$_A$ (pH 2)**	**Tube 5$_B$ (pH 4)**	**Tube 5$_C$ (pH 6)**	**Tube 5$_D$ (pH 7)**	**Tube 5$_E$ (pH 8)**	**Tube 5$_F$ (pH 10)**	**Tube 5$_G$ (pH 12)**
0 min.	0	0	0	0	0	0	0
10 min.	0	2	4	5	4	2	0

TABLE 8-5 Effect of pH on Enzyme Activity
Prediction: **(variable student answers)**
Conclusion: **(variable student answers)**

13. Plot the data from table 8-5 for your ten minute reading in figure 6-6

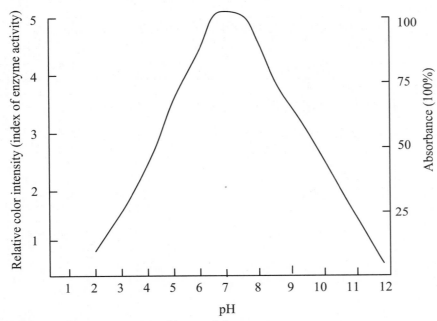

Figure 8-6 Effect of pH on catechol oxidase activity

14. Over what pH *range* does catechol oxidase catalyze catechol to benzoquinone? **pH 4-10**
15. What is the *optimum* pH for catechol oxidase? **pH 7**

8.6 Experiment: Necessity of Cofactors for Enzyme Activity

TABLE 8-6 Is Copper a Cofactor for Catechol Oxidase?		
Prediction: (variable student answers)		
	Relative Color Intensity or Absorbance	
Time	Tube 6_A: with PTU	Tube 6_B: without PTU
0 min	0	0
10 min	0	5
Conclusion: **Copper is required—it is a co-factor.**		

13. Did benzoquinone form in tube 6A? In tube 6B? **In 6A, no. In 6B, yes.**

14. From this experiment, what can you conclude about the necessity for copper for catechol oxidase activity?
Copper is a necessary co-factor for catechol oxidase.

15. What substance used in this experiment contained copper? **Catechol**

Name _____

Section No. _____

ENZYMES: CATALYSTS OF LIFE

Pre-lab Questions

1. For every 10°C rise in temperature, the rate of most chemical reactions will: a. double; b. triple; c. increase by 100 times; d. stop.

2. When an enzyme becomes denatured, it: a. increases in effectiveness; b. loses its requirement for a cofactor; c. forms an enzyme-substrate complex; d. loses its ability to function.

3. Catechol oxidase: a. is an enzyme found in potatoes; b. catalyzes the production of catechol; c. has as its substrate benzoquinone; d. is a substance that encourages the growth of microorganisms.

4. Enzymes function by: a. being consumed (used up) in the reaction; b. lowering the activation energy of a reaction; c. combining with otherwise toxic substances in the cell; d. adding heat to the cell to speed up the reaction.

5. pH is a measure of: a. an enzyme's effectiveness; b. enzyme concentration; c. the hydrogen ion concentration; d. none of the above.

6. An enzyme may lose its ability to function because of: a. excessively high temperatures; b. a change in its three-dimensional structure; c. a large change in the pH of the environment; d. all of the above.

7. The relative color intensity used in the experiments of this exercise: a. is a consequence of production of benzoquinone; b. is an index of enzyme activity; c. may differ depending on the pH, temperature, or presence of cofactors, respectively; d. all of the above.

8. Enzymes are: a. biological catalysts; b. agents that speed up cellular reactions; c. proteins; d. all of the above.

9. Enzyme specificity refers to the: a. need for cofactors for the function of some enzymes; b. fact that enzymes catalyze one particular substrate or a small number of structurally similar substrates; c. effect of temperature on enzyme activity; d. effect of pH on enzyme activity.

10. The substance that an enzyme combines with is: a. another enzyme; b. a cofactor; c. a coenzyme; d. the substrate.

ENZYMES: CATALYSTS OF LIFE

Answers to Pre-lab Questions
in Lab Manual Order

1. d		6. d	
2. b		7. d	
3. d		8. c	
4. b		9. a	
5. a		10. d	

Answers to Pre-lab Questions
in Instructor's Manual Order

1. a		6. d	
2. d		7. d	
3. a		8. d	
4. b		9. b	
5. c		10. d	

Answers to Post-lab Questions

1. Eggs may contain bacteria such as *Salmonella*. Considering what you've learned in this exercise, explain how cooking eggs makes them safe to eat. **The high cooking temperatures denature bacterial enzymes, killing the bacteria.**

2. As you demonstrated in this experiment, high temperatures inactivate catechol oxidase. How is it that some bacteria live in the hot springs of Yellowstone Park at temperatures as high as 73°C? **The enzymes of these particular bacteria do not become denatured at extremely high temperatures.**

3. Why do you think high fevers alter cellular functions? **They cause enzymes to denature.**

4. Some surgical procedures involve lowering a patient's body temperature during periods when blood flow must be restricted. What effect might this have on enzyme-controlled cellular metabolism? **Lowers the rate of enzyme reactions; cellular processes are slowed, so demand for oxygen is not as great.**

5. At one time it was believed that individuals who had been submerged under water for longer than several minutes could not be resuscitated. Recently this has been shown to be false, especially if the person was in cold water. Explain why cold-water "drowning" victims might survive prolonged periods under water. **Cold slows cellular metabolism so less oxygen is required.**

6. Explain what happens to catechol oxidase when the pH is on either side of the optimum. **Slight changes in three-dimensional structure makes fit of active site less than perfect, slowing activity.**

7. What would you expect the pH optimum to be for an enzyme secreted into your stomach? **Low; in the acid range.**

8. Is it necessary for a cell to produce one enzyme molecule for every substrate molecule that needs to be catalyzed? Why or why not? **No. Enzymes are not used up during reactions so they can be reused.**

9. Explain the difference between *substrate* and *active site*. **The substrate is the molecule of the substance being acted upon by an enzyme molecule. The active site is a region of the enzyme molecule to which the substrate molecule binds.**

10. The photo shows slice of two apples. The one on the left sat on the counter for 15 minutes prior to being photographed. The one on the right was sliced immediately prior to the photo being taken. a. Explain as thoroughly as possible what you see and why the two slices differ. **The browning is due to the production of benzoquinone formed when the cut cells are exposed to oxygen.** b. If you don't want a cut apple to brown, what can you do to prevent it? **Cover the surface with an oxygen-impervious plastic wrap. Placing it in the refrigerator will slow the formation of benzoquinone.**

EXERCISE 9

PHOTOSYNTHESIS: CAPTURE OF LIGHT ENERGY

Materials and Equipment

9.1 Test for Starch

Per student
- dropper bottle of iodine (I_2KI) solution
- dropper bottle of glucose solution
- depression (spot) plate
- dropper bottle of starch solution
- dropper bottle of dH_2O

9.2 Experiment: Effects of Light and Carbon Dioxide on Starch Production

Per student group (4)
- two 400-mL beakers
- hot plate in fume hood
- petri dish halves
- forceps
- bottle of 95% ethanol (EtOH)
- square of aluminum foil
- heat resistant glove
- source of dH_2O

Per lab room
- Fast Plants[TM] 9 to 10 days old, grown for four days in three different environments:
   - I. normal conditions w/ both light and carbon dioxide
   - II. in dark, w/ normal carbon dioxide
   - III. in light, but w/ carbon dioxide removed

9.3 Experiment: Relationship Between Light and Photosynthetic Products

Per student group (4)
- china marker
- heat resistant glove
- hot plate in fume hood
- petri dish halves
- two 400-mL graduated beakers
- bottle of 95% ethanol
- forceps
- I_2KI in foil-wrapped stock bottle

Per lab room
- dH_2O carboy or tap
- light-grown geranium plant or leaves of geranium plant (see *Notes*)
- dark-grown geranium plant or leaves of geranium plant (kept in dark place; see *Notes*)

9.4 Experiment: Necessity of Photosynthetic Pigments for Photosynthesis

Per student group (4)
- colored pencils or pens
- hot plate in fume hood
- petri dish halves
- bottle of 95% ethanol (EtOH)
- two 400-mL beakers
- heat-resistant glove
- bottle of iodine solution
- forceps

Per lab room
- dH_2O carboy or tap
- variegated *Coleus* or geranium (*Pelargonium*) plants

9.5 Experiment: Absorption of Light by Chloroplast Extract

Per student
- hand-held spectroscope (optional)

Per lab room
- several spectroscope set-ups
- lamp sockets (1 per spectroscope)
- beaker, 50 mL (1 per spectroscope; see *Note*)
- colored filters (blue, green, red) (1 per spectroscope)
- sets of colored pencils (violet, blue, green, yellow, orange, red)
- 10 x 75 mm corked test tubes containing spectroscope
- inside-frost showcase lamps, 40-watt (1 per spectroscope) *Note*: Keep extra lamps on hand to replace any that burn out.
- ring stands (1 per spectroscope)
- utility jaw clamps (1 per spectroscope)

9.6 Separation of Photosynthetic Pigments by Paper Chromatography

Per student
- chromatography paper, Whatman No. 1, 3 cm x 15 cm sheets
- metric ruler
- pencil

Per student pair
- chromatography chamber with solvent
- chloroplast pigment extract in foil-wrapped dropping bottle (see *Notes*)
- colored pencils (green, blue-green, yellow, orange)

9.7 Structure of the Chloroplast

None required.

Preparation of Materials and Equipment

9.1 Test for Starch

Iodine (I_2KI) solution (100 mL):

potassium iodide (KI)	7 g
iodine (I_2)	10 g
dH$_2$O	100 mL

Dissolve the potassium iodide in the water. Add the iodine and stir until dissolved. Store in foil-wrapped or brown glass bottle.

Yield: 100 mL I$_2$KI is sufficient for 2 or 3 student groups (8 to 12 students) per experiment.

Starch solution (1L):

soluble starch (potato)	10 g
dH$_2$O	1000 mL

Make a thin paste by combining the starch and a small amount of the water. Heat the remainder of the water to boiling. Remove boiling water from burner and add starch paste while stirring constantly.

Yield: 1000 mL starch solution is sufficient for 200 student groups.

Glucose solution (100 mL):

glucose (dextrose)	10 g
dH$_2$O	100 mL

Yield: 100 mL is sufficient for 100 student groups.

9.2 Experiment: Effects of Light and Carbon Dioxide on Starch Production

Iodine (I_2KI) solution (See above)

9.3 Experiment: Relationship Between Light and Photosynthetic Products

Iodine (I_2KI) solution (See above)

9.4 Experiment: Necessity of Photosynthetic Pigments for Photosynthesis

Iodine (I_2KI) solution (See above)

9.5 Experiment: Absorption of Light by Chloroplast Extract

Colored filters: Filters can be made by placing layers of cellophane between glass plates used for 2 x 2 projection slides. Use one layer of red cellophane and three layers each for blue and green. These will not be perfectly monochromatic.

Monochromatic filters can be purchased (see *Ordering Information*).

Preparation of pigment extract (300 mL):

Chemicals and Solutions

acetone (CH_3COCH_3) chilled, 200 mL   95% ethanol, 100 mL

Materials and Equipment

whole-leaf spinach, 10-oz., frozen, 1 pkg.	Buchner funnel
paper toweling	side-arm filter flask
carrot root, 1 medium	aspirator or vacuum pump
vegetable peeler	Whatman No. 1 filter paper
Funnel	Beaker
brown glass bottle *or* Wheaton bottle wrapped in aluminum foil	

CAUTION: PERFORM EXTRACTION IN FUMEHOOD

Procedure

1. Thaw frozen spinach.
2. Press leaves between paper towels until *thoroughly dry*.
3. Carotene content of spinach leaves is variable. To ensure adequate carotene, add a handful of carrot peelings to the spinach leaves during extraction.
4. Extract pigments from leaves in chilled acetone in covered beaker for 10 min.
5. Decant and save acetone; cover to prevent evaporation.
6. Further extract pigments from leaves in 95% ethanol for 5 min.
7. Decant ethanol and combine with acetone extract.
8. Vacuum filter through Buchner funnel with Whatman No. 1 filter paper to remove debris.
9. Store in brown glass or foil-wrapped bottle and refrigerate until use.
10. This extract is generally too concentrated to give satisfactory results in a spectroscope and should be diluted, 1 part pigment extract to 4 parts acetone-ethanol solvent. Properly diluted, both the absorption bands and the unabsorbed portions of the spectrum will be clearly visible.

Shelf life: several weeks under refrigeration.
Yield: 300 mL undiluted pigment extract is generally adequate for 75 students to perform parts II and III.

Note: Frozen spinach can be used as directed above, or fresh spinach can be used. Break apart the fresh spinach leaves and disrupt the cells with a mortar and pestle before continuing the extract at step 3.

9.6 Separation of Photosynthetic Pigments by Paper Chromatography

Pigment extract: as in part II.

Chromatography solvent (100 mL):	petroleum ether	90 mL
	acetone (CH_3COCH_3)	10 mL

> **CAUTION: Solvents are HIGHLY FLAMMABLE. Keep tightly closed.**

Shelf life: indefinite, but acetone preferentially evaporates. Fresh solvent should be prepared each day to ensure good results.

Yield: 100 mL solvent is adequate for approximately 4 chromatography chambers.

9.7 Structure of the Chloroplast

None required.

Notes

9.2 Experiment: Effects of Light and Carbon Dioxide on Starch Production

Brassica rapa Fast Plants™ seedlings can be grown in film canisters. Drill a small hole in the bottom of each canister and insert an absorbent cotton string to act as a wick. Fill with moist fine potting mix, seed, and water until water drips through the wick. Set the canisters so that the wick is immersed in water or on a water wicking fabric. Plants will need continuous high light intensity once growth is begun. Plant about 1 week before putting the canisters and plants into the different treatments. The plants should remain in the various treatment conditions for 4 days prior to the lab experiment.

Use a glass desiccator to create the environment without CO_2. Place water in the bottom of the desiccator, then set the canisters on the platform with string wicks extending into water. Also place an open container of KOH pellets inside the desiccator before sealing it. The KOH removes the CO_2 from the atmosphere trapped inside. The "normal condition" plants and the "without CO_2" remain under lights, but the "dark grown" plants should have a box placed over them, or place them in a dark cupboard.

9.3 Experiment: Relationship Between Light and Photosynthetic Products

Portions of the leaves of all geranium plants should be masked with aluminum foil (attach with paper clips) a week before use. Place half the plants (labeled "Dark-grown") in the dark at least two days before use so that all starch may be translocated from the leaves. Illuminate the other plants (labeled "Light-grown") with continuous bright fluorescent light for two days prior to use to ensure maximum starch production. A starch reaction should be plainly visible only in the uncovered portion of the light-grown leaves.

9.5 Experiment: Absorption of Light by Chloroplast Extract

Use 50-mL beakers to hold 10 x 75 mm test tubes of pigment extract and acetone-ethanol solvent. The pigment breaks down in the presence of light. Keep several tubes on reserve in the refrigerator.

SLD Lighting sells 20" x 24" colored theatre gel transparency films. The films are not completely monochromatic, but are much more so than others available from biological supply houses or craft supply stores.

9.6 Separation of Photosynthetic Pigments by Paper Chromatography

Insert a micropipet into a cork that fits the pigment extract-containing dropping bottle *or* flame the tip of a disposable glass pipet to reduce the diameter of the opening. Either method will produce droplets that won't flood the chromatography paper.

Follow your institution's guidelines for disposal of waste solvents at the completion of this exercise. Waste solvent bottles (not glass) should be stored in a fume hood.

The order of pigments, top to bottom, on the paper following chromatographic separation is: xanthophylls, carotenes, chlorophyll a, chlorophyll b.

Ordering Information

See General Laboratory Supplies list on page vii for basic items

9.1 Test for Starch

depression (spot) plate	Carolina	74-3043
Glucose	Sigma	G8270
iodine, I_2	Fisher	I37-100
potassium iodide, KI	Fisher	P410-100
starch, potato	Fisher	S71202

9.2 Experiment: Effects of Light and Carbon Dioxide on Starch Production

35 mm film canister	local film processing center	
95% ethanol	Carolina	86-1283
aluminum foil	purchased locally	
iodine, I_2	Fisher	I37-100
potassium iodide, KI	Fisher	P410-100
Basic RCBr (Wisconsin Fast Plants™) seeds, (200)	Carolina	15-8805

9.3 Experiment: Relationship between Light and Photosynthetic Products

potassium iodide, KI	Fisher	P410-100
iodine, I_2	Fisher	I37-100
starch, potato	Fisher	S71202
95% ethanol	Carolina	86-1283

9.4 Experiment: Necessity of Photosynthetic Pigments for Photosynthesis

95% ethanol	Carolina	86-1283
potassium iodide, KI	Fisher	P410-100
iodine, I_2	Fisher	I37-100
Coleus (can purchase from local greenhouse; should have both white/yellow areas and green areas)	Carolina	15-7312

9.5 Experiment: Absorption of Light by Chloroplast Extract

95% ethanol	Carolina	86-1283
Acetone	Fisher	A18-500
grating spectroscope	Carolina	75-5330
inside-frost showcase lamps, 40 watt	local electrical supply	
lamp sockets	hardware store	
ring stands	Fisher	14-670B
sidearm filtering flask	Fisher	10-180E
spectroscope (hand held)	Ward's	25W 4996
utility jaw clamps	Fisher	05-769-5
cellophane (red, blue, green)	art and craft supply store	
Monochromatic gel light filters		
Brilliant Blue - SLD Lighting R69		
Moss Green - SLD Lighting R89		
Light Red - SLD Lighting R26		

9.6 Separation of Photosynthetic Pigments by Paper Chromatography

Acetone	Fisher	A18-500
chromatography paper, Whatman No. 1	Fisher	05-714
petroleum ether	Fisher	E139-500

9.7 Structure of the Chloroplast

None required.

Answers to In-text Questions

9.1 Test for Starch

2. Record your observations. How can you identify the presence of starch? Observations: **Water and starch solution droplets appear yellowish (color of iodine solution), while starch solution droplet appears bluish-black to very dark brown. Starch can be identified by production of dark brown-black color using iodine test.**

9.2 Experiment: Effects of Light and Carbon Dioxide on Starch Production

TABLE 9-1 Effect of Light and Carbon Dioxide on Starch Presence

Fast Plants™ Growing Condition	Appearance	Prediction	Starch Presence and Location
I. Normal conditions with both light and carbon dioxide	**Healthy, deep green color of shoots; plant may have buds**	**If light and carbon dioxide are both necessary for photosynthesis, then plants will show abundant starch**	**Plants darkly stained, starch produced and/or stored throughout**
II. In dark, with normal carbon dioxide	**Plants stunted, yellowed**	**If light is necessary for photosynthesis, then plants will have little starch**	**Very little, if any, starch staining. (Staining due to remnant starch.)**
III. In light, but with carbon dioxide removed	**Plants stunted, yellowed**	**If carbon dioxide is necessary for photosynthesis, then plants will have little starch**	**Very little, if any starch staining. (Staining due to remnant starch.)**

8. What does this staining pattern in plants of the three treatments indicate? **Both light and carbon dioxide are necessary for starch production, for photosynthesis to occur.**

9. What conclusion can you draw about the effect of light on the presence of starch? **Light is necessary for production of starch.**

10. What conclusion can you draw about the effect of carbon dioxide on the presence of starch? **Carbon dioxide is necessary for production of starch.**

11. Write a conclusion either accepting or rejecting the hypothesis. **The data support the stated hypothesis.**

9.3 Experiment: Relationship between Light and Photosynthetic Products

2. Write a prediction regarding starch presence, and thus photosynthesis activity, for each growing condition and leaf treatment area in Table 9-2.

TABLE 9-2 Relationship between Light and Starch Production

Geranium Plant Growing Condition	Prediction		Starch Presence and Location	
	Masked Areas	Unmasked Areas	Masked Areas	Unmasked Areas
Light-grown	If light is necessary for photosynthesis, then masked areas will have no starch	If light is necessary for photosynthesis, then unmasked areas will have starch	No starch staining except often for small amount along veins, especially near edges of mask due to translocation of photosynthates from adjoining area	Uniform starch staining
Dark-grown	If light is necessary for photosynthesis, then masked areas of dark-grown plants will have no starch	If light is necessary for photosynthesis, then unmasked areas of dark-grown plants will have no starch	No starch staining	No starch staining

What does the blue-black coloration of the leaf indicate? **That photosynthesis occurred, producing carbohydrates (starch).**

Why did the masked area fail to stain? **The light-dependent reactions require light in order for photosynthesis to proceed. In absence of light, no carbohydrates will be produced and any starch present in tissues initially will be used up.**

Write a conclusion accepting or rejecting the hypothesis. **The data support the hypothesis.**

9.4 Experiment: Necessity of Photosynthetic Pigments for Photosynthesis

1. Make a prediction regarding starch presence and photosynthetic activity for each pigmentation area:
If chlorophyll is necessary for photosynthetic activity, then starch will be present in leaf areas with green coloration, but not present in areas with other pigment colors visible.

5. How does the pattern of starch storage relate to the distribution of chlorophyll? **Starch is present where chlorophyll is present, but not where only carotenoids and/or anthocyanins are present. (Sometimes very observant students will see that there are small amounts of starch present in non-green leaf areas immediately adjacent to green areas. This is due to translocation of photosynthates from actively photosynthesizing areas.)**

6. Write a conclusion either accepting or rejecting the hypothesis. **The data support the hypothesis.**

9.5 Experiment: Absorption of Light by Chloroplast Extract

2. Observe the spectrum produced by the three colored filters using the spectroscope.
Which color or colors are absorbed when a red filter is placed between the light and the prism? **Depending on the specific red filter used, students generally observe that colors *other than red* are absorbed. Red wavelengths are transmitted through the red filter.**

When a blue filter is used? **Depending on the specific blue filter used, students generally observe that colors *other than blue* are absorbed. Blue wavelengths are transmitted through the blue filter.**

A green filter? **Depending on the specific green filter used, students generally observe that colors *other than green* are absorbed. Green wavelengths are transmitted through the green filter.**

Make a general statement concerning the color of a pigment (filter) and the absorption of light by that pigment **Light wavelengths transmitted through a pigment or filter are those we see. The pigment or filters absorbs the other wavelengths.**

4. How does the absorption spectrum of the chloroplast extract compare with the absorption spectrum of the green filter? **The chloroplast extract absorbs more strongly in green wavelengths than a green filter with somewhat less absorption in the yellow wavelengths.**
How might you explain the difference in absorption by the green filter and by the chloroplast pigment extract? **Accessory pigments (carotenoids) are yellow-orange pigments and could account for the difference.**

9.6 Separation of Photosynthetic Pigments by Paper Chromatography

9. What pigments are contained within the chloroplasts of spinach leaves? **Chlorophyll a and b, and several carotenoids are visible.**

What common "vegetable" is particularly high in carotenes? **Carrots.**

9.7 Structure of the Chloroplast

Figure 9-8 labels, left to right.
 Starch
 Thylakoid disks
 Chloroplast membrane
 Stroma
 Thylakoid disks

PHOTOSYNTHESIS: CAPTURE OF LIGHT ENERGY

Pre-lab Questions

1. A device useful for viewing the spectrum of light is a: a. spectroscope; b. volumeter; c. chromatogram; d. chloroplast.

2. Which of the following pigments would you find in a geranium leaf? a. chlorophyll, xanthophyll, phycobilins; b. chlorophyll a, chlorophyll b, carotenoids; c. phycocyanin, xanthophyll, fucoxanthin; d. carotenoids, chlorophylls, phycoerythrin.

3. Which reagent would you use to determine the distribution of the carbohydrate stored in leaves? a. starch; b. Benedict's solution; c. chlorophyll; d. I_2KI

4. Products and byproducts of photosynthesis do NOT include: a. O_2; b. $C_6H_{12}O_6$; c. CO_2; d. H_2O.

5. The ultimate source of energy trapped during photosynthesis is: a. CO_2; b. H_2O; c. O_2; d. sunlight.

6. A paper chromatogram is useful for: a. measuring the amount of photosynthesis; b. determining the amount of gas evolved during photosynthesis; c. separating pigments based upon their physical characteristics; d. determining the distribution of chlorophyll in a leaf.

7. An example of a heterotrophic organism is: a. a plant; b. a geranium; c. a human; d. none of the above.

8. Grana are: a. the same as starch grains; b. the site of ATP production within chloroplasts; c. part of the outer chloroplast membrane; d. contained within mitochondria and nuclei.

9. The raw materials used for photosynthesis include: a. O_2; b. $C_6H_{12}O_6$; c. $CO_2 + H_2O$; d. CH_2O.

10. Organisms capable of producing their own food are known as: a. autotrophs; b. heterotrophs; c. omnivores; d. herbivores.

PHOTOSYNTHESIS: CAPTURE OF LIGHT ENERGY

Answers to Pre-lab Questions
in Lab Manual Order

1. c		6.	d
2. a		7.	c
3. c		8.	a
4. c		9.	b
5. b		10.	d

Answers to Pre-lab Questions
in Instructor's Manual Order

1. a		6.	c
2. b		7.	c
3. d		8.	b
4. c		9.	c
5. d		10.	a

Answers to Post-lab Questions

1. Is starch stored in the leaves of some plants? **Yes.** Would you expect leaves in a temperate climate plant to be the primary area for long-term starch storage? Why or Why not? What part(s) of a plant might be better suited for long-term starch storage? **In temperate plants, leaves are only used as short term storage organs. The carbohydrates produced may be exported to other organs, such as the roots or tubers. For example, potatoes are tubers. These organs may remain throughout the winter and the starch becomes available the next spring for renewed growth.**

2. Examine the photo at right, which shows the location of starch in two geranium leaves treated in much the same way as you did in Part IV of your experiments. Explain the results you see. **Lighter areas were masked; darker areas are where light struck the leaf and photosynthesis occurred. In the darker areas, starch was stored, which reacted to iodine to produce the dark color.**

3. Examine the photograph at right of a *Coleus* leaf. Describe an experiment that would allow you to determine whether the deep purple portion of the leaf is photosynthesizing. **One possible experiment would involve illuminating the plant with bright light for several hours prior to experiment. Map color pattern of leaf and then extract pigments by boiling leaf first in water and then in alcohol. Perform starch test by flooding leaf with I$_2$KI. Photosynthesizing parts of leaf would stain black, indicating presence of starch, a product of photosynthesis. Compare stained areas with map of color pattern.**

4. The photo at right was taken through a spectroscope. What color was the pigment extract used to produce this spectrum? **Red.** What color(s) did this extract absorb? **All wavelengths/colors *except* red.**

5. Would you illuminate your house plants with a green light bulb? Why or why not? **No. Green wavelengths are the least useful for photosynthesis. Most of the green light would be reflected, little absorbed.**

6. Examine this electron micrograph of a chloroplast. a. Identify the stack of membranes labeled A. **Granum.** b. Identify the region labeled B. **Stroma.** c. Would the production of organic compounds during the light-independent reactions occur in region B or on the membranes labeled A? **B.** d. Would you expect the plant in which this structure was found to have been illuminated with strong light immediately before it was prepared for electron microscopy? Why or why not? **No. A chloroplast that had been illuminated with strong light would probably contain starch grains. This one does not.**

7. Numerous hypotheses have been proposed for the extinction of the large dinosaurs. Recently, evidence has been found of the impact of a large meteor at about the time of this mass extinction. The amount of dust and debris put into the atmosphere upon impact, as well as atmospheric heating, would have been enormous. Using your knowledge of photosynthesis, speculate as to why the dinosaurs became extinct. **Large amounts of dust and debris in the atmosphere would have reduced the light reaching plants. Plants that herbivorous dinosaurs ate could have died, leading to widespread starvation of herbivorous dinosaurs. Carnivorous dinosaurs preyed upon herbivorous dinosaurs and each other, so as the herbivores died out, there were no prey for carnivores, and eventually they too, died out.**

8. Explain the statement: "Without autotrophic organisms, heterotrophic life would cease to exist." **Heterotrophic organisms must obtain their nutrients from the carbohydrates stored by autotrophic organisms. The ultimate source of virtually all energy is the sun, with that energy being captured by autotrophs.**

9. Why do you suppose that a chloroplast kept in darkness for some time prior to being fixed for electron microscopy does not contain starch? **Starch grains located in chloroplasts are often only temporary. This starch is usually converted to sucrose and transported to storage organs such as roots.**

10. With the results of the preceding experiments in mind, what might you do to increase the vigor of your house plants? **Increase light level (dependent upon particular species). Increase CO_2 level (impractical for individuals, but practiced in some large greenhouses).**

RESPIRATION: ENERGY CONVERSION

Materials and Equipment

10.1 Aerobic Respiration

A. Carbon Dioxide Production

Per student group (4)
- 600-mL beaker
- phenol red solution
- china marker
- hot plate *or* laboratory burner, wire gauze square, tripod, and matches or flint lighter
- three respiration bottle apparatus
- heat resistant glove

Per lab room
- germinating pea seeds
- ungerminated (dry) pea seeds

B. Oxygen Consumption

Per student group (4)
- volumeter
- eighty germinating pea seeds
- glass beads
- non-absorbent cotton
- marker fluid in dropping bottle
- metric ruler
- ¼ teaspoon measure
- china marker
- bottle of potassium hydroxide (KOH)
- eighty ungerminated (dry) pea seeds

10.2 Fermentation

Per student group (4)
- bottle of 1% starch
- 25-mL graduated cylinder
- china marker
- three 50-mL beakers
- 0.5% amyloglucosidase in bottle fitted with graduated 5-mL pipet and pipet pump
- three glass stirring rods
- 1/4 teaspoon measure (optional)
- metric ruler
- three fermentation tubes (preferably graduated)

Per lab room
- 0.5 g pieces fresh yeast cake
- 37°C incubator
- balance and weighing paper (optional)

10.3 Experiment: Effect of Temperature on Goldfish Respiration

Per student group (4)
- crushed ice
- clock
- Celsius thermometer with clip
- aquarium (see *Notes*) filled with dechlorinated tap water
- plastic dishpan
- one goldfish

10.4 Ultrastructure of the Mitochondrion

None required.

Preparation of Materials and Equipment

10.1 Aerobic Respiration

A. Carbon Dioxide Production

Respiration bottle assembly: Respiration bottle consists of the following components: 8-oz. bottle fitted with 2-hole rubber stopper; thistle tube with solid rubber stopper; bent soft-glass tubing; 16 x 125 mm test tubes. Assemble these components as illustrated in figure 10-1 of the lab manual. Thistle tube stem must be cut off to fit into the bottle. Glass tubing is cut to approximately 28 cm lengths, then bent to shape with the three sides approximately 8 cm, 8 cm, and 11 cm in length. You may want to construct a support for the respiration bottle apparatus to prevent tipping.

Phenol red solution (Approx. 1 L): Exact preparation of dilute phenol red solution depends upon the mineral composition of your local tap water. Start with a liter of dH_2O and add a small pinch (approx. 0.2–0.4 g) phenol red crystals. The solution should be approximately pH 7.0 and appear to be a pale pink when a small amount is in a beaker. If not pale pink, add a drop or two of dilute HCl or NaOH to adjust color. Test this solution before class by blowing through a straw into a small amount in a beaker. About 90 seconds of blowing should produce a pink to yellow color change.
   Yield: 1 L phenol red solution should be adequate for 60 student groups.

Germinating pea seeds: Germinate non-green pea seeds on moist filter paper or paper toweling 48 to 72 hours before needed in lab. Germination process can be speeded up by soaking the pea seeds in water for two to three hours before placing them on the lined trays.
   Yield: One 12-in. tray should be enough for 1 to 2 student groups (see *Notes*).

B. Oxygen Consumption

Volumeter assembly: Volumeters are ordered from Ward's (see *Ordering Information*).

Marker fluid: Add a few drops of food coloring to water to make a fluid that is easily seen in the pipets. Supply in dropping bottles.

Germinating pea seeds: See above.

10.2 Fermentation

| *10% glucose* (100 mL): | glucose (dextrose) | 10 g |
| | dH_2O to make | 100 mL |

   Yield: 100 mL 10% glucose is adequate for 6 student groups.

| *1% starch* (1 L): | soluble starch (potato) | 10 g |
| | dH_2O | 1000 mL |

   Make a thin paste by combining the starch and a small amount of the water. Heat the remainder of the water to boiling. Remove boiling water from burner and add starch paste while stirring constantly.
   Yield: 1 L starch solution should be adequate for 30 student groups.

| *1% amyloglucosidase* (100 mL): | amyloglucosidase | 1.0 g |
| | dH_2O | 100 mL |

   Shake and allow to stand one hour. Filter through a Buchner funnel and Whatman 1 filter paper. Add 2 to 3 drops toluene (to act as preservative), stopper tightly and refrigerate.
   Dispense in class in a bottle fitted with a 1-hole rubber stopper into which a 5-mL graduated pipet has been inserted. Provide a pipet pump.
   Shelf life: several days if refrigerated.
   Yield: 100 mL enzyme solution is sufficient for 20 student groups.

10.3 Experiment: Effect of Temperature on Goldfish Respiration Rate

None required.

10.4 Ultrastructure of the Mitochondrion

None required.

Notes

10.1 Aerobic Respiration

A. Experiment: Carbon Dioxide Production

The water must cover the end of the glass tubing exiting the respiration bottle. Similarly, the liquid in the test tube, whether water or phenol red must also cover the other end of the glass tubing.

Support the test tubes with a test tube rack.

The number of pea seeds needed to half-fill a respiration bottle will vary depending upon the size of seed and the size of the bottle used. (We have suggested a wide-mouth 8-oz. bottle, but other sizes may also suffice.) We have found that 85 g dry pea seeds will fill one 8-oz. bottle approximately half full after imbibition. The preparer should determine the number of seeds necessary well before the peas are needed.

B. Experiment: Oxygen Consumption

It may be more convenient and time-saving to set up volumeters before lab. Students are thus spared the necessity of handling the KOH pellets. One set-up can last throughout an entire day, but germinating pea seeds and KOH pellets should be replaced each day.

10.2 Fermentation

Fermentation tubes with a graduated scale on the tail may be purchased from Carolina Biological Supply (see *Ordering Information*). They are more expensive than non-graduated tubes, but the markings eliminate the need to calculate the volume of gas evolved with the equation given in the lab manual.

Cheaper non-graduated fermentation tubes are also available, if desired (Carolina 73-2345).

If cake yeast is unavailable, dry granulated yeast (1/4 teaspoon per beaker) is an acceptable substitute, though results may be slower to appear.

10.3 Experiment: Effect of Temperature on Goldfish Respiration Rate

The instructor may wish to place the goldfish in the jar of room temperature water before class to allow the fish as much time as possible to acclimate.

Dechlorinate water by allowing it to stand 24 hours before introducing the fish, or use commercial chlorine remover (see *Ordering Information*).

A wide variety of glass containers can be used as aquaria, such as food service containers, large beakers, or jars. Do use glass, however, rather than plastic or other material, for relatively rapid conductance of temperature changes and for visibility.

Ordering Information

See General Laboratory Supplies list on page vii for basic items

10.1 Aerobic Respiration

A. Carbon Dioxide Production

tubing, glass apparatus, 8 mm o.d.	Fisher	S37608E
thistle tube	Fisher	S67537
phenol red, crystal	Fisher	S93322

B. Oxygen Consumption

Volumeter	Ward's	14 V 8300
non-absorbent cotton	Fisher	07-895
potassium hydroxide pellets	Fisher	P250-500

10.2 Fermentation

starch, soluble	Fisher	S71202
glucose (dextrose)	Sigma	G8270
amyloglucosidase (from Rhizopus)	Sigma	A7255
fermentation tube, graduated	Carolina	73-2360
Yeast—purchase from local grocery store		

10.3 Experiment: Effect of Temperature on Goldfish Respiration Rate

rectangular jar bath, 1.7 L	Local aquarium shop	
chlorine/chloramine neutralizer	Local aquarium shop	
glass fishbowl aquarium, 1 gal	Local aquarium shop	
gold fish	Local aquarium shop	
plastic dishpan	Local housewares supply	
round glass battery jar, 4 qt	Ward's	17W 1003
Thermometer	Carolina	74-5460
thermometer holder	Carolina	74-5500

10.4 Ultrastructure of the Mitochondrion

None required.

Answers to In-text Questions

10.1 Aerobic Respiration

A. Experiment: Carbon Dioxide Production

8. Make a prediction about carbon dioxide production in each of the three bottles: **The germinating peas will produce carbon dioxide. Those that have been boiled will be dead and thus will not produce carbon dioxide. The ungerminated peas will not produce any detectable carbon dioxide.**

9. Phenol red solution is mostly water. When the phenol red solution is basic (pH > 7), it is pink; when it is acidic (pH < 7), the solution is yellow. The phenol red solution in the stock bottle is
   pink (color); therefore, the stock solution is **basic** (acidic/basic).

TABLE 10-1 CO2 Evolution by Pea Seeds		
Pea Seeds	**Indicator Color (Phenol Red)**	**Conclusion (CO_2 Present or Absent)**
Germinating—unboiled	yellow	+
Germinating—boiled	pink	-
Ungerminated	pink	-

Which set(s) of seeds underwent respiration? **The germinating, unboiled seeds.**

What happened during boiling that caused the results you found? (Hint: Think "enzymes.") **The enzymes that are needed for respiration were denatured and thus no respiration occurred.**

Write a conclusion, accepting or rejecting the hypothesis. **(Answer varies depending upon student's hypothesis.)**

B. Experiment: Oxygen Consumption

TABLE 10-2 Respiratory Rate as Measured by Oxygen Consumption
(Results will vary)

12. In Figure 10-3, graph the consumption of oxygen over time.

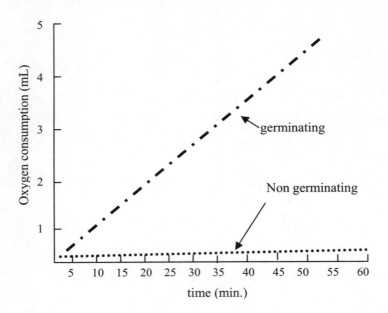

Figure 10-3 Oxygen consumption by germinating and nongerminating pea seeds.

12. How do the respiratory rates for germinating and nongerminating seeds compare? **The respiratory rate in the germinating seeds is much greater than the nongerminating.**
How do you account for this difference? **Germination results in a high metabolic rate with a great deal of cellular respiration.**

10.2 Fermentation

5. Write a prediction about gas production in each tube.
Tube 1: Gas will be produced.
Tube 2: No gas will be produced.
Tube 3: Gas will be produced.

Tube 1	Solution	Distance from Tip of Tube to Fluid Level (mm)			Volume[a] of Gas Evolved (mm³)
		20 min.	**40 min.**	**60 min.**	
1	10% glucose + yeast		**(tail likely to be empty)**		**most**
2	1% starch + yeast		**(no change in tail)**		**none**
3	1% starch + yeast+ amylase		**(part of tail empty)**		**some**

TABLE 10-3 Evolution of Gas by Yeast Cells

Did your results conform to your predictions? If not, speculate on reasons why this might be so. **(Answer will vary with student's prediction.)**
What gas accumulates in the tail portion of the fermentation tube? **Carbon dioxide.**

10.3 Experiment: Effect of Temperature on Goldfish Respiration

1. Make a prediction regarding the outcome of your experiment. Identify the independent and dependent variables and enter them in Table 10-4.

TABLE 10-4 Operculum Movement of Goldfish as a Function of Temperature						
Prediction: As temperature rises, the metabolic rate of the goldfish will increase as a result of the need to increase the amount of oxygen available for respiration.						
Independent Variable: temperature						
Dependent Variable: Number of openings and closings of gill cover (a reflection of respiration rate)						
RESULTS						
Trial	Starting temp. -------- ^{0}C	25 ^{0}C	20 ^{0}C	15 ^{0}C	10 ^{0}C	5 ^{0}C
1						
2						
3	**The opercular action should decrease with decreasing temperature, falling a low as 102 per minute)**					
Average						

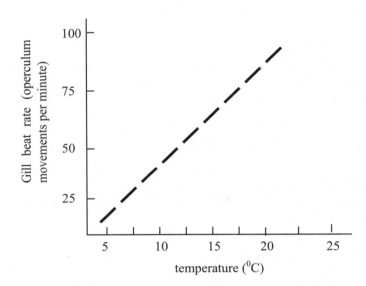

Figure 10-5 Relationship between gill beat rate and temperature in goldfish.

9. Make a conclusion about your results, accepting or rejecting the hypothesis. **Answer will vary depending upon student's hypothesis.**
What controls might you have used for this experiment? **Fish held at room temperature for the duration of the experiment.**
At which temperature was the gill beat rate highest? **The highest temperature used (assuming it was not so high as to kill the fish!)**
What is the relationship between the increase in water temperature and gill beat rate in goldfish? Why? **There is a direct relationship—the higher the temperature, the more numerous the gill beat rate. As the temperature rises, the metabolic rate of the goldfish increases due to the increased need for oxygen.**

10.4 Ultrastructure of the Mitochondrion

Figure 10-7 Transmission electron micrograph of a mitochondrion (18,600x).
Labels: (top to bottom) outer membrane; crista; inner membrane; intermembrane compartment; matrix

RESPIRATION: ENERGY CONVERSION

Pre-lab Questions

1. The "universal energy currency" of the cell is: a. O_2; b. $C_6H_{12}O_6$; c. ATP; d. H_2O.

2. The purpose of the thermobarometer in a volumeter is to: a. judge the amount of O_2 evolved during respiration; b. determine the volume changes as a result of respiration; c. indicate oxygen consumption by germinating pea seeds; d. indicate volume changes resulting from changes in temperature or barometric pressure.

3. As temperatures rise, the body temperatures of _____ organisms rise.: a. ectothermic; b. endothermic; c. autotrophic; d. heterotrophic.

4. Products of aerobic respiration include: a. glucose; b. oxygen; c. carbon dioxide; d. starch.

5. A metabolic pathway is: a. a single, specific reaction that starts with one compound and ends up with another; b. a sequence of chemical reactions that are part of the metabolic process; c. a series of events that occurs only in autotrophs; d. all of the above.

6. Which of the following enzymes breaks down starch into glucose? a. kinase; b. maltase; c. fructase; d. amylase.

7. "Efficiency" of a respiration pathway refers to the: a. number of steps in the pathway; b. amount of CO_2 produced relative to the amount of carbohydrate entering the pathway; c. amount of H_2O produced relative to the amount of carbohydrate entering the pathway; d. amount of ATP energy produced relative to the energy content of the carbohydrate entering the pathway.

8. Oxygen is necessary for life because: a. photosynthesis depends upon it; b. it serves as the final electron acceptor during aerobic respiration; c. it is necessary for glycolysis; d. all of the above.

9. Yeast cells undergoing alcoholic fermentation produce: a. ATP; b. ethanol; c. CO_2; d. all of the above.

10. Phenol red is used in the experiments as: a. an O_2 indicator; b. a CO_2 indicator; c. a sugar indicator; d. an enzyme.

RESPIRATION: ENERGY CONVERSION

Answers to Pre-lab Questions
in Lab Manual Order

1. b	6. b		
2. c	7. a		
3. c	8. d		
4. d	9. b		
5. d	10. d		

Answers to Pre-lab Questions
in Instructor's Manual Order

1. c	6. d		
2. d	7. d		
3. a	8. b		
4. c	9. d		
5. b	10. b		

Answers to Post-lab Questions

1. Explain the role of the following components in the experiment on carbon dioxide production:
    germinating pea seeds—**experimental condition**
    ungerminated (dry) pea seeds—**control**
    germinating, boiled pea seeds—**control**
    phenol red solution—**carbon dioxide indicator**

2. If you performed the experiment on oxygen consumption without adding KOH pellets to the test tubes, what results would you predict? **The marker fluid movement would give results that are unable to be interpreted.** Why? **If there is no KOH present to absorb the carbon dioxide, then there would be no way to determine if the movement of the fluid was due to carbon dioxide evolution or oxygen consumption. For example, if more carbon dioxide is produced than oxygen consumed, the marker droplet might actually move out of the side arm pipet.**

3. Sucrose (table sugar) is a disaccharide composed of glucose and fructose. Glycogen is a polysaccharide composed of many glucose subunits. Which of the following fermentation tubes would you expect to product the greatest gas volume over a 1 hour period? **Tube 1 > Tube 2 > Tube 3** Why? **Fermentation in Tubes 2 and 3 is dependant upon the yeast having enzymes capable of breaking down the sucrose and glycogen. If not, then there are more glucose units available in Tube 1. If the enzymes are present, then glycogen might actually produce more carbon dioxide.**
    Tube 1: glucose plus yeast
    Tube 2: sucrose plus yeast
    Tube 3: glycogen plus yeast

4. Bread is made by mixing flour, water, sugar, and yeast to form a dense dough. Why does the dough rise? **The dough rises because bubbles form inside the elastic dough, causing it to expand.** What gas is responsible for the holes in bread? **The yeast cells are using the sugar for respiration. In the process, they produce CO_2, which forms the bubbles (holes).**

5. Warmer water holds less dissolved oxygen than cooler water. Use this information plus that which you gleaned from this experiment to more fully explain why the gill beat rate of a fish increases as water temperature increases. **As the temperature of the fish increases with the increase in environmental temperature, the physiological need for oxygen also increases. At the same time, the dissolved oxygen in water is decreasing. In order for the goldfish to obtain sufficient oxygen for cellular respiration, the gill beat rate would have to increase to pass more water over the gills.**

6. Examine the electron micrograph of the mitochondrion on the right. a. What portions of aerobic respiration occur in region b? **Kreb's cycle and electron transport phosphorylation.** b. What substance is produced as hydrogen ions cross from the space between the inner and outer membranes into region b? **ATP.** c. What portion of cellular respiration takes place *outside* of this organelle in the cytoplasm? **Glycolysis.**

7. Oxygen is used during aerobic respiration. What biological process is the source of the oxygen? **Photosynthesis.**

8. Compare aerobic respiration, anaerobic electron transport, and fermentation in terms of: a. efficiency of obtaining energy from glucose. **Aerobic respiration is much more efficient than either anaerobic electron transport or fermentation (38% vs. about 7%).** b. end products. **Aerobic: $6 CO_2 + 6 H_2O + 36 ATP$; anaerobic electron transport: $6 CO_2 + H_2SO_4 + 2 ATP$; fermentation: lactate or ethanol + 2 ATP.**

9. How would you explain this statement: "The ultimate source of our energy is the sun"? **The energy of sunlight is captured by photosynthetic organisms. Animals (or other heterotrophic organisms) utilize this energy when they eat plant material. If another animal eats the plant eater, the animal eater is utilizing energy that *originally* came from the sun. We also rely on the sun's energy when we burn fossil fuels (substances that originated in plant life) and when we utilize solar energy directly.**

10. The first law of thermodynamics seems to conflict with what we know about ourselves. For example, after strenuous exercise we run out of "energy." We must eat to replenish our energy stores. Where has that energy gone? What form has it taken? **The energy has been utilized to cause muscular contraction. Much of the energy "lost" is not lost at all, but simply converted to heat, another form of energy.**

MITOSIS AND CYTOKINESIS: NUCLEAR AND CYTOPLASMIC DIVISION

Materials and Equipment

11.1 Chromosomal Structure

Per student
- coverslip
- disposable pipette and bulb
- compound microscope (oil immersion preferable)
- microscope slide pre-chilled in cold 40% methanol
- paper toweling

Per student pair
- Metric ruler
- dropper bottle of Permount mounting medium
- tube of HeLa cells

Per lab room
- Coplin staining jars with Stain 1 and 2
- 1-L beaker containing dH_2O

11.2 The Cell Cycle in Plant Cells: Onion Roots

Per student
- compound microscope
- Prepared slide of onion, *Allium*, root tip mitosis

11.3 The Cell Cycle in Animal Cells: Whitefish Blastula

Per student
- prepared slide of whitefish blastula mitosis
- compound microscope

11.4 Chromosome Squashes

Per student
- *Allium* (onion) or *Narcissus* root tips
- two dissecting needles
- sharp razor blade
- compound microscope
- microscope slide and coverslip

Per student pair
- acetocarmine stain in dropping bottle
- burner and matches
- iron alum in dropping bottle

11.5 Simulating Mitosis

Per student pair
- forty-four pop beads each of two colors
- eight magnetic centromeres

Preparation of Materials and Equipment

11.1 Chromosomal Structure

Preparation of microscope slides: Chill clean microscope slides in 40% methanol in Coplin staining jars in freezer or ice bath until use.

40% methanol (100 mL):	methanol, absolute	40 mL
	distilled water	60 mL

11.2 The Cell Cycle in Plant Cells: Onion Roots

None required.

11.3 The Cell Cycle in Animal Cells: Whitefish Blastula

None required.

11.4 Chromosome Squashes

Allium (onion) or Narcissus (daffodil) root tips: Obtain *Narcissus* or *Allium* bulbs from a garden supply center. *Narcissus* is more available in the fall; store in a refrigerator until needed.

Gently scrape the bulb plate (not the roots themselves) with a scalpel and place the bulbs in coarse, wet gravel. Alternatively, the bulbs may be suspended in a jar or 100 mL beaker of water by toothpicks inserted through the bulb and resting on the rim of the jar or beaker. Allow at least a week for roots to grow, changing the water twice a day.

When roots are about 1 cm long, harvest the root tips (5 mm to 1 cm) by cutting with a sharp razor blade or scalpel. Place the root tips in acetic alcohol to fix for 24 hours. (A camel-hair brush may be handy for transferring the root tips.) The roots will keep indefinitely when refrigerated in the fixative.

Roots may be hydrolyzed for class use. Before class (at most one day), decant the fixative, rinse 1 minute in dH_2O, then place roots in 1 N hydrochloric acid (HCl) at 60°C for 8 to 10 minutes. Wash roots thoroughly in two changes of dH_2O, then place roots in water. All HCl must be rinsed off or staining may be inhibited.

Acetic alcohol (40 mL):	95% ethanol	30 mL
	Glacial acetic acid	10 mL

Prepare mixture in a fume hood.
Shelf life: indefinite.
Yield: 40 mL acetic alcohol is sufficient to hydrolyze many root tips.

1 N HCl (100 mL): Measure 8.3 mL concentrated (12N) HCl into a 100-mL volumetric flask and dilute to 100 mL with distilled water.

Acetocarmine stock solution (100 mL): Acetocarmine solution may be purchased (see *Ordering Information*) or may be prepared as follows:

	carmine (alum lake; C.I. Natural Red 4)	1 g
	glacial acetic acid	45 mL
	dH_2O	55 mL
	ferric acetate, saturated, aqueous	2 drops

Add acid slowly to water while stirring. Bring to a boil. Dissolve carmine in the boiling 45% acetic acid. Cool and decant. Add 2 drops of a saturated, aqueous solution of ferric acetate and allow to stand for 12 hours. Filter and store in a refrigerator.

Ferric acetate may be omitted if steel dissecting needles are used to tease apart the tissue. The iron in the needles (the rustier the better, for this purpose) reacts with the acetic acid in the dye, but this method requires more experience to produce clearly evident mitotic figures.

Shelf life: indefinite.
Yield: 100 mL stock solution should be adequate for 400 student pairs.

Ferric acetate: Very soluble in water. Prepare saturated solution, filter and store in an amber bottle or in the dark.

| *Iron alum, 5%* (100 ml): | iron alum [FeNH$_4$(SO$_4$)$_2$•12H$_2$O] | 5 g |
| | dH$_2$O to make | 100 mL |

       Crystals of iron alum must be pale violet; discard any yellowish crystals. Grind iron alum in a mortar, then weigh out 5 g. Dissolve in dH$_2$O.
       Shelf life: short. Prepare fresh when needed.
       Yield: 100 mL iron alum solution is enough for 400 student pairs.

Notes

11.1 Chromosomal Structure

       The human chromosome spread kit (see *Ordering Information*) contains one tube of prepared HeLa cells per student pair, Stains 1 and 2 sufficient to fill one Coplin jar each, 15 mL Permount, #1 coverslips, and printed background and procedural information.

       Stains can be re-used if students are careful to drain Stain 1 as well as possible to prevent cross-contamination of Stain 2.

       Students can view slides mounted with Permount immediately at magnification *not* involving oil immersion. To view with oil immersion (necessary to actually view chromosomal structure and to count chromosomes), allow Permount to dry at least one hour. Alternatively, coverslips can be mounted in dH$_2$O and viewed immediately.

       Phone Cell Serv/College Division to check for availability and schedule shipment as early as possible. (Consult *Sources of Materials and Supplies* for phone number. Additional information available at www.cellservkits.com/NewFiles/Kit4.html)

11.3 The Cell Cycle in Animal Cells: Whitefish Blastula

       Prepared slides of Parascaris (*Ascaris*) embryo mitosis (see *Ordering Information*) are good substitutes for whitefish blastulae.

11.4 Chromosome Squashes

       Narcissus is preferred to *Allium* for root tip squashes because many more roots are produced per bulb (50 to 100) and because their chromosomes can be differentiated on the basis of appearance. Conversely, *Allium* chromosomes appear to be much alike. Additionally, onion bulbs purchased in a grocery store may have been treated to inhibit sprouting and so may produce few roots.

       Narcissus root tips will often show a greater abundance of mitotic figures when harvested and fixed at noon or midnight.

Ordering Information

       See General Laboratory Supplies list on page vii for basic items

11.1 Chromosomal Structure

Methanol	Carolina	87-4950
Coplin staining jar	Carolina	74-2160
Human Chromosome Spread Kit	Call CellServ	

11.2 The Cell Cycle in Plant Cells: Onion Roots

prepared slide, onion (*Allium*) bulb, median l.s. or root tip —Triarch 14-2b

11.3 The Cell Cycle in Animal Cells: Whitefish Blastula

prepared slide, whitefish, mitosis, sections of blastula—Triarch ZL6-111
prepared slide, *Parascaris,* embryo mitosis, sections of uterus—Triarch ZE2-13

11.4 Chromosome Squashes

See General Laboratory Supplies list on page vii for basic items

Allium or *Narcissus* bulbs	local garden supply	
camel-hair brush	Local art supplies store	
carmine (alum lake; C. I. Natural Red 4)	Fisher	C579-25
glacial acetic acid	Fisher	A38-500
acetocarmine stain	Carolina	84-1423
hydrochloric acid, 1N	Fisher	SA48-500
iron alum (ferric ammonium sulfate)	Fisher	S93237
ferric acetate	Fisher	50-827-860
Alcohol burner	Fisher	S41892

11.5 Simulating Mitosis

chromosome simulation Biokit	Carolina	17-1100

Answers to In-text Questions

11.1 Chromosomal Structure

13. …Now examine Figure 11-4, an electron micrograph of a human chromosome. Label the two chromatids, centromere and the duplicated chromosome.

Figure 11-4 labels: centromere (top line), chromatid (top bracket) duplicated chromosome (middle bracket), chromatid (bottom bracket)

11.2 The Cell Cycle in Plant Cells: Onion Roots

B. Cytokinesis in Onion Cells

What is the difference between chromatin and chromosomes? **Chromatin is the DNA before it has condensed into chromosomes. There is no difference in the chemical makeup, just the appearance.**

Figure 11-6 labels: (First listed is the name of the cell cycle; thereafter, labels are top to bottom)
1. Interphase
nucleus
cytoplasm
chromatin
nucleolus
nuclear envelope

2.
cytoplasm

3. Metaphase
cytoplasm
pole
spindle fibers
spindle equator (this leader has an arrowhead)
sister chromatids
pole
spindle (bracket to right of image)

4.
cytoplasm

5. Telophase
cytoplasm
nuclear envelope
chromosome
cell plate formation
chromosome
nuclear envelope

6.
daughter cell (top left bracket)
daughter cell (bottom left bracket
cytoplasm (top right leader)
cytoplasm (bottom right leader)

C. Duration of Phases of the Cell Cycle

1. Examine the meristem region of an onion root tip slide. Count the number of cells in each of the stages of mitosis plus interphase in one field of view. Repeat this procedure for other fields of view until you count 100 cells. Record your data in Table 11-2.

(Numbers will vary; those in parentheses are illustrative)

TABLE 11-2 Determining Duration of Cell Cycle Phases			
Phase	**Number seen**	**Approx.% total**	**Duration (hrs)**
Interphase	**Most frequent (by far) (870)**	**91.1**	**21.9**
Prophase	**second most frequent(54)**	**5.7**	**1.4**
Metaphase	**of approx. equal frequency with anaphase and telophase (14)**	**1.5**	**0.4**
Anaphase	**least frequent (5)**	**0.5**	**0.1**
Telophase	**of approx. equal frequency with metaphase (11)**	**1.1**	**0.2**
Total	**(954)**		**24**

11.3 The Cell Cycle in Animal Cells: Whitefish Blastula

A. Interphase and Mitosis

(d) Telophase. **Telophase** is characterized by the arrival of the individual (daughter) chromosomes at the poles. A nuclear envelope forms around each daughter nucleus. Find a telophase cell.
Is the spindle still visible? **No.**

Is there any evidence of a nuclear envelope forming around the chromosomes? **(Possibly, depending on what the student is looking at.)**

B. Cytokinesis in Animal Cells

11.4 Chromosome Squashes

6. Examine the preparation with your light microscope. Identify all stages of the cell cycle that have been described above.
What do you notice about the shape of the cells after this preparation? **They are rather irregular in shape.**

Name _____

Section No. _____

MITOSIS AND CYTOKINESIS: NUCLEAR AND CYTOPLASMIC DIVISION

Pre-lab Questions

1.   The correct sequence of stages in *mitosis* is: a. interphase, prophase, metaphase, anaphase, telophase; b. prophase, metaphase, anaphase, telophase; c. metaphase, anaphase, prophase, telophase; d. prophase, telophase, anaphase, interphase.

2.   The process of cytoplasmic division is known as: a. meiosis; b. cytokinesis; c. mitosis; d. fission.

3.   The product of chromosome duplication is: a. two chromatids; b. two nuclei; c. two daughter cells; d. two spindles.

4.   During prophase, duplicated chromosomes: a. consist of chromatids; b. contain centromeres; c. consist of nucleoproteins; d. all of the above.

5.   Chromatids separate during: a. prophase; b. telophase; c. cytokinesis; d. anaphase.

6.   Cell plate formation: a. occurs in plant cells but not in animal cells; b. begins during telophase; c. is a result of fusion of Golgi vesicles; d. all of the above.

7.   Centrioles and a starburst cluster of spindle fibers would be found in: a. both plant and animal cells; b. only plant cells; c. only animal cells; d. none of the above.

8.   Reproduction in prokaryotes occurs primarily through the process known as: a. mitosis; b. cytokinesis; c. furrowing; d. fission.

9.   The genetic material (DNA) of eukaryotes is organized into: a. centrioles; b. spindles; c. chromosomes; d. microtubules.

10.   During the S period of interphase: a. cell growth takes place; b. nothing occurs since this a resting period; c. chromosomes divide; d. synthesis (or replication) of the nucleoproteins takes place.

MITOSIS AND CYTOKINESIS: NUCLEAR AND CYTOPLASMIC DIVISION

Answers to Pre-lab Questions
in Lab Manual Order

1. d		6. d	
2. c		7. d	
3. b		8. d	
4. a		9. d	
5. b		10. c	

Answers to Pre-lab Questions
in Instructor's Manual Order

1. b		6. d	
2. b		7. c	
3. a		8. d	
4. d		9. c	
5. d		10. d	

Answers to Post-lab Questions

1. Distinguish among interphase, mitosis, and cytokinesis. **Interphase—period when nuclei are not dividing. Mitosis—division of the nucleus. Cytokinesis—division of the cytoplasm.**

2. Distinguish between the structure of a duplicated chromosome before mitosis and the chromosome produced by separation of two chromatids during mitosis. **Prior to mitosis, each chromosome consists of two chromatids. During anaphase the chromatids separate, so each chromosome now consists of a *single* chromatid. (Replication of this single-chromatid chromosome occurs during interphase to give rise to two chromatids.)**

3. If the chromosome number of a typical onion root tip cell is 16 before mitosis, what is the chromosome number of each newly formed nucleus after nuclear division has taken place? **16.**

4. In plants, what name is given to a region where mitosis occurs most frequently? **Meristem.**

5. The cells in the following photomicrographs have been stained to show microtubules comprising the spindle apparatus. Identify the stage of mitosis in each and label the region indicated on b. **A is anaphase; B is telophase, and the indicated region is the cell plate. C is prophase.**

6. Name two features of animal cell mitosis and cytokinesis you can use to distinguish these processes from those occurring in plant cells. a. **animals—furrowing during cytokinesis; plants—cell plate formation.** b. **animals—astral spindle formed by spindle fibers radiating from centrioles; plants—spindle not radiating from centrioles.**

7. Observe photomicrographs a and b in the figure below. Is (a) from a plant or an animal? **Plant.** Note the double nature of the blue "threads." Each individual component of the doublet is called a **sister chromatid**. Is (b) from a plant or an animal? **Animal.**

8. Why do you suppose cytokinesis generally occurs in the cell's midplane? **So that each daughter cell gets about half of the cytoplasm and cytoplasmic components.** What would happen if a cell underwent mitosis but not cytokinesis? **A cell with more than one nucleus in the cytoplasm would be formed.**

9. Why must the DNA be duplicated during the S phase of the cell cycle, prior to mitosis? **So that the number of chromosomes in each daughter cell will be the same as that in the parent cell.**

10. What would happen if a cell underwent mitosis but not cytokinesis? **The resulting cell would have two complete (and identical) sets of chromosomes.**

MEIOSIS: BASIS OF SEXUAL REPRODUCTION

Materials and Equipment

12.1 Demonstrations of Meiosis Using Pop Beads

Per student pair

- forty-four pop beads each of two colors (red and yellow, for example)
- eight pieces string, each 40 cm long
- colored pencils

- eight magnetic centromeres
- marking pens
- meiotic diagram cards

Per student group (table)

- bottle of 95% ethanol

- tissues

12.2 Meiosis in Animal and Plant Cells

Per student pair

- scissors

- tape or glue

Per student group (table)

- set of demonstration slides of meiosis in animal testes and lily anther
- set of demonstration slides of meiosis in mammalian ovary

Preparation of Materials and Equipment

12.1 Demonstrations of Meiosis using Pop Beads

A. Meiosis without Crossing Over

Simulated pop bead chromosomes: Construct from chromosome simulation Biokits (2 kits per room, see *Ordering Information*), or purchase pop beads and magnetic centromeres separately from Carolina Biological Supply Co. One Biokit per room provides 1800 beads, 900 of each color (enough beads for 11 student pairs), plus 60 magnetic centrioles (enough for 7 student pairs).

Construct "chromosomes" by attaching chains of pop beads to each side of a centromere (see lab manual figure 12-7). All beads within a "chromosome" should be the same color. Make 2 chains of one color and 2 chains of another color per student pair.

B. Meiosis with Crossing Over

None required.

C. Demonstrating Independent Assortment

Simulated pop bead chromosomes: In addition to the pop-bead chromosomes from parts A and B, construct 4 more chains per student pair. Make the chains a different length and different colors from those in part A.

12.2 Meiosis in Animal and Plant Cells

None required.

Notes

12.1 Demonstrations of Meiosis Using Pop Beads

Chromosome simulation Biokits are very expensive, but may be used year after year.

Students should label individual beads only with the marking pens provided. Markings may then be removed with 95% ethanol.

12.2 Meiosis in Animal and Plant Cells

Many stages in *Lilium* microsporogenesis are available. You may not have room to include all stages listed, and so should select those that are most appropriate.

Order several grasshopper testis slides, in order to demonstrate the major stages of meiosis in animal cells.

Ordering Information

See General Laboratory Supplies list on page vii for basic items

12.1 Demonstrations of Meiosis Using Pop Beads

chromosome simulation Biokit	Carolina	17-1100

12.2 Meiosis in Animal and Plant Cells

grasshopper testis, section, prepared slide	Triarch	ZK3-18
Lilium, anthers, c.s., prepared slides: Early prophase	Triarch	18-3
Lilium, anthers, c.s., prepared slides: Middle prophase	Triarch	18-3a
Lilium, anthers, c.s., prepared slides: Late prophase	Triarch	18-4
Lilium, anthers, c.s., prepared slides: First meiotic division	Triarch	18-5
Lilium, anthers, c.s., prepared slides: Second meiotic division	Triarch	18-6

Answers to In-text Questions

12.1 Demonstrations of Meiosis Using Pop Beads

PROCEDURE

3. How many sister chromatids are there in a duplicated chromosome? **Two.**
How many chromosomes are represented by four sister chromatids? **Two.** By eight? **Four.**
What is the diploid number of the starting (parental) nucleus? **Four.**

A. Meiosis without Crossing Over

3. Meiosis II.
(d) Telophase II…
If the parental nucleus was from a male, what is the gamete called? **Sperm.**
If female? **Egg or ovum.**
Is the parental nucleus diploid or haploid? **Diploid.**
Are the nuclei produced after the first meiotic division diploid or haploid? **Haploid.**
Are the nuclei of the gametes diploid or haploid? **Haploid.**

What is the genotype of each gamete nucleus after meiosis II? (The genotype is the genetic composition of an organism, or the alleles present. Another way to ask this question is: What alleles are present in each gamete nucleus?
AfE, AfE, aFe, aFe, OR Afe, Afe, aFE, aFE

(There are different possibilities for completing Fig. 12-8, depending upon the choices that students made in Meiosis I. One possibility below.)

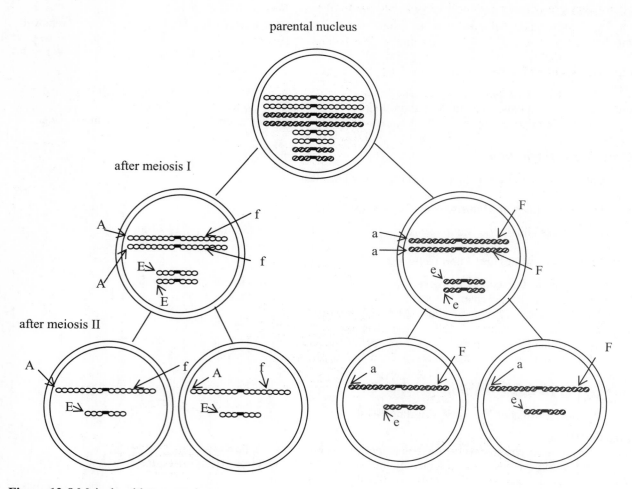

Figure 12-8 Meiosis without crossing over

B. Meiosis with Crossing Over

4.   What are the genotypes of the gamete nuclei? **AfE, afE, AFe, aFe**

Is the distribution of alleles present in the gamete nuclei after crossing over the same as that which was present without crossing over? **No.**

Is the distribution of alleles present in the gamete nuclei after crossing over the same as that in the nuclei after the first meiotic division? **No.**

Crossing over provides for genetic recombination, resulting in increased variety. How many different genetic types of daughter chromosomes are present in the gamete nuclei without crossing over (Figure 12-8)? **Two.**

How many different types are present with crossing over (Figure 12-11)? **Four.**

What is the difference between a gene and an allele? **A gene is a sequence of nucleotides that provide instructions for the production of a trait (such as hair color or flower petal color). An allele is an alternative form of that gene, such as the sequence that provides instruction for the productions of a particular hair color or flower petal color.**

Let's look at a single set of alleles on your model chromosomes that are, say, the alleles for pigmentation, A and a. Both alleles were present in the parental nucleus. How many are present in the gametes? **One.**

(There are different possibilities for completing Fig. 12-11, depending upon the choices that students made when breaking the beads and rejoining them to simulate crossing over. Indeed, it would be possible to come up with the same gamete genotype as the students came up with without crossing over. If a student does that, suggest they put letters on all of the beads and see what happens.)

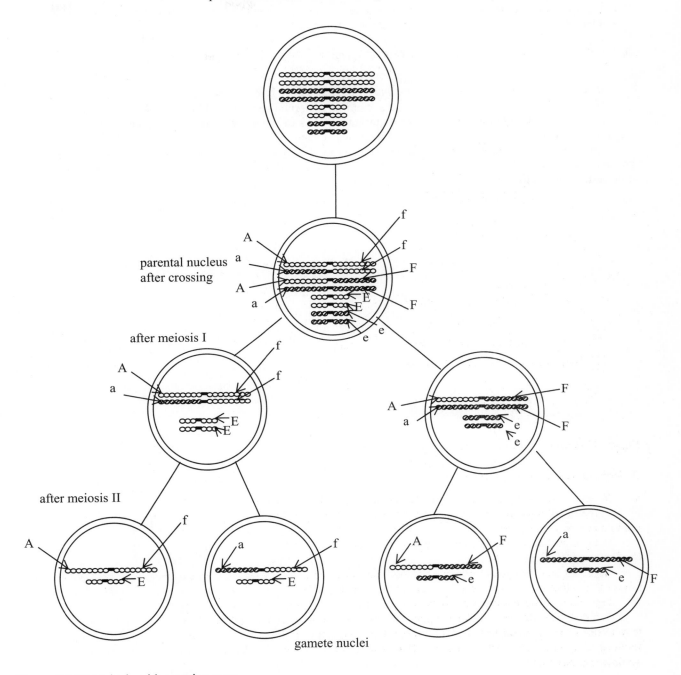

parental nucleus before crossing over

parental nucleus after crossing

after meiosis I

after meiosis II

gamete nuclei

Figure 12-11 Meiosis with crossing over.

C. Demonstrating Independent Assortment

Does the distribution of the alleles for enzyme production to different gametes on the second set of homologues have any bearing on the distribution of the alleles on the first set (alleles for skin pigmentation and earlobe condition)? **No.**

Because the genes for enzyme production and those for skin pigmentation and earlobe attachment are on different homologous chromosomes, these genes are **nonlinked**, while the genes for skin pigmentation and earlobe attachment are **linked** because they are on the same chromosome.

D. Nondisjunction and the Production of Gametes with Abnormal Chromosome Number

3.

How many chromosomes are found in gamete nuclei? **Three in two and one in two.**

How does this compare to the chromosome number in normal gametes? **There would be two in each.**

Recall that each chromosome bears a unique set of genes and speculate about the effect of non-disjunction on the resulting zygotes formed from fertilization with such a gamete.

There would be too many copies of a gene in some gametes, but perhaps more importantly, in some gametes the genes for some traits would be totally absent and this could lead to death of the organism, or minimally, something lacking from that organism.

12.2 Meiosis in Animal and Plant Cells

C. Meiosis in Plants

2. As you examine the slides, cut out pictomicrographs on pages 175 and 177 and arrange them on Figure 12-19 to depict the meiotic events leading to microspore formation. Label each photo with terms provided.
The figure below shows the meiotic order of events (Figure 12-19 completed).

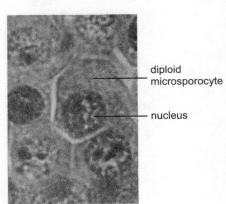
diploid
microsporocyte

nucleus

Interphase

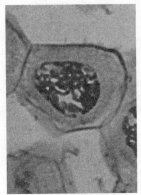

Early Prophase I
Labels: nucleus, chromosomes

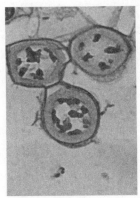

Mid-Prophase I
Label: chromosome

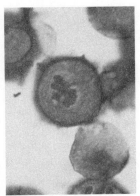

Late Prophase I
Label: chromosomes

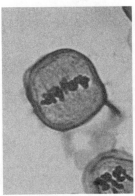

Metaphase I
Labels: spindle equator, spindle, spindle fibers, pole

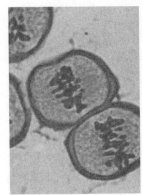

Early Anaphase I
Label: spindle fibers

Later Anaphase I
Labels: pole, homologous chromosomes

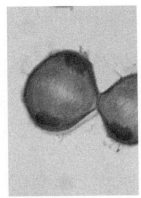

Telophase I
Labels: pole, homologous chromosomes, spindle fibers

Cytokinesis I
Labels: cell plate

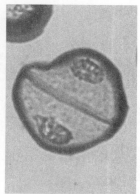

Interkinesis
Labels: nuclei, cell wall, daughter cells

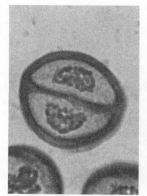

Prophase II
Labels: daughter cells, nuclei

Metaphase II
Labels: chromosomes, spindle equator

Anaphase II
Labels: sister chromatids (unduplicated chromosomes)

Telophase II
Labels: cell plate, nuclei

Cytokinesis
Labels: cell plate, nuclei

Note the following correction: There are two photos showing early anaphase, therefore the photo below was not used. The photo showing Telophase II also shows Cytokinesis, therefore there is no photo in the last box.

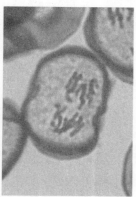

MEIOSIS: BASIS OF SEXUAL REPRODUCTION

Pre-lab Questions

1. The term "2n" means: a. the diploid chromosome number is present; b. the haploid chromosome number is present; c. chromosomes within a single nucleus exist in homologous pairs; d. a and c.

2. Non-disjunction: a. results in gametes with abnormal chromosome numbers; b. occurs at anaphase; c. results when homologues fail to separate properly in meiosis; d. is all of the above.

3. Recombination of alleles on non-sister chromatids occurs during: a. anaphase I; b. meiosis II; c. telophase II; d. crossing over.

4. DNA duplication occurs during: a. interphase; b. prophase I; c. prophase II; d. interkinesis.

5. If both homologous chromosomes of each pair exist in the same nucleus, that nucleus is: a. diploid; b. unable to undergo meiosis; c. haploid; d. none of the above.

6. Humans: a. don't undergo meiosis; b. have 46 chromosomes; c. produce gametes by mitosis; d. all of the above.

7. Gametogenesis in male animals results in: a. four sperm; b. one gamete and three polar bodies; c. four functional ova; d. a haploid ovum and three diploid polar bodies.

8. Alternative forms of genes are called: a. homologues; b. locus; c. loci; d. alleles.

9. In higher animals, meiosis results in the production of: a. egg cells (ova); b. gametes; c. sperm cells; d. all of the above.

10. In meiosis, the number of chromosomes _____, while in mitosis, it _____. a. is halved, is doubled; b. is halved, remains the same; c. is doubled, is halved; d. remains the same, is halved.

EXERCISE 12

MEIOSIS: BASIS OF SEXUAL REPRODUCTION

Answers to Post-lab Questions

1. If a cell of an organism had forty-six chromosomes before meiosis, how many chromosomes would exist in each nucleus after meiosis? **23.**

2. What basic difference exists between the life cycles of higher plants and higher animals? **Higher plants have two completely different body forms. Haploid gametophytes produce gametes, while the diploid sporophytes produce spores. Animals have no such alternation of generations.**

3. In animals, meiosis results directly in gamete production, while in plants meiospores are produced. Where do the gametes come from in the life cycle of a plant? **Gametangia in/on a haploid gametophyte.**

4. How would you argue that meiosis is the basis for sexual reproduction in plants, even though the *direct* result is a spore rather than a gamete? **The spore is the first cell of the gametophyte generation. As it divides, it gives rise to the gametophyte, which in turn produces gametes. Without meiosis, the gamete-producing plant would never be produced, and sexual reproduction would be impossible.**

5. Suppose one sister chromatid of a chromosome has the allele *H*. What allele will the other sister chromatid have? (Assume crossing over has not taken place.) *H.*

6. Suppose that two alleles on one homologous chromosome are *A* and *B*, and the other homologous chromosome's alleles are *a* and *b*. How many different genetic types of gametes would be produced *without* crossing over? **2.** What are those types? **AB, ab.** If crossing over were to occur, how many different genetic types of gametes could occur? **4.** List them. **AB, ab, Ab, aB.**

7. Assume that you have built a homologous pair of *duplicated* chromosomes, one chromosome red and the other yellow. Describe the appearance of two non-sister chromatids after crossing over. **See Figure 12-10, page 164 of the lab manual for an illustration.**

8. Examine the meiotic diagram at right. Describe in detail what's wrong with the diagram. **The distribution of chromosomes in two of the four gamete nuclei is erroneous. The two left-most gamete nuclei should both contain a single red chromosome; the two right-most should both have a single yellow chromosome.**

9. Observe the photo at right, which shows a stage of meiosis occurring in a flower anther. Are the cells shown haploid or diploid? **Haploid.**

10. From a genetic viewpoint, of what significance is fertilization? **Fertilization reestablishes the diploid condition.**

HEREDITY

Materials and Equipment

13.1 Monohybrid Crosses

Per student group (table)
- genetic corn ears illustrating monohybrid and dihybrid crosses

Optional
- pop beads used in *Meiosis* exercise
- bottle of 70% ethanol
- marking pen
- simulated chromosomes with centromeres and meiotic diagram cards from *Meiosis* exercise
- cotton balls
- hand lens

13.1.C.1 Week 1—Observation of F_1 Hybrid Gametophytes

Per student
- 2-week-old *C-fern*™ culture in petri dish
- dissecting microscope
- sterile dH$_2$O
- sterile pipet
- marking pen
- calculator (optional)

Materials needed to prepare for students
- petri dish, sterile, 60 x 15 mm
- sterile spore spreader
- marking pen
- fluorescent light bank
- pre-sterilized *C-fern*™ Spores of an F_1 Hybrid (Wild Type x Polka Dot)
- Basic *C-fern*™ Medium
- sterile dH$_2$O
- sterile pipet
- culture dome

13.1.C.3 Week 3—Observation of F_2 Sporophytes

Per student
- 4-week-old *C-fern*™ culture in petri dish
- dissecting microscope
- dissecting needle or toothpicks
- calculator (optional)

Preparation of Materials and Equipment

13.1 Monohybrid Crosses

70% ethanol (95 mL):

95% ethanol	70 mL
distilled water	25 mL

13.1.C.1 Week 1—Observation of F_1 Hybrid Gametophytes

Melt Basic *C-fern*™ medium in boiling water bath. The 160 mL bottle of media will require approximately 15 minutes to melt. Aseptically pour the media into sterile 60 x 15 mm petri dishes. Fill the dishes about ¾ full with about 15 mL/60 mm dish. One bottle of media (160 mL) will prepare approximately 10 petri dishes. Allow the dishes to cool undisturbed. The dishes of media may be stored at room temperature.

Suspend the pre-sterilized spores in 4 mL sterile distilled water. Invert the vial several times to wet the spores, and then dispense and spread three drops per dish. Yield: Over 30 petri dishes. Plan to inoculate the cultures and place under lights at least 10 days prior to the first class period. Fully mature gametophytes require approximately 10 days from starting to reach maturity.

13.1.C.3 Week 3—Observation of F₂ Sporophytes

Maintain the cultures established for Exercise 13.1.C.1 for this exercise.

Notes

An excellent resource, "Culture Instructions for *C-fern*™ Investigations," is available from Carolina Biological.

A kit can be purchased from Carolina Biological that will include all materials needed to conduct the *C-fern*™ experiments as well as more specific culture information.

Ordering Information

See General Laboratory Supplies list on page vii for basic items

genetic corn mounts, monohybrid cross	Carolina	17-6810
genetic corn mounts, dihybrid cross	Carolina	17-6900
chromosome simulation BioKit	Carolina	17-1100
C-fern™ Investigations: Genetics in Action Mendelian Genetics Kit (Will include all of the necessary materials)	Carolina	15-6708
Booklet: Culture Instructions for *C-fern*™ Investigations. Phone Carolina Biological to request		

If ordered separately:

Basic *C-fern*™ Medium	Carolina	15-6780
sterile pipet	Carolina	1-5840
pre-sterilized *C-fern*™ Spores of an F₁ Hybrid (Wild Type x Polka Dot)	Carolina	15-6760
sterile spore spreader	Carolina	70-3414
culture dome	Carolina	15-6792
lighting system	Carolina	97-1944

Answers to In-text Questions

13.1 Monohybrid Crosses

A. Monohybrid Problems with Complete Dominance

1. For each of these diploid genotypes, indicate all possible genotypes of the gametes that can be produced by the organism:

Diploid Genotype	Potential Gamete Genotype(s)
FF	**All F**
ff	**All f**
Ff	**Half F, half f**

2. Give the diploid genotype produced by fusion of the following gamete genotypes.

Gamete genotype	X	Gamete Genotype	→	Diploid Genotype
F		*F*		**FF**
F		*F*		*Ff*
F		*F*		ff

3. A man has the genotype *FF*. What is the genotype of his gamete (sperm) nuclei? **All F**
A woman has attached earlobes. What is her genotype? *ff*
What allele(s) do her gametes (ova) carry? **All *f***
These two individuals produce a child. Show the genotype of the child by doing the cross.

Sperm genotype *F*　　x　　Ovum genotype *f*　　→　child's genotype *Ff*

What is the phenotype of the child? (That is, does this child have attached or free earlobes?) **Free**

4. (a) What is the phenotype (color) of the flowers with the following genotypes?

Genotype	Phenotype
AA	**Purple**
Aa	**White**
Aa	**Purple**

A white-flowered garden pea is crossed with a homozygous dominant purple-flowered plant.
(b) Name the genotype(s) of the gametes of the white-flowered plant. *a*
(c) Name the genotype(s) of the gametes of the purple-flowered plant. *A*
(d) Name the genotype(s) of the plants produced by the cross. *Aa*
(e) Name the phenotype(s) of the plants produced by the cross. **Purple.**
(f) The Punnet square is a convenient way to perform the mechanics of a cross.

	a	a
A	Aa	Aa
A	Aa	Aa

(g) A heterozygous plant is crossed with a white-flowered plant. Fill in the Punnett square, then give the genotypes and phenotypes of all the possible genetic outcomes.

	a	a
A	Aa	Aa
a	aa	aa

Possible genotypes: *Aa, aa*　　　Possible phenotypes: **purple (*Aa* genotype) and white (*aa* genotype)**
(i) What is the probability of an individual from part (g) having the genotype *aa*? **50%**

B. An Observable Monohybrid Cross

2. Let the letter "*P*" represent the gene for kernel color.
(a) What genotypes produce a purple phenotype? *PP, Pp*
(b) Which allele is dominant? **Purple, *P***
(c) What is the genotype of the yellow kernels on the F_2 ear? *pp*
(d) You are given an ear with purple kernels. How do you determine its genotype with a single cross?
Perform a test cross by crossing the purple, dominant phenotype, with a homozygous recessive (yellow.) If the purple kernels are *PP*, offspring kernels will be all purple (*Pp*). If purple kernels are *Pp*, offspring kernels will be half purple (*Pp*) and half yellow (*pp*).

107

C. Experiment: Monohybrid Heredity in a Fern

C.1 Week 1—Observation of F₁ Hybrid Gametophytes

2. Do all the gametophytes have the same phenotype? Describe any differences you observe. **Students should observe both hermaphroditic and male gametophytes, and also see that some are a uniform green and others have a "polka dot" appearance.**

Which of the phenotypes would you designate as a mutant? Why? **Instructors can introduce the concept of wild type (standard) versus mutant phenotypes. Polka dot phenotype (caused by clumping of chloroplasts) is clearly distinct from wild type uniform green phenotype.**

3. (a) Why is it important to take a random sample from the cultures? **To avoid bias and collect representative data. It's human nature to notice and fix on one of the phenotypes during sampling. Unless this is avoided, the collected data will not be representative of the population.**
(b) What is a suitable method of collecting data that would ensure a random sample? **As an example, students should adjust their microscopes to a magnification that allows them to clearly distinguish the phenotypes. They should then randomly move the petri dish to a region containing gametophytes and then count and classify all the heart-shaped gametophytes in one field of view. Repeat the procedure until a total count of at least 50 has been obtained. A grid method could also be used by setting the petri dish atop a grid photocopied onto a transparency sheet.**

5. (a) Are the plants in the culture dish haploid or diploid? **Haploid.**
(b) What products will result from the fertilization events in the culture? **Zygotes, which then will grow into sporophyte ferns.**
Will they be haploid or diploid? **Diploid.**
(c) If the F1 sporophyte is heterozygous for a single mutant trait, what genotypes will be present in the spores? **Half spores will have one allele, half spores will have other allele. In this instance, if chloroplast trait is designated "CP", both *CP* and *cp* will be present in spores.**
What genotypes will be present in the gametophytes? **Half gametophytes will have one allele, one genotype, *CP*, and the other half of the gametophytes will have the other allele, the other genotype, *cp*.**
(d) What is the expected ratio of genotypes? **Approximately 1:1**
(e) What is the approximate phenotypic ratio of the gametophytes? **Should be approximately 1:1.**
(f) Can you determine the dominance relationships from the data in Table 13-1?
No, because the gametophytes are haploid. Each allele present is expressed in these haploid organisms, so it is not possible to determine dominance relationships from these data.
(g) Predict the genetic outcome of the fertilizations taking place in the cultures by formulating a hypothesis to explain the inheritance of the trait. Indicate expected ratios of both the gametophyte and the F2 generations. **Common hypothesis is that *CP* allele is dominant to *cp* allele, in which case one would expect to see a 3 normal :1 polka dot phenotypic ratio, produced by 1:1 ratio of F1 gametophytes.**

C.2 Data Analysis

In the space below, diagram the crosses involved in the F1 and F2 generations, indicating which generations/ structures are haploid, and which are diploid.

P cross: *CP* X   *cp*   →   F1 sporophytes *CPcp*
       haploid   haploid   diploid

F1 sporophytes produce spores with genotypes *CP* and *cp*. These grow into haploid gametophytes producing eggs and sperm.

Self-fertilizations produce all possible combinations of F2, can be visualized with Punnett Square:

	CP	*cp*
CP	*CPCP*	*CPcp*
cp	*CPcp*	*cpcp*

F2 diploid sporophytes would have approximate ratio of 1*CPCP* : 2*CPcp* : 1*cpcp*

1. Transfer your individual or group data from the Totals columns in Table 13-1 to Table 13-4 and calculate χ^2.
Data varies.
2. How many degrees of freedom are there? **One.**
Is your hypothesis supported or not supported? **Varies.**
If not, what might be changed in your hypothesis or in the experimental design? **Varies.**

C.3 Week 3—Observation of F2 Sporophytes

1. Are the young sporophytes haploid or diploid? Why? **Sporophytes are diploid. Each is produced from fusion of egg and sperm, followed by subsequent mitotic cell divisions.**

5. Restate your hypothesis regarding the inheritance of the mutant and wild-type alleles, and your prediction of the genetic outcome in the F_2 sporophytes. **Common hypothesis is that *CP* allele is dominant to *cp* allele, in which case one would expect to see a 3 normal :1 polka dot phenotypic ratio, produced by 1:1 ratio of gametophytes.**

6. How many degrees of freedom are there? **One.**
What is the approximate probability? **Varies according to student data.**
Is your hypothesis supported or not supported? **Varies according to student data.**
Which allele is the dominant allele? ***CP*, or normal, allele**
Which is recessive? ***cp*, or polka dot, allele**
If gametophytes had not expressed the phenotype, would you be able to form a hypothesis from observations of the gametophyte generation? **No.** Why or why not? **There would have been no observations to provide data to aid in formulation of an hypothesis.**

13.2 Dihybrid Inheritance

A. Dihybrid Problems

1. (a) List all possible genotypes for an individual with pigmented iris and dimpled chin. ***PPDD, PpDD, PPDd, PpDd***
(b) List the possible genotypes for an individual with pigmented iris but lacking a dimpled chin. ***PPdd, Ppdd***
(c) List the possible genotypes of a blue-eyed, dimple-chinned individual. ***ppDD, ppDd***
(d) List the possible genotypes of a blue-eyed individual lacking a dimpled chin. ***ppdd***

2. An individual is heterozygous for both traits (eye pigmentation and chin form).
(a) What is the genotype of such an individual? *PpDd*
 (b) What are the possible genotypes of that individual's gametes? *Pd, PD, pD, pd*
 (c) Two individuals heterozygous for both eye pigmentation and chin form have children. What are the possible genotypes of those F1 offspring? *PPdd, PPDd, PPDD, Ppdd, PpDd, PpDD, ppDD, ppDd, ppdd*
 (d) What is the ratio of the genotypes? *PPDD:2PPDd:4PpDd:2Ppdd:1PPDD:2PpDD:1ppDD:2ppDd:1ppdd*
What is the phenotypic ratio? **9 pigmented, dimpled:3 pigmented, undimpled:3 blue-eyed, dimpled:1 blue-eyed, undimpled.**
(e) Recalling the discussion of probability in section 13.1, state the probability of a child from part (d) having the following genotypes. *ppDD* **1/16;** *PpDd* **4/16;** *PPDd* **2/16**
 (f) State the probability that three children born to the parents in part (d) will have the genotype *ppdd*.
1/16 X 1/16 X 1/16 = 0.00024 = 0.024%
What is the probability that three children born to these parents will have dimpled chins and pigmented eyes?
9/16 X 9/16 X 9/16 = 0.1779 = 17.8%
 (g) What is the genotype of the F1 generation when the father is homozygous for both pigmented eyes and dimpled chin, but the mother has blue eyes and no dimple? *PpDd*
What is the phenotype of this individual? **Pigmented eyes, dimpled chin.**

B. An Observable Dihybrid Cross

1. ….Which genotypes of the parents produced the F2 generation kernels? *PpSs X PpSs*
2. Set up a Punnett square of this dihybrid cross: What is the predicted phenotypic ratio? **9:3:3:1**
3. Which traits seem dominant? **Generally purple color and smooth kernels**
Which traits seem recessive? **Generally yellow color and shriveled kernels.**
4. Calculate the actual phenotypic ratio you observed: **Varies.**
   Do your observed results differ from the expected results? **Varies.**
5. Use the chi-square test to determine if the deviation from the expected results can be accounted for by chance alone. **Varies.**

13.3 Some Readily Observable Human Traits

(Results vary for each student.)

Name _____

Section No. _____

HEREDITY

Pre-lab Questions

1. In a monohybrid cross: a. only one trait is being considered; b. the parents are always dominant;
    c. the parents are always heterozygous; d. no hybrid is produced.

2. The physical appearance and physiology of an organism, resulting from interactions of its genetic makeup
    and its environment, is its: a. phenotype; b. hybrid vigor; c. dominance; d. genotype.

3. The genetic makeup of an organism is its: a. phenotype; b. genotype; c. locus; d. gamete.

4. The gametophyte of a fern is: a. haploid; b. photoautotrophic; c. a structure that produces eggs and/or
    sperm; d. all of the above.

5. A Punnett square is used to determine: a. probable gamete genotypes; b. possible parental phenotypes;
    c. possible parental genotypes; d. possible genetic outcomes of a cross.

6. A chi-square test is used to: a. determine if experimental data adequately matches what was expected;
    b. analyze a Punnett square; c. determine parental genotypes producing a given offspring genotype;
    d. determine if a trait is dominant or recessive.

7. When both dominant and recessive alleles are present within a single nucleus, the organism is _____ for the
    trait: a. diploid; b. haploid; c. homozygous; d. heterozygous.

8. An allele whose expression is completely masked by the expression or effect of its allelic partner is:
    a. homologous; b. homozygous; c. dominant; d. recessive.

9. If you can roll your tongue: a. you have at least one copy of the dominant allele T; b. you must have two
    copies of the recessive allele t; c. you must be male; d. you are haploid.

10. Possible gamete genotypes produced by an individual of genotype $PpDd$ are: a. Pp and Dd; b. all $PpDd$;
    c. PD and pd; d. PD, Pd, pD, and pd.

111

HEREDITY

*Answers to Pre-lab Questions
in Lab Manual Order*

1.	a	6.	d
2.	b	7.	d
3.	d	8.	a
4.	a	9.	d
5.	d	10.	a

*Answers to Pre-lab Questions
in Instructor's Manual Order*

1.	a	6.	a
2.	a	7.	d
3.	b	8.	d
4.	d	9.	a
5.	d	10.	d

Answers to Post-lab Questions

1. Explain the implications of Mendel's law of segregation as it applies to distribution of alleles in gametes. **Each diploid organism contains two alleles for each trait. Those alleles will be separated (segregated) into different gametes.**

2. Assume that production of hairs on a plant's leaves is controlled by a single gene with two alleles *H* (dominant) and *h* (recessive). Hairy leaves are dominant to smooth (non-hairy) leaves. a. Name the genotype(s) of a smooth-leaved plant. **hh** b. Name the genotype(s) of a hairy-leaved plant. **HH or Hh** c. What are the possible genotypes of gametes produced by the smooth-leaved plant? **All h** d. What are the possible gametes produced by the hairy-leaved plant? **Gametes could be all H if homozygous or a heterozygous individual would produce half H and half h.**

3. Non-true-breeding hairy-leaved plants are crossed with smooth-leaved plants. a. What genotypic and phenotypic ratios would you expect for the potential offspring? **1Hh : 1 hh; 1 hairy-leaved plant : 1 smooth-leaved plant.** b. Suppose you perform such a cross, collect data, and do a chi-square test to aid in data analysis. How many degrees of freedom would there be? **One** c. Suppose your chi-square value is very large (>25). What does this indicate about your experiment and/or hypothesis?

4. What genotypic ratio would you expect in the gametophyte generation of C-ferns produced by F_1 spores if two traits on separate chromosomes were being followed? **9:3:3:1**

5. Were dominant and recessive traits observed equally in both gametophytes and sporophytes of C-ferns? **Approximately 1:1 phenotypic ratio.** How did you determine which character was dominant and which was recessive? **Cross the F_1 to produce an F_2 in order to determine dominance relationships.**

6. Suppose you have two traits controlled by genes on separate chromosomes. If sexual reproduction occurs between two heterozygous parents, what will be the genotypic ratio of all possible gametes? **1 AB : 1 Ab : 1 aB : 1 ab**

7. Explain the usefulness of the chi-square test. **Briefly, the chi-square test allows you to determine if data supports, or does not support, a hypothesis. The test compares the observed results of an experiment or observation to expected results, and the chi-square distribution tables indicate when deviation from expected results is likely to be due to chance rather than to an incorrect hypothesis.**

8. Suppose students in previous semesters had removed some of the corn kernels from the genetic corn ears before you counted them. What effect would this have on your results? **Results would be skewed because data would be missing.**

9. Assume that one allele is completely dominant over the other for the following questions. a. Two individuals heterozygous for a *single* trait have children. What is the expected phenotypic ratio of the possible offspring? **3:1** b. Two individuals heterozygous for *two* traits have children. What would be the expected phenotypic ratio of the possible offspring? **9:3:3:1.** c. Crossing two individuals heterozygous for two traits results in the same phenotypic ratio as for a single trait. Are the genes for these two traits on separate chromosomes or on the same chromosome? Explain your answer. (Remember that the gene for each trait is located at a locus, a physical region on the chromosome.) **The loci would be linked, the traits being on the same chromosome.**

10. How does probability differ from actuality? **Probability is a prediction of what *might* occur, while actuality describes what has really happened.**

EXERCISE 14

NUCLEIC ACIDS: BLUEPRINTS FOR LIFE

Materials and Equipment

14.1 Isolation and Identification of Nucleic Acids

Per student pair

- culture tube of *Halobacterium salinarum*
- glass rod
- sterile pipette (5 or 10 mL)
- two 10-mL graduated cylinder
- agarose gel plate with methylene blue stain
- test tube rack

- cotton applicator stick
- 10 mL 95% ethanol in test tube
- bent inoculating needle
- two test tubes
- china marker
- dropping pipet

Per lab bench

- DNA standard solution in dropper bottle
- TBE buffer solution bottle in dropping bottle

- 1% albumin solution in dropper bottle
- paper towels

Per lab room

- raw egg white in beaker
- white light transilluminator or other source of white light

- source of dH_2O

14.2 Modeling the Structure and Function of Nucleic Acids and Their Products

Per student pair

- DNA puzzle kit

Per lab room

- DNA model

14.3 Principles of Genetic Engineering: Recombination of DNA

Per student group

- nutrient agar plate containing ampicillin, incubated with *E. coli* Strain 1 on one half, and *E. coli* Strain 2 on the other half
- nutrient agar plate containing streptomycin, incubated with *E. coli* Strain 1 on one half, and *E. coli* Strain 2 on the other half
- nutrient agar plate containing *both* ampicillin and streptomycin, incubated with a mating solution of both *E. coli* Strain 1 and *E. coli* Strain 2 spread across the plate (The mating solution is designed to allow bacterial conjugation to occur.)
- demonstration nutrient agar plates showing growth of *E. coli* Strain 1 and *E. coli* Strain 2

Preparation of Materials and Equipment

14.1 Isolation and Identification of Nucleic Acids

Halobacterium salinarum cultures: Purchase *H. salinarum* from Ward's Natural Science, Inc., (see *Ordering Information*) as freeze-dried cultures or living cultures on agar slants. Store on *Halobacterium* agar (see *Ordering Information*) slants at 4°C, retransferring onto fresh agar slants at least every 6 months to maintain viability.

Class cultures are started by aseptically streaking loopfuls of bacteria from the surface of a growing culture onto new *Halobacterium* agar slants. *Halobacterium* grows slowly and should be incubated about 2 weeks at 37°C. DO NOT try to streak *Halobacterium* with a loopful of sterile dH_2O, as standard microbiological technique would suggest; the cells will rupture from osmotic shock.

Bent inoculating needle: Bend the terminal 5 mm of each inoculating needle into a U-shaped hook.

DNA standard solution (200 mL): Add 1 drop glacial acetic acid to 200 mL dH$_2$O. Add 0.1 g DNA, stirring until dissolved. It may be necessary to heat gently to get the DNA into solution. Store frozen.
> *Shelf life:* 2 to 3 years if kept frozen.
> *Yield:* 200mL DNA standard solution should be sufficient for approximately 60 student groups.

Agarose gel plate with methylene blue stain (500 mL): 0.1% methylene blue in 0.8% agarose:

methylene blue	.05 g
agarose	4 g
dH$_2$O	500 mL

To the 500 mL of dH$_2$O, add the methylene blue. Stir until dissolved on a stirring hot plate. Once the stain is dissolved, bring the solution to a boil. Slowly add the agarose with constant stirring. Boil and stir until agarose is fully dissolved. Pour standard size petri dishes, approximately 15 mL/plate. Allow to cool.
> *Shelf life:* Plates may be stored in refrigerator for several weeks. However make sure the plates do not dessicate.
> *Yield:* 500 mL will pour approximately 33 plates.

10X TBE buffer stock solution:

TRIS base	108 g
Boric acid	55.0 g
0.5 M EDTA (pH 8.0)	40.0 mL

1% Albumin solution:

albumin, soluble	1 g
dH$_2$O	100 mL

> *Shelf life:* Solution should be kept refrigerated. Discard after 1 month.
> *Yield:* 100 mL should be sufficient for 100 students.

14.2 Modeling the Structure and Function of Nucleic Acids and Their Products

None required.

14.3 Principles of Genetic Engineering: Recombination of DNA

Purchase Introductory Bacterial Conjugation kit (21-1125) from Carolina Biological Supplies. Upon receipt of this kit, store the antibiotic solutions at 4°C for up to one month, or in the freezer for up to three months until use. Slants may be stored at 4°C for up to three months. Other materials may be stored at room temperature (about 25°C) for at least one year.

The set-up takes some time. The first activities include inoculating three liquid cultures of each bacterial strain and preparing LB agar plates. The LB plates should be prepared within 10 days of the lab activity, and stored at 4°C until use. The liquid cultures may be started 1 to 4 days before the first lab day.

Preparing LB Agar Plates: One to 10 days before the scheduled lab, prepare at least 16 agar plates as follows: 4 LB plain, 4 LB+amp, 4 LB+str, and 4 LB+str+amp. The kit has enough material to prepare up to 48 agar plates. Use good aseptic technique and work in an area away from drafts and heavy activity.

1. Loosen the caps and place the bottles of LB agar in a boiling water bath for 30 to 40 minutes or in a microwave oven for 7 to 10 minutes, or until the agar has melted completely. Swirl the agar and make certain that no lumps are present.
2. Allow the agar to cool until the bottle can be held comfortably in a bare hand (20 to 30 minutes). Swirl every 5 to 7 minutes to ensure even cooling. Since antibiotics are inactivated by high temperature, the agar must be cooled to about 55°C before the antibiotic solutions are added. While the agar is cooling, label one of the four bottles "+amp" to designate it for the addition of ampicillin. Label one of the four bottles "+str" to designate that a vial of streptomycin solution will be added to this bottle. The third bottle should be labeled "+str/amp" because streptomycin and ampicillin will be added to it. The fourth bottle, labeled "LB," will contain plain agar.

3. Carefully cut the top of the plastic sleeve containing the sterile petri plates and save the sleeve for storing the poured plates and remaining plates. Remove the plates from the sleeve, being careful to keep the lids in place. Set aside four stacks of petri plates each of 4 plates. Label the bottoms of the petri dishes in each stack as follows:
   Stack 1: "LB"
   Stack 2: "LB+str"
   Stack 3: "LB+amp"
   Stack 4: "LB+str+amp"

4. When the agar has cooled to "comfortably warm," aseptically add one vial of ampicillin solution to the agar bottle labeled "+amp". Add one vial of streptomycin solution to the bottle labeled "+str" and one vial of each antibiotic solution to the bottle labeled "+str+amp." Work quickly, and do not place open caps down on the lab bench. Immediately after the addition of the antibiotic solution, replace the cap on the agar bottle and swirl the agar to thoroughly mix the antibiotics.

5. Pour the melted agar from each bottle into the appropriately labeled culture plates. Lift the lid of each plate and pour enough agar to just cover the bottom (about 3 mm in depth). Replace the lids.

6. Allow the agar to solidify. Return the plates to the storage sleeve or wrap them with plastic wrap and store them topside-down in a refrigerator at 4°C until use. Keep the plates away from the rear wall of the refrigerator to prevent freezing.

Preparing Liquid Cultures: Materials for preparing liquid cultures include Str^r slant culture (I), 6 sterile plastic loops, Amp^r slant culture (II), permanent lab marker, 6 bottles of LB broth (10 mL), masking or labeling tape, Bunsen burner, lighter and 10% bleach (or disinfectant)

If there is enough time, it is a good idea to streak a fresh plate of each culture the day before you want to make the liquid culture. The liquid culture should be made from one colony to ensure purity. If there is not enough time to do this, satisfactory cultures can be made from the slant provided in this kit. It would be a good idea to have the procedure described below clearly visualized in your mind so that you can work with speed for the actual inoculation.

1. Cleanse the lab bench with 10% chlorine bleach or another disinfectant. Using tape (for easy cleanup), label three bottles of LB broth as "I" and three bottles as "II."

2. Loosen the cap of each bottle so it sits loosely on the top of the bottle. Loosen the caps on the slant culture vials, but not too much and light the Bunsen burner.

3. Aseptically, pick up a small cell mass (about 10% of the area of the yellow loop) from the Strain "I" slant culture vial and transfer LB broth labeled "Strain I".

4. Immerse the tip of the loop into the broth and agitate it to dislodge the cell mass. Break it up with the loop, if possible. Reflame the neck of the bottle and then replace the cap tightly. Repeat steps 3 for the other two bottles of LB labeled "I."

5. Repeat steps 3 using the slant culture vial containing Strain II and the three bottles of LB broth labeled "II."

6. Incubate the liquid cultures for 24 hours in a shaking water bath prewarmed to 37°C, or on a shaking platform in an incubator prewarmed to 37°C. If no mechanical shaker is available, incubate 2 to 3 days at 37°C, or at room temperature for 4 days. Cultures may be refrigerated for one week if not used immediately.

Confirming Antibiotic Resistance in Each Bacterial Strain: You will need, sterile loops, plain LB agar plate, LB agar+str plate, LB agar+amp plate, LB agar+str+amp plate, laboratory marker.

1. On the bottom surface, draw a line down the middle of each of the four different agar plates. Write "I" on one side of the line, and "II" on the other side.

2. Obtain the *E. coli* I and II broth cultures. Strain I has a gene for streptomycin resistance (Str^r) in the chromosome. Strain II has a gene for ampicillin resistance (Amp^r) on a plasmid (see Laboratory Manual Figure 14-16).

3. Using sterile loop, inoculate *E. coli* I lightly to the agar in the middle of each section marked "I" on each of the four plates.

4. Using a new loop, inoculate *E. coli* II lightly to the agar in the middle of each section marked "II" on each plate. Allow the plates to sit briefly so the liquid can soak in before the plates are inverted for incubation. Incubate the plates overnight at 37°C, or for 36 to 48 –48 hours at room temperature.

5. Prepare an LB agar+amp+str "mating" plate to bring the cells of *E. coli* strains I and II into close proximity so that conjugation (mating) and the transfer of DNA between cells can occur. Using a sterile loop, place 0.1 mL (2-3drops) of Strain I sample on the mating plate. Then, using a new sterile loop, place 0.1 mL (2-3drops) of Strain II sample on the mating plate, approximately half inch away from strain 1. Use a new sterile loop to mix Strains I and II all over the surface of "mating" plate to allow for conjugation. Incubate the plates overnight at 37°C or for 24 to 48 hours at room temperature.

6. Test for recombination as follows: Slightly lift the lid of the agar "mating" plate containing the "suspected" recombinant cells and pick up some bacteria using a sterile transfer loop. Streak some of these bacteria onto the LB+amp plate. Repeat this process for the LB+str and LB+amp+str plates so that each plates has been inoculated with suspected "recombinant" cells from the mating plate. A new sterile loop should be used for each transfer. Incubate the plates overnight at 37°C or for 24 to 48 hours at room temperature.

Expected results:

Contents of Petri Plates	E. coli strain 1	E. coli strain 1I	Recombinant
LB	+	+	
LB+str	+	-	+
LB+amp	-	+	+
LB+str+amp	-	-	+

(+) = bacteria growth (-) = no bacterial growth

Notes

14.1 Isolation and Identification of Nucleic Acids

Halobacterium growth medium is very expensive. Two pairs of students may be able to extract sufficient nucleic acid from a single slant culture of *Halobacterium* with slight modification: One pair of students harvests bacterial cells **from the top half of a slant culture** using a cotton applicator stick as described. The second pair of students adds 1.5 mL dH$_2$O into the same slant culture and scrapes the remaining bacterial cells into that liquid for cell lysis. That cell suspension can then be poured into a test tube for isolation of the nucleic acids.

While plate cultures will produce greater quantities of bacterial cells for nucleic acid isolation, *Halobacterium* growth medium desiccates readily. Resulting salt crystals on the agar surface could interfere with the exercise. We therefore suggest that slant cultures be used throughout.

14.2 Modeling the Structure and Function of Nucleic Acids and Their Products

The DNA model is purchased as a scale model kit and must be assembled (assembly time about 1 hr.) and painted. A paint set specifically for this model can be purchased, also from Carolina Biological. A simpler kit is also available.

The tRNA pieces supplied in the DNA puzzle kit do not show the base sequence making up the anticodon. We suggest that you write the 3-letter base sequence on the pieces when you receive the kit (C-G-U for alanine, A-C-C for glycine).

14.3 Principles of Genetic Engineering: Recombination of DNA

Setting up the experiment takes some time, so plan ahead. The materials provided are much more than you will need for a demonstration experiment. Refill kit that contains two bacterial cultures and two antibiotics can be bought separately (see *Ordering Information*).

Ordering Information

See General Laboratory Supplies list on page vii for basic items

14.1 Isolation and Identification of Nucleic Acids

Halobacterium salinarum, living culture	Ward's	85 V 0987
H. salinarum, freeze-dried culture with growth medium	Ward's	85 V 1874
Halobacterium medium, 12 slant tubes	Ward's	88 V 0170
Halobacterium medium, dehydrated, for 1 liter	Ward's	88 V 0055
ethanol, 95%	Carolina	86-1281
inoculating needle	Ward's	14 V 0956
DNA, from salmon testes	Sigma	D1626
bottle, tincture ("Wheaton"), 250 mL	Carolina	71-6826
TRIS base	Fisher	BP152-500
boric acid	Fisher	A73-500
EDTA	Fisher	E478-500
methylene blue	Fisher	M291-25
Agarose	Fisher	AC-18644-0250
Bovine albumin, fraction V	Sigma	A3059

14.2 Modeling the Structure and Function of Nucleic Acids and Their Products

DNA puzzle kit	Carolina	17-1050
DNA Model Kit B	Carolina	17-1058
DNA Model Kit B Paint Set	Carolina	17-1060

14.3 Principles of Genetic Engineering: Recombination of DNA

Bacteria Conjugation Kit	Carolina	21-1125
Perishables Refill Kit	Carolina	21-1125A

Answers to In-text Questions

14.1 Isolation and Identification of Nucleic Acids

A. Isolation of Nucleic Acids

B. Identification—Test for DNA

TABLE 14-1 Identification of Contents Extracted from *Halobacterium*

Droplet Code	Droplet Contents	Color
P	Precipitate in TBE buffer	**Bluish purple**
D	DNA standard	**Bluish purple**
A	1% albumin	**Colorless**
C	TBE buffer	**Colorless**

Name the substance(s) present in the material you isolated from *Halobacterium*. **DNA**

What is the purpose of the DNA standard droplet? **To illustrate what a positive test for DNA appears as.**

What is the purpose of the TBE buffer droplet? **This is a control. It demonstrates that the TBE does not react to the methylene blue. Because the precipitate is in the TBE buffer, if any color reaction occurs it would indicate the reaction is due to the presence of something other than the TBE buffer.**

14.2 Modeling the Structure and Function of Nucleic Acids and Their Products

A. Nucleic Acid Structure

2… Note the small notches and projections in the nitrogen-containing bases. Will the notches of adenine and thymine fit together? **Yes**
Will guanine and cytosine? **Yes**
Will adenine and cytosine? **No**
Will thymine and guanine? **No**

The notches and projections represent bonding sites. Make a prediction about which bases will bond with one another. **Adenine will bond to thymine and cytosine will bond to guanine.**

Will a purine base bond with another purine? **No.**
Will a purine base bond with both types of pyrimidines? **No.**

5… What do you notice about the *direction* in which each strand is running? (That is, are both 5' carbons at the same end of the strands?) **No. The 5' carbons are at one end of one strand and the 5' end is at the opposite end of the other strand. That is to say, they are antiparallel.**

7… Compare the structural formulas of ribose (Figure 14-13) and deoxyribose (Figure 14-4). How do they differ? **Deoxyribose lacks an oxygen at the 2' carbon.**

Why is the sugar of DNA called *deoxy*ribose? **Because it has one less oxygen atom compared to ribose.**

B. Modeling DNA Replication

C. Transcription: DNA to RNA

What is the sequence from left to right of nitrogen bases on the mRNA strand? **A-C-G-U-G-G-A-C-G**
4. …By what avenue do you suppose the mRNA exits the nucleus? (*Hint*: Reexamine the structure of the nuclear membrane, as described in Exercise 6.) **Via the pores in the nuclear envelope.**

To *transcribe* means to "make a copy of." Is transcription of RNA from DNA the formation of an exact copy? **No.**
Explain. **Transcription produces a copy in the language of complementary base pairs.**

D. Translation—RNA to Polypeptides

2.… Will a particular tRNA bond with *any* amino acid, or is each tRNA specific? **It's specific.**

3. Now let's do some translating. In the space below, list the sequence of bases on the *messenger* RNA strand, starting at the left. (left, 3' end) **A-C-G-U-G-G-A-C-G** (right, 5' end).

The first codon on the mRNA model is (5' end) **G-C-A** (3' end).

6. Move the tRNA-amino acid complex onto the P site of the ribosome template sheet and fit the codon and anticodon together. In the boxes below, indicate the codon, anticodon, and the specific amino acid attached to the tRNA.

mRNA codon$_1$ = CGA

tRNA anticodon$_1$ = CGU

amino acid$_1$ = alanine

7. Now identify the second mRNA codon and fill in the boxes.

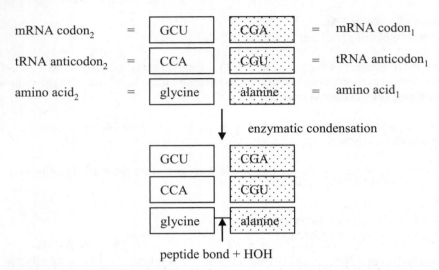

mRNA codon₂	=	GCU	CGA	=	mRNA codon₁
tRNA anticodon₂	=	CCA	CGU	=	tRNA anticodon₁
amino acid₂	=	glycine	alanine	=	amino acid₁

9. Separate amino acid₁ from its tRNA and link it to amino acid₂.

mRNA codon₂	=	GCU	CGA	=	mRNA codon₁
tRNA anticodon₂	=	CCA	CGU	=	tRNA anticodon₁
amino acid₂	=	glycine	alanine	=	amino acid₁

enzymatic condensation

GCU	CGA
CCA	CGU
glycine	alanine

peptide bond + HOH

10. What amino acid will tRNA₁ pick up? **Alanine**

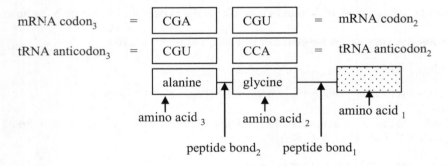

mRNA codon₃	=	CGA	CGU	=	mRNA codon₂
tRNA anticodon₃	=	CGU	CCA	=	tRNA anticodon₂
		alanine	glycine		

amino acid ₃   amino acid ₂   amino acid ₁

peptide bond₂   peptide bond₁

Record the tripeptide that you have just modeled. **Alanine-glycine-alanine.**

A gene probably consists of **many** deoxyribonucleotides.

14.3 Principles of Genetic Engineering: Recombination of DNA

TABLE 14-2 Bacterial Growth on Antibiotic-containing Plates			
Growth of Bacteria on Nutrient Agar Containing:			
Strain of *E. coli*	**Ampicillin**	**Streptomycin**	**Ampicillin plus Streptomycin**
Strain 2 (donor)	+	-	X
Strain 1 (recipient)	-	+	X
"Mating mixture"	X	X	+

120

3. … Was Strain 2 susceptible or resistant to ampicillin? **Resistant**
To Streptomycin? **Susceptible.**

Was Strain 1 susceptible or resistant to Ampicillin? **Susceptible.**
To Streptomycin? **Resistant.**

Make a conclusion about the presence and location of a gene in each of the two strains of *E. coli* for resistance to each of the antibiotics.

   Strain 2: **The gene for resistance to Streptomycin is on the plasmid. Strain 2 is missing the gene for Ampicillin resistance.**

   Strain 1: **The gene for resistance to Ampicillin is on the chromosome. Strain 1 is missing the gene for Streptomycin resistance.**

Make a conclusion about what happened when the two strains were mixed together. Incorporate your observations concerning antibiotic resistance into your conclusion. **When the two strains were mixed together, conjugation took place and the gene for Ampicillin resistance was transferred from the plasmid of strain 2 to the chromosome of Strain 1, rendering Strain 1 resistant to Ampicillin. The plate containing both antibiotics would have growth on it as a consequence of cells that show resistance to both streptomycin and ampicillin.**

NUCLEIC ACIDS: BLUEPRINTS FOR LIFE

Pre-lab Questions

1. A nucleotide may consist of: a. deoxyribose or ribose; b. purines or pyrimidines; c. phosphate groups; d. all of the above.

2. Deoxyribose is: a. a 5-carbon sugar; b. present in RNA; c. a nitrogen-containing base; d. one type of purine.

3. Nitrogen-containing bases between two complementary DNA strands are joined by: a. polar covalent bonds; b. hydrogen bonds; c. phosphate groups; d. deoxyribose sugars.

4. Which of the following is consistent with the principle of base pairing? a. purine-purine; b. pyrimidine-pyrimidine; c. adenine-thymine; d. guanine-thymine.

5. The individuals responsible for constructing the first model of DNA structure were: a. Wallace and Watson; b. Lamarck and Darwin; c. Mendel and Meischer; d. Crick and Watson.

6. Replication of DNA: a. takes place during interphase; b. results in two double helices from one; c. is semiconservative; d. all of the above.

7. An anticodon: a. is a three-base sequence of nucleotides on tRNA; b. is produced by translation of RNA; c. has the same base sequence as does the codon; d. is the same as a gene.

8. Transcription of DNA: a. results in formation of a complementary strand of RNA; b. produces two new strands of DNA; c. occurs on the surface of the ribosome; d. is semiconservative.

9. Bacterial plasmids: a. are the only genetic material in bacteria; b. may carry genes for antibiotic resistance; c. may be transferred between bacteria during the process of conjugation; d. are both b and c.

10. The difference between deoxyribose and ribose is that ribose: a. is a six-carbon sugar; b. bonds only to thymine, not uracil; c. has one more oxygen atom than deoxyribose has; d. all of the above.

EXERCISE 14

NUCLEIC ACIDS: BLUEPRINTS FOR LIFE

Answers to Pre-lab Questions
in Lab Manual Order

1.	d	6.	c
2.	a	7.	d
3.	d	8.	a
4.	c	9.	a
5.	b	10.	d

Answers to Pre-lab Questions
in Instructor's Manual Order

1.	d	6.	d
2.	a	7.	a
3.	b	8.	a
4.	c	9.	d
5.	d	10.	c

Answers to Post-lab Questions

1. The following diagram represents some of the puzzle pieces used in this section. a. Assembled in this form, do they represent a (an) amino acid, base, portion of messenger RNA, or deoxyribonucleotide? **Portion of messenger RNA.** b. Justify your answer. **The sugar is ribose, as indicated by the presence of a single oxygen atom in the five carbon ring. The base is uracil. Therefore, the best answer of the choices is "a portion of messenger RNA."**

2. Why is DNA often called a double helix? **DNA consists of two strands linked by hydrogen bonds. The strands are twisted into a helix.**

3. State the following ratios: a. guanine to cytosine in a double-stranded DNA molecule? **1 : 1.** b. adenine to thymine? **1 : 1.**

4. Define: a. replication—**Production of a new strand of DNA from an old strand;** b. transcription—**Production of a strand of RNA using DNA as a template;** c. translation—**Production of a polypeptide from information supplied by RNA;** d. codon—**A 3-base sequence on mRNA;** e. anticodon—**A 3-base sequence on tRNA.**

5. What does it mean to say that DNA replication is *semiconservative*? **When replication occurs, two new helices of DNA are produced. Each contains one old strand of DNA (called "conserved"), and one newly synthesized strand.**

6. a. If the base sequence on one DNA strand is ATGGCCTAG, what will the sequence be on the other strand of the helix? **TACCGGATC.** b. If the original strand serves as the template for transcription, what will the sequence be on the newly formed RNA strand? **UACCGGAUC.**

7. a. What amino acid would be produced if *transcription* took place from a nucleotide with the 3-base sequence ATA? **Tyrosine.** b. Suppose a genetic mistake took place during *replication* and the new DNA strand had the sequence ATG. What would be the 3-base sequence on an RNA strand transcribed from this series of nucleotides? **UAC.** c. Which amino acid would this codon result in? Explain. **Tyrosine. Different triplets (three letter sequences) of mRNA may code for the same amino acid.**

8. a. What is a plasmid? **A small circle of DNA in some bacterial cells. This plasmid is *not* part of the bacterial chromosome.** b. How are plasmids used in genetic engineering? **Foreign sequences of nucleotides are inserted into the plasmid. When the bacterium reproduces, each new bacterial cell contains a hybrid plasmid and thus produces the substance for which the foreign nucleotide sequence coded.**

9. How does bacterial conjugation differ from the process by which eukaryotic gene products are produced by bacteria? **Bacterial conjugation is the transfer of genetic material between two bacteria. Genetic engineering (recombinant DNA) produces a new strain of bacteria by incorporating the nucleotide sequence from a eukaryotic cell into the plasmid of a prokaryotic bacterium.**

10. What kinds of molecules are present in bacterial cells in addition to the DNA you might have isolated in section 14.1? **RNA, proteins, lipids, carbohydrates, and inorganics.**

BIOTECHNOLOGY: BACTERIAL TRANSFORMATION

Materials and Equipment

15.1 Experiment: Bacterial Transformation

Per student group

- microcentrifuge tube rack
- micropipeter and tips to transfer 10µL
- X-gal/IPTG LG agar plate (optional)
- three X-gal/IPTG LB agar plates
- microcentrifuge tube containing 1 mL transformation solution, labeled TS
- three to four empty microcentrifuge tubes labeled BC, C1 and C2 (optional)
- microcentrifuge tube containing 10µL wild- type pUC 19 plasmid
- sterile disposable inoculating loops or wire loops and Bunsen burner

- ice bucket and ice
- water bath
- microcentrifuge
- beaker

Per lab room

- wall clock or timer
- 37°C incubator (optional)
- 50-mL polypropylene tube containing bacterial culture (*E. coli* K-12 strain JM 101)

- transfer hood (optional)

Preparation of Materials and Equipment

15.1 Experiment: Bacterial Transformation

LB media for bacteria starter culture:

LB media:

LB media	2.5 g
distilled water	100 mL

Mix and heat to boiling to dissolve. Dispense 15 mL into 50 mL polypropylene tubes. Sterilize in autoclave for 15 minutes at 15 lbs. Pressure and 121°C. Store in refrigerator until needed.

Class cultures should be inoculated with approximately 20 µL of bacterial cells. Incubate the inoculated media with constant shaking for 4 to 5 hours at 37 °C or at room temperature overnight.

Plasmid preparation:

Resuspend the plasmid DNA in 200µL sterile distilled water. Dissolve the plasmid DNA by mixing the solution with clean pipet tip. Store the plasmid DNA solution in a refrigerator or freezer for future use.

Transformation solution:

calcium chloride	5.4 g
sterile distilled water	35 mL

Store in refrigerator or freezer for future use.

X-Gal/IPTG LB agar plates:

X-Gal stock solution: X-Gal   40 mg
    Prior to use add 200µL dimethyl formamide. The solution may be stored in a freezer.
IPTG stock solution: IPTG   40 mg
    Prior to use add 200µL sterile distilled water. The solution may be stored in a freezer.
Ampicillin stock solution: ampicillin   100 mg
    (100 mg/mL)
    Prior to use add 1 mL sterile distilled water. The solution may be stored in a freezer.

X-Gal/IPTG LB agar with antibiotic:

LB agar media	4.1 gm
distilled water	110 mL

Mix in 500mL flask and heat to boiling to dissolve. Sterilize in autoclave for 15 minutes at 15lbs. pressure and 121°C. After autoclaving, allow the agar to cool to approximately 50°C (agar is still molten, but you should be able to hold your hand on the bottle several seconds). Aseptically transfer 20μL of X-Gal solution and 20μL of IPTG solution and 100μL of antibiotic solution to the molten agar. Mix the contents by gently swirling the solution. Pour approximately 25mL of media into sterile petri plates. Allow to cool and solidify. Invert the plates and store in refrigerator until needed.

X-Gal/IPTG LB agar plates without antibiotic are prepared as above but omit the addition of the antibiotic solution.

Notes

15.1 Experiment: Bacterial Transformation

Kits for similar experiments can be purchased from various vendors. Though generally more expensive in cost/student, the ordering process and preparation time is more efficient.

Ordering Information

See General Laboratory Supplies list on page vii for basic items

15.1 Experiment: Bacterial Transformation

50 mL polypropylene tube	Fisher	05-538-55A
Ampicillin	Carolina	21-6880
calcium chloride	Fisher	AC42352-250
Dimethylformamide	Fisher	BP2610-100
E.coli K-12 strain JM101	Wards	85-W-1866
inoculating loop	Fisher	13-070-1
IPTG	Fisher	BP1755-1
LB agar	Fisher	DF0445-17-4

(Can also purchase LB +amp+X-Gal agar from Carolina 21-6604)

LB broth	Fisher	DF0445-17-4
Microcentrifuge	Fisher	05-090-7
microcentrifuge tube	Fisher	05-669-30
micropipetter set	Fisher	21-377-250

(For micropipetter - check with vendor for correct tips)

PUC 19 plasmid	New England Biolabs	N3041S
Waterbath	Fisher	15-460-10
X-Gal	Carolina	21-7190

(Can also purchase Ampicillin/X-Gal from Carolina 21-6874)

Answers to In-text Questions

15.1 Experiment: Bacterial Transformation

12. Make arrangements with your instructor to check the bacterial plates after the appropriate period of incubation has passed. Record the date and time. **Fill in date and time**

TABLE 15-3 Results of Transformation Experiment			
Predictions: If competent bacteria are transformed by plasmids that contain genes for antibiotic resistance and ß-galactosidase activation, then they will form blue colonies on media containing ampicillin, substrate (X-gal), and inducer (IPTG). If competent bacteria are not transformed, then there will be no growth on this media. If competent bacteria are not transformed, then there will be growth on this media minus the antibiotic.			
Plate	Colonies (yes or no)	Color of colonies	Other comments
B	Yes	blue	
C1	No		
C2 (optional)	Yes	Not blue	
Conclusions: The predictions are accepted and the hypothesis is supported			

14. How do your results compare with those of the rest of the class? **The class results are consistent.**

15. What can you conclude from the results of the C1 control plate? **It is a negative control in that competent bacteria that were not transformed can't grow on the on media containing ampicillin, substrate (X-gal), and inducer (IPTG).**

16. *Optional.* What can you conclude from the results of the C2 control plate? **It is a positive control in that competent bacteria that were not transformed can grow on the on media containing only substrate (X-gal) and inducer (IPTG).**

17. Look over these results and draw some conclusions about whether your predictions should be accepted or rejected. Is your hypothesis supported or falsified? **The predictions are accepted and the hypothesis is supported.**

18. If you were to use the plasmid DNA from the blue colonies to insert a foreign gene and the insertion site was within the *lacZ* gene (Figure 15-6), how could you detect bacteria with a plasmid that contains the inserted foreign gene? **Their colonies will not be blue.**

15.2 Bacterial Transformation on the Internet

1. Visit the National Center for Biotechnology Information. The current address is http://www.ncbi.nlm.nih.gov/Database/index.html

2. Type "plasmid" into the *Entrez* search and retrieval system. What kind of databases does it search?

> **Nucleotide**
> **Protein**
> **Genome**
> **Etc.**

5. Visit the Human Genome Project. The current address is http://www.ornl.gov/TechResources/Human_Genome/home.html
What is the Human Genome Project? **"…The U.S. Human Genome Project [was] a 13-year effort coordinated by the Department of Energy and the National Institutes of Health. The project originally [was] planned to last 15 years, but effective resource and technological advances accelerated the completion date to 2003. Project goals were to**

- *identify* **all the approximately 30,000 genes in human DNA,**
- *determine* **the sequences of the 3 billion chemical base pairs that make up human DNA,**
- *store* **this information in databases,**
- *improve* **tools for data analysis,**
- *transfer* **related technologies to the private sector, and**
- *address* **the ethical, legal, and social issues (ELSI) that may arise from the project."**

6. Another great site is managed by the Cold Spring Harbor Laboratory: http://www.cshl.org/
Be sure to search for plasmids and visit the DNA Learning Center. What is Barbara McClintock famous for in the field of plant genetics?
"Barbara McClintock discovered that certain genes can move around the chromosomes. She called these movable genes 'transposable elements'; the press called them 'jumping genes.' [Al] Hershey and McClintock were both awarded the Nobel Prize for their work at Cold Spring Harbor."

8. Use your favorite search engine to find five sites that have something to do with plasmids or bacterial transformation. List them below with a brief summary of their contents.

e.g.,

http://histmicro.yale.edu/history1.htm - Plasmids: Histories of a Concept
http://bccm.belspo.be/db/lmbp_search_form.php - a plasmid catalogue
http://en.wikipedia.org/wiki/Plasmid - article in free on-line encyclopedia
http://www.escience.ws/b572/L2/L2.htm - Stan Metzenberg's lecture on bacterial plasmids
http://www.mun.ca/biochem/courses/4103/topics/transformation.html - Martin E. Mulligan's overview of bacterial transformation

Name _____

Section No. _____

BIOTECHNOLOGY: BACTERIAL TRANSFORMATION

Pre-lab Questions

1. Characteristics of genetically engineered plants and plant products include: a. better nutrition; b. longer storage lives; c. resistance to disease and insects; d. all of the above.

2. Transformed cells contain: a. transformants; b. new genes; c. bacteria; d. none of these choices.

3. In genomic libraries: a. naturally and artificially selected plants are genetically engineered; b. DNA fragments are stored in plasmids; c. a virus is used to transform human cells; d. none of the above are done.

4. A tiny loop of double-stranded DNA describes a: a. bacterium; b. DNA ligase; c. plasmid; d. antibiotic.

5. The wild-type pUC19 plasmid (blue plasmid) contains genes for: a. antibiotic resistance; b. activation of β-galactosidase production; c. both a and b; d. none of these choices.

6. Enzymes used to insert a foreign gene into a plasmid include: a. DNA ligase; b. vectors; c. restriction enzymes; d. both a and c.

7. In the preceding experiment, bacteria that form blue colonies on X-gal/IPTG LB agar containing antibiotic also contain: a. a gene for antibiotic resistance; b. an active *lacZ* gene; c. an inactive *lacZ* gene; d. both a and b.

8. A molecule or anything else that transports new genes into a cell is called a: a. vector; b. plasmid; c. restriction enzyme; d. bacterium.

9. The presence of an antibiotic in the media where the bacteria are grown enables the selection of colonies grown from: a. transformed cells; b. nontransformed cells; c. cells that have the gene for resistance to the antibiotic; d. both a and c.

10. In this treatment of bacteria with cold transformation solution followed by heat-shock, the procedure: a. makes the cell wall porous; b. allows for plasmids to enter the cells; c. creates competent cells; d. does all of these choices.

BIOTECHNOLOGY: BACTERIAL TRANSFORMATION

Answers to Post-lab Questions

1. Define bacterial transformation. **Bacteria become transformed when they pick up new genes that are carried into cells in plasmids (tiny circles of double-stranded DNA).**

2. What does the term *vector* mean in the field of biotechnology? **Vectors are the gene-carrying vehicles that can enter, replicate, and express themselves within bacteria and other types of cells. Scientists use manipulated vectors such as plasmids to introduce foreign genes into bacteria.**

3. Draw and label a typical plasmid used by scientists to transform bacteria. **See figure 15-2.**

4. How are restriction and DNA ligase enzymes used to insert a foreign gene into a plasmid? **Plasmids with the matching restriction sites are cut open with restriction enzymes, foreign DNA fragments fill the gap, and DNA ligase seals its ends to the cut ends of the plasmid.**

5. When is a plasmid considered a recombinant ? **After insertion of the foreign DNA.**

6. What two general types of products can be harvested from cultures of transformed bacteria? **Duplicated recombinant plasmids and the gene product coded for in the inserted foreign DNA.**

7. In the process of bacterial transformation, how are the bacteria that contain a plasmid identified? **The plasmids used in this experiment contain a gene for ampicillin resistance. Transformed bacterial cells are easily identified as only they produce bacterial colonies when grown on solid LB agar media containing this antibiotic.**

8. How are transformed bacteria that contain a plasmid with an inserted foreign gene identified? **The plasmids used in this experiment also contain the *LacZ* gene, which activates β-galactosidase. This enzyme cleaves X-gal, which is also present in the media. The products of this reaction, in the presence of an inducer (IPTG), give rise to blue-colored bacterial colonies.**

9. Name the two elements needed for procedures similar to bacterial transformation to be useful in human gene therapy. **1. Knowledge 2. Ready availability of the human genome and suitable vectors.**

10.   At the time this exercise was written the media campaign in support of golden rice was being launched. Search the Internet for the roots of the controversy over this genetically enhanced plant. Briefly describe the benefits of, and the concerns over, its introduction to the rice-growing areas of the world. **Rice is the major food staple of much of the world, including a number of relatively poor, populous countries. However, it is deficient in carotenoids, which are molecules needed to make vitamin A. This deficiency is linked to a condition of progressive blindness that afflicts as many as a quarter million children a year. Golden rice contains introduced genes for carotenoids. The inventors and the company with the distribution rights in a humanitarian gesture offered to make golden rice seeds freely available to the world's poor countries. This came at a time of worldwide controversy over the safety of genetically modified commodities, including so-called "Frankenfoods." The probable medical advantages were clear, but some people felt that this was a calculated effort to sway world opinion. They were concerned that it had the potential to hasten the widespread introduction of other products with introduced genes before adequate testing for possible effects on human health and the environment.**

EXERCISE 16

EVOLUTIONARY AGENTS

Materials and Equipment

Per student group (4)

- two plastic dishpans (12 in. x 7 in.)
- 4000 small (8 mm diam.) white
- 4000 small red beads (optional)
- small bowl
- strainer or coarse sieve (9.5 mm mesh)
- ruler with a cm scale

- fifty large (10 mm diam.) white beads
- fifty large red beads
- fifty large pink beads
- pair long forceps
- calculator
- one large gray bead

Per lab room

- clock with a second hand

Preparation of Materials and Equipment

None required.

Notes

The large and small beads used in this exercise (with the exception of the optional 4000 small red beads) are available as a set, Evolutionary Agents Bead Set, from Carolina Biological Supply (see *Ordering Information.*).

If an instructor decides to substitute beads of his or her own choosing for this exercise, select approximately the same sizes as given here (8 and 10 mm), or else the type of sieve used and the timing of the various procedures will need to be adjusted.

4000 small (8 mm) beads will fill a pan of dimensions 12 in. x 7 in. to a depth of approximately 2 inches. Students should "strain" the "pond" from one pan into the other pan.

Ordering Information

See General Laboratory Supplies list for general supplies

Evolutionary agents beads set	Carolina	17-1165
sieve, coarse, 9.5 mm mesh	Fisher	04-883G
plastic dishpan or polypropylene sterilizing tray,12 in. x 7 3/4 in. x 5 1/8 in. (or purchase from local housewares supply)	Carolina	62-9380

Answers to In-text Questions

What percentage of our population is homozygous for black coats? **9%**

16.1 Natural Selection

A. Experiment: Natural Selection Acting Alone

TABLE 16-1 Large-Bead Counts Before and After Four Rounds of Simulated Predation				
Population	**White Beads**	**Pink Beads**	**Red Beads**	**Total Beads**
Initial				
Before	10	20	10	40
After	8	10	4	22
Second Generation				
Before	18	24	8	50
After	15	14	4	33
Third Generation				
Before	23	22	5	50
After	19	12	3	34
Fourth Generation				
Before	27	19	4	50
After	20	12	2	34

These bead counts are examples

TABLE 16-2 Allele and Genotype Frequencies Due to Selection by Simulated Predation					
Population	p	q	p^2	$2pq$	q^2
Initial	.5	.5	.25	.5	.25
First generation after selection	.59	.41	.35	.48	.17
Second generation after selection	.67	.33	.45	.44	.11
Third generation after selection	.74	.26	.54	.39	.07
Fourth generation after selection	.76	.24	.58	.36	.06

7. …When you are finished, copy the frequency of the red allele from Table 16-1 to Table 16-3 (Selection Alone column) and plot this data in Figure 16-2. **Fill in points.**

9. If you had started with a pond filled with small red beads as a background, how would the frequency of the red allele change? **The red and, to a lesser extent, the pink large beads compared to the large white beads would be harder for a "predator" to locate and therefore the red allele will increase over the generations.**

10. …Which kind of selection is illustrated by simulated predation of white, pink, and red beads in a white pond? Explain why you made this choice. **The simulated predation exercise illustrates directional selection as the proportion of the white individuals (an extreme phenotype) in the population is increasing over the generations.**

11. …how would the frequency of the color genes in each pond compare after a large number of generations? **The allele fixed in the population will be the one that when homozygous produces the most cryptic phenotype, white in white "ponds" and red in red "ponds."**

TABLE 16-3 Frequency of Red Allele (q) Due to Selection and Migration		
Prediction (Selection Alone): If the large beads are removed from a "pond" of white smaller beads, then the pink and red large beads will be chosen at respectively higher rates than the white large beads and the red allele will decrease over the generations.		
Prediction (Selection and Migration): If five large red beads (migrants) are added to the above "pool" before removal of the large beads, then the resulting decrease in the red allele will be less. over the generations.		
Generation	**Selection Alone**	**Selection and Migration**
1	.41	.52
2	.33	.44
3	.26	.41
4	.24	.39
Conclusion (Selection Alone): The prediction is accepted.		
Conclusion (Selection and Migration): The prediction is accepted.		

B. Experiment: Effect of Gene Flow on Natural Selection

4. How does migration influence the effectiveness of selection in this example? **It decreases the effectiveness of selection as it adds new red alleles to the population.**

6. How would migration have influenced the change in gene frequencies if white instead of red individuals had entered the population? **The rate of decrease in the red allele would have increased over the generations along with the frequency of heterozygotes and homozygotes with the red phenotype.**

16.2 Mutation

TABLE 16-4 Change in Allele Frequencies Due to Mutation			
Population	p	q	r
Initial	.5	.5	
New generation with mutation	.48	.5	.02

TABLE 16-5 Numbers of Each Phenotype Two Generations After a Single Mutation				
Color	Genotype	Frequency	X 50	Number of Individuals
White	p^2	.23	x 50	12
Pink	$2pq$	.48	x 50	24
Red	q^2	.25	x 50	12
Gray	$2pr$	.02	x 50	1
Dark red	$2qr$	.02	x 50	1
Black	r^2	.00	x 50	0

What effect will natural selection have on these phenotypes in a white pond? **Compared to the white phenotype, the other phenotypes will be more vulnerable to natural selection due to predation.**

How could conditions change to favor the selection of the rare black allele? **A gray or similar "pond" would confer a cryptic advantage to phenotypes with the rare black allele.**

16.3 Genetic Drift

TABLE 16-6 Allele Frequencies Produced by Genetic Drift			
		Actual Frequency in	
	Expected Frequency	Small cluster	Large cluster
n		10	20
p	.5	.6	.43
q	.5	.4	.57

6. …What effect does the size of the number of individuals participating in reproduction have on gene flow to the next generation? **The larger the number of individuals in a population that participate in reproduction, the more likely it is for the genes in the next generation to have the same frequencies as those of the initial population.**

9. Now calculate the allele frequencies in the new pond and record them in Table 16-7. How do they compare with the frequencies that characterized the pond from which these migrants came?

TABLE 16-7 Allele Frequencies in a Founder Population		
Allele Frequency	Initial Population	Founder Population
p	.5	.33
q	.5	.67

Example

134

16.4 Nonrandom Mating

TABLE 16-8 Phenotype Changes Due to Nonrandom Mating Color		
	Number in	
Color	Initial Generation	Next Generation
White	10	30
Pink	20	20
Red	10	30

TABLE 16-9 Genotype Frequency Changes Due to Nonrandom Mating		
Genotype Frequency	Initial Generation	Next Generation
p^2	.25	.38
$2pq$	.5	.25
q^2	.25	.37

5. What happens to the frequency of the heterozygote genotype in subsequent generations? **Assuming that individuals will continue to mate only with individuals of the same color, the gene frequency of the heterozygote will continue to decrease.**

Name _____

Section No. _____

EVOLUTIONARY AGENTS

Pre-lab Questions

1. A process which results in individuals of two populations losing the ability to interbreed is referred to as: a. stabilizing selection; b. fusion; c. speciation; d. differential migration.

2. If a population is in Hardy-Weinberg equilibrium and $p = 0.6$: a. $q = 0.5$; b. $q = 0.4$; c. $q = 0.3$; d. $q = 0.16$.

3. Two ways in which new alleles can become incorporated in a population are: a. mutation and genetic drift; b. selection and genetic drift; c. selection and mutation; d. mutation and gene flow.

4. Natural selection operates directly on: a. the genotype; b. individual alleles; c. the phenotype; d. color only.

5. A shift from expected allele frequencies, resulting from chance is known as: a. natural selection; b. genetic drift; c. fission; d. migration.

6. Two populations that have no gene flow between them are likely to: a. become more different with time; b. become more alike with time; c. become more alike if the directional selection pressures are different; d. stay the same unless mutations occur.

7. If a new allele appears in a population the Hardy-Weinberg formula: a. cannot be used because no equilibrium exists; b. can be used, but only for two alleles at a time; c. can be used by lumping all but two phenotypes in one class; d. can be expanded by adding more terms.

8. The process that discriminates between phenotypes with respect to their ability to produce offspring is known as: a. natural selection; b. gene flow; c. genetic drift; d. migration.

9. Genetic drift is a process that has a greater effect on populations that: a. are large; b. are small; c. are not affected by mutation; d. do not go through bottlenecks.

10. If all conditions of Hardy-Weinberg equilibrium are met: a. allele frequencies move closer to 0.5 each generation; b. allele frequencies change in the direction predicted by natural selection; c. allele frequencies stay the same; d. all allele frequencies increase.

EVOLUTIONARY AGENTS

*Answers to Pre-lab Questions
in Lab Manual Order*

1.	c	6.	c
2.	b	7.	d
3.	c	8.	d
4.	a	9.	b
5.	a	10.	b

*Answers to Pre-lab Questions
in Instructor's Manual Order*

1.	c	6.	a
2.	b	7.	d
3.	d	8.	a
4.	c	9.	b
5.	b	10.	c

Answers to Post-lab Questions

1. What effect would increasing gene flow between two populations have on their genetic make-up? **It would make them genetically more and more alike.**

2. How can selection cause two populations to become different with time? **If each population is in a different environment and adapts to different conditions, they will become increasingly different genetically with time.**

3. Describe how the effects of directional selection may be offset by gene flow. **If directional selection eliminates one allele, but new migrants replace it, the frequencies may stay the same.**

4. In addition to mutation, what other mechanism allows for new genetic information to be introduced into a population? Explain your answer. **The other mechanism is gene flow. Mutations introduce new genes into a population by changing the DNA in a gene. Gene flow does it by new organisms immigrating into a population and interbreeding with old members.**

5. What is the fate of most new mutations? **Most are harmful and are lost via natural selection or genetic drift.**

6. If a population has three codominant color alleles, how many phenotypes are possible? **Six.**

7. What effects can non-random mating exert on a population? **It causes changes in gene frequencies.**

8. What two evolutionary agents are most responsible for decreases in genetic variation in a population? **Genetic drift and directional selection.**

9. If a population has three color alleles and one is dominant over the other two, how many phenotypes are possible? **Four.**
   a. **Homozygotes with two dominant alleles and heterozygotes with the dominant allele, regardless of the other allele, will be the dominant color;**
   b. **Homozygotes with two non-dominant alleles will be a second color;**
   c. **Homozygotes with the other two non-dominant alleles will be a third color;**
   d. **Heterozygotes with one each of the non-dominant alleles will be a fourth color.**

10. In humans, birth weight is an example of stabilizing selection. What does this mean to the long-term average birth weight of human babies? **It should stay about the same, generation after generation.** How might the increasing number of Caesarean sections be affecting this characteristic? **Caesarean sections tend to decrease selection against large birth weights and allow more individuals with large birth weights to pass that trait along to another generation. Therefore, caesarean sections tend to create more variation and variance in birth weight.**

EVIDENCES OF EVOLUTION

Materials and Equipment

17.1 Experiment: Natural Selection

Per student group (4)
- calculator
- metric ruler
- flat of dandelion seedlings, labeled "Mowed" or "Unmowed"
- trowel or large spoon
- knife or single-edged razor blade

Per lab room
- several dishpans half-filled with water
- paper towels

17.2 Geologic Time

Per student pair
- one 4.6-m rope or string
- masking tape
- meter stick and/or metric ruler
- calculator

17.3 The Fossil Record and Human Evolution

1 set of skull reproductions, including:
- *Dryopithecus africanus*
- *Australopithecus afarensis*
- *Australopithecus africanus*
- *Australopithecus robustus*
- *Homo habilis*
- *Homo erectus*
- *Homo sapiens neanderthalensis*
- *Homo sapiens sapiens*
- *Pan troglodytes*

Optional materials
- collection of fossil plants and animals
- wall chart of human evolution
- guide to fossils

Preparation of Materials and Equipment

17.1 Experiment: Natural Selection

Dandelion seedlings: Distribute approximately 50 dandelion seeds over the surface of moistened commercial potting soil in each growing flat. Cover lightly with additional potting soil, and water daily. Dandelion seeds usually germinate without pretreatment. Maintain in greenhouse for two to three months minimum. Plants may be grown for longer periods of time, resulting in more robust and easily handled plants.

Notes

17.1 Experiment: Natural Selection

Site selection for collection of dandelion seed is crucial for the effectiveness of this exercise. Select two areas that are as alike as possible with respect to soil type, aspect, and moisture, but which differ in mowing regime. Cemeteries might provide likely sites if you can find a cemetery with an old, unmown area as well as a regularly-mown section. Similarly, dandelion seed heads collected from a walking path vs. those from an adjacent unmowed field could be used. Select sites that have been subject to a particular mowing regime for as many years as possible. Alternatively, another weedy species could be chosen.

Collect at least thirty mature, fully opened seed heads from each of the two populations.

Students with backgrounds in statistics could perform simple statistical tests on the collected data, such as standard deviations, and t-tests.

In discussing your results, remind students that the genetic differences in these two populations probably have two sources: genetic drift and founder effect, and natural selection. Dandelions also can exhibit high gene flow from air-borne dispersal of seeds, resulting in disruptions of local adaptations.

17.3 The Fossil Record and Human Evolution

Skull reproductions can be quite expensive. However, many Anthropology Departments maintain such skulls and might be willing to loan them. Similarly, collections of fossils might be borrowed from geological collections.

The recommended specimens (see *Ordering Information*) are relatively inexpensive plaster casts of half-skull restorations mounted on wood plaques. A wide variety of more expensive specimens are available from biological supply companies. Contact companies directly for ordering information.

Ordering Information

See General Laboratory Supplies list on page vii for basic items

17.1 Experiment: Natural Selection

17.2 Geologic Time

17.3 The Fossil Record and Human Evolution

"The Evolution of Man", wall chart			
basic fossil collection	Carolina	POM 23300 or GEO5325	
fossil hominid half-skull restorations:			
Dryopithecus africanus	Ward's	80V 1505	
Australopithecus afarensis	Carolina	28-1505	
Australopithecus africanus	Carolina	28-1571	Ward's 80 V 1515
Australopithecus robustus	Carolina	28-8215	
Homo habilis	Carolina	28-1723	Ward's 80 V 1512,
Homo erectus	Carolina	28-5408	Ward's 80 V 1652,
Homo sapiens neanderthalensis	Carolina	28-4525	Ward's 80 V 1658
Homo sapiens sapiens	Carolina	28-4550	Ward's 80 V 1660
Pan troglodytes, full skull replica	Carolina	24-6592	Ward's 80 V 1775
"Fossils: A Guide to Prehistoric Life"	Carolina	GEO8791	

Answers to In-text Questions

17.1 Experiment: Natural Selection

This experiment tests the hypothesis that *dandelion populations grown for generations under different mowing regimes will have different growth forms*. Write a prediction regarding this experiment in Table 17-2. **Predictions will vary. Many will predict that seedlings grown from plants in frequently mowed areas will be shorter than those from unmowed areas.**

What would you predict the dandelion plants grown from seeds produced in mowed and unmowed areas to look like? **Again, predictions will vary but most commonly refer to height.**

8…Are there noticeable differences in the distribution of shoot-to-root ratios between descendants of dandelions from intensely mowed versus unmowed areas? If so, what are those differences? **Most commonly, dandelions from intensely mowed areas will show generally smaller shoot-to-root ratios than the dandelions from unmowed areas.**

If you failed to detect a difference between seeds grown from plants of mowed versus unmowed populations, speculate on the reason(s) for this failure. Does this failure necessarily mean that natural selection is not occurring? **No, not necessarily. Result could be due to nonrandom sampling of the parent plants. Also, mowing regimes might not have been continuous over time or established for very long. In this case, the selection pressures might be fluctuating or not established for long.**

Explain the results of this demonstration in terms of the effects of natural selection on the genetic makeup of the two dandelion populations. **Generally, this exercise illustrates that dandelions with shorter shoot-to-root ratios are favored in mowed areas since they would retain more photosynthetic area than would taller dandelions. The shorter dandelions would be better able to flower and reproduce in the mowed environment, and so would become more common in the population over time.**

17.2 Geologic Time.

Over what proportion of the earth's history were there only single-celled living organisms? **2.6 by with prokaryotes only / 4.6 by = 0.56 = 56%**
Over what proportion of the earth's history have multicelled organisms existed? **0.58 by / 4.6 by = 0.126 = 12.6%**
Over what proportion of the earth's history have mammals been a dominant part of the fauna? **0.225 by / 4.6 by = 0.048 = 4.8%**
Over what proportion of the earth's history have modern humans existed? **0.0001 by / 4.6 by = 0.00002 = 0.002%**

17.3 The Fossil Record and Human Evolution

1 (a) Do any of the fossils resemble organisms now living? If so, describe the similarities between fossil and current forms. **Answers will vary depending on fossil collection used.**

(b) Are there fossils in the collection that are unlike any organisms currently living? If so, describe the features that appear to be most unlike today's forms. **Answers vary.**

2. In Table 17-3, record your observations of the changes that occurred over time.

TABLE 17-3 Skull Characteristics of Human Ancestors and Relatives, from (- - -) = Most Primitive to (+ + +) = Most Advanced					
Genus and Species	**Teeth**	**Jaw structure**	**Cranium**	**Muscle attachments**	**Nose**
Dryopithecus	----	----	----	----	----
Australopithecus afarensis	--	--	--	--	--
Australopithecus africanus	-	-	-	-	----
Australopithecus robustus	+	-	+	---	---
Homo habilis	++	++	+	+-	+
Homo erectus	++	+-	++	+-	+
Homo sapiens neanderthalensis	+++	++	+++	+	++
Homo sapiens sapiens	+++	+++	+++	+++	+++
Pan troglodytes	--	--	--	--	--

(Note that answers rely on comparison, and are somewhat subjective.)

3. (a) Study the skull of *Dryopithecus* and the skull of *A. afarensis*. What resemblances do you see between the two specimens? **Both have protruding lower jaw, receding small cranium and somewhat similar teeth.**

(b) What structural differences do you see between the two skull specimens? ***Dryopithecus*** **has smaller cranial capacity, no brow ridge.** ***Australopithecus*** **has an overall larger skull (assuming specimens are adult.)**

(c) What advances do you see in skull characteristics between *Dryopithecus* and *Australopithecus africanus*? ***Australopithecus*** **has a larger cranium, a less protruding jaw, and teeth that meet vertically.**

(d) Between *Dryopithecus* and *Australopithecus robustus*? ***A. robustus*** **has larger brow ridges and jaw musculature attachments, a larger cranial capacity, and the teeth are more uniform.**

4. (a) What changes from primitive to advanced characteristics do you see in the evolutionary line from *A. afarensis* to *Homo sapiens sapiens*? **All changes in features in table 17-3 are visible.**

(b) What is the trend in cranial capacity between the ancestral *A. afarensis* and *Homo erectus*? **Greatly increasing cranial capacity.**

(c) Between *Homo erectus* and *Homo sapiens*? **An increase in cranial capacity.**

(d) What differences do you see between the skulls of Neandertal man and modern humans? **Neandertals had a more protruding lower face, prominent brow ridges, larger muscle attachment areas around the nose and no chin. The Neandertal cranium was more flat, with a lower forehead.**

(e) How do the cranial capacities of Neandertal man and modern humans compare? **Very similar. In fact, some anthropologists posit that Neandertals had larger cranial capacity than modern humans.**

6. (a) How does the chimpanzee skull compare to the human skull with respect to primitive and advanced anatomical features? **A chimp has larger, more pronounced canine teeth, a smaller cranium, more robust and longer jaw, more prominent brow ridge, protruding jaw, and no chin relative to that of modern human.**

(b) How does the chimpanzee skull compare to the skull of *Dryopithecus,* the apelike hominid ancestor? **They are rather similar.** ***Dryopithecus*** **has a narrower, v-shaped jaw with teeth that are more vertically oriented than the chimpanzee.** ***Dryopithecus*** **also has less pronounced brow ridge than the chimpanzee.**

Name _____

Section No. _____

EVIDENCES OF EVOLUTION

Pre-lab Questions

1. The major mechanism of evolution is: a. adaptive radiation; b. drift; c. fitness; d. natural selection.

2. Hominids with evolutionarily advanced skull characteristics would have: a. many large, specialized teeth; b. a large cranium with prominent vertical forehead; c. prominent eyebrow ridges; d. a long jaw and muzzle.

3. A catastrophic global event in which major groups of species disappear is called: a. adaptive radiation; b. natural selection; c. mass extinction; d. evolution.

4. The earth was formed approximately: a. 4600 years ago; b. 1 million years ago; c. 1 billion years ago; d. 4.6 billion years ago.

5. The human ancestor whose populations dispersed from Africa to other parts of the world was: a. *Homo sapiens sapiens*; b. *Australopithecus afarensis*; c. *Dryopithecus*; d. *Homo erectus*.

6. Fossils: a. are remains of organisms; b. are formed when organic materials are replaced with minerals; c. provide evidence of evolution; d. are all of the above.

7. An organism whose genetic makeup allows it to produce more offspring than another of its species is said to have greater: a. fitness; b. evolution; c. adaptive radiation; d. selection.

8. Evolution is: a. the difference in survival and reproduction of a population; b. the process that results in changes in the genetic makeup of a population over time; c. a group of individuals of the same species occupying a given area; d. change in an individual's genetic makeup over its lifetime.

9. The first living organisms appeared on the earth approximately: a. 4.6 billions years ago; b. 3.8 billion years ago; c. 1 billion years ago; d. 6400 years ago.

10. The organism believed to be the common ancestor of modern apes and humans is: a. *Australopithecus africanus*; b. *Homo habilis*; c. the chimpanzee; d. *Dryopithecus.*.

EXERCISE 17

EVIDENCES OF EVOLUTION

*Answers to Pre-lab Questions
in Lab Manual Order*

1. b   6. c
2. d   7. b
3. a   8. a
4. d   9. b
5. b   10. d

*Answers to Pre-lab Questions
in Instructor's Manual Order*

1. d   6. d
2. b   7. a
3. c   8. b
4. d   9. d
5. d   10. a

Answers to Post-lab Questions

1. Define the following terms: a. *evolution*—**the gradual change over time in the frequency of alleles within a population of organisms;** b. *natural selection*—**the evolutionary process causing differential survival and reproduction among individuals within a population that differ in one or more traits;** c. *population*—**a group of individuals of the same species, living in the same given area;** d. *species*—**one or more populations of individuals that interbreed under natural conditions and produce fertile offspring.**

2. Describe how natural selection would operate to change the genetic makeup of a dandelion population that had been growing in an unmowed area if that area became subject to frequent low mowing. **Populations have natural variation in their frequency of various alleles. Interactions with the environment or other organisms may favor (or conversely, be detrimental to) individuals with certain genetic makeup. Those individuals may then show enhanced (or reduced) survival and/or reproduction. With the next generation, the offspring of that parental generation will likely carry more of those "favored" traits, and so on through generations, resulting in a gradual change in the genetic makeup of the population.**

3. Which event occurred first in the earth's history?
   a. Photosynthesis or eukaryotic cells? **photosynthesis**
   b. Vertebrate animals or flowering plants? **vertebrate animals**
   c. Extinction of dinosaurs or origin of hominids? **extinction of dinosaurs**

4. What primitive characteristics are visible in the skull pictured below? **There is a sagittal crest. The forehead is relatively low and sloping and the brow ridge is prominent. The teeth are large and perhaps somewhat specialized, and the lower jaw is elongated. The nose is not protruding from the face.**

5. Describe anatomical changes in the skull that occurred in human evolution between a *Dryopithecus*-like ancestor and *Homo sapiens*. **Changes include a greatly-increased cranial capacity with a prominent vertical forehead; reduction in size, number and specializations of teeth; lower jaw and muzzle shortened; much reduced eyebrow ridges and no keel for muscle attachments; and the development of a prominent nose with a distinct bridge.**

6. Compare the slope of the forehead of chimpanzees with that of modern humans. **The forehead of chimpanzees greatly slopes in contrast to the higher vertical and rounded forehead of modern humans.**

7. Compare the teeth of *Australopithecus afarensis* and *Homo sapiens*.
   a. Describe similarities and differences between the two species. **A. afarensis has large specialized teeth while those of modern humans are smaller and less specialized.**
   b. Write a hypothesis about dietary differences between the two species based on their teeth. **The large, specialized teeth of A. afarensis may have been adapted for grinding hard foods, with relatively large canines adapted for tearing. In contrast, the smaller teeth of modern humans seem to be adapted for a huge diversity of generally softer foods.**

143

8. Why was the development of bipedalism a major advancement in human evolution? **Bipedalism allowed the hands to be freed for purposes other than locomotion. As hands evolved, tool use also could develop.**

9. Do you believe humans are still evolving? If not, why not? If yes, explain in what ways humans may be evolving. **Most biologists believe that *Homo sapiens* is no longer evolving organically, because our big brains allow us to circumvent natural selection and alter our environment and also control our own mating. However, some people believe that human *culture* is evolving.**

10. Humans have selectively bred many radically different domestic animals. (For example, think of St. Bernard and chihuahua dogs.) Does this activity result in evolution? Why or why not? **Selective breeding of domestic animals is artificial selection, where specific traits are selected to fulfill some human purpose, such as to increase meat yield or for a particular aesthetic reason. *Evolution* results from the environmental imposition of conditions that determine the fitness of individuals and resulting proportion of alleles among individuals of future populations. Therefore, artificial selection, by definition, cannot result in evolution. You could also make an argument that humans are part of the environment for dogs and thus are agents of natural selection.**

TAXONOMY: CLASSIFYING AND NAMING ORGANISMS

Materials and Equipment

18.1 Constructing a Dichotomous Key

Per lab room
- several meter sticks or metric height charts taped to wall

18.2 Using a Taxonomic Key

A. Some Microscopic Members of the Freshwater Environment

Per student
- compound light microscope
- glass microscope slide
- coverslip
- dissecting needle

Per student group (table)
- test tube rack
- cultures of freshwater organisms (see *Note*)
- Protoslo solution or methyl cellulose in dropping bottle
- one disposable plastic pipette per culture

B. Common Trees and Shrubs

Per student group (table)
- set of eight tree twigs with leaves (fresh or herbarium specimens) *or* trees and shrubs in leafy condition (see *Notes*)

Preparation of Materials and Equipment

18.1 Constructing a Dichotomous Key

None required.

18.2 Using a Taxonomic Key

A. Some Microscopic Members of the Freshwater Environment

Methyl cellulose (100 mL):	methyl cellulose	10 g
	dH$_2$O	90 mL

Mix 10 g methyl cellulose with 45 mL boiling water. Immediately remove from heat and allow mixture to stand for 20 minutes. Add 45 mL of cool water and mix thoroughly. Place at 10°C (top shelf of refrigerator) until solution becomes transparent. Dispense in dropping bottles.

Yield: 100 mL is sufficient to fill 3 to 4 dropping bottles.

B. Common Trees and Shrubs

None required.

Notes

18.2 Using a Taxonomic Key

A. Some Microscopic Members of the Freshwater Environment

Living algal cultures can be maintained for several days if held in bright indirect light at cool room temperature. When ordering these cultures, specify a shipping date at least 2 days before cultures are needed. Also be aware that cultures that are shipped at the end of a week or just before a holiday may spend several days in uncontrolled temperature conditions.

The cultures are generally adequate for about twice as many students as specified in the Carolina Biological Supply catalogue. Number each culture and instruct students to obtain a drop from each, verifying their identification of each culture with the instructor before proceeding to the next.

Students should use at least two drops of water to make a wet mount on a microscope slide in order to avoid crushing the algal colonies. A drop of Protoslo Quieting Solution or methyl cellulose may be needed to slow down the swimming motion.

B. Common Trees and Shrubs

Fresh material is generally superior to herbarium specimens. Be careful to select only specimens found in the key. Many campus plantings are horticultural varieties of non-native species and thus may not "key-out" correctly with the necessarily simplified, non-universal key in the lab manual.

Ordering Information

18.1 Constructing a Dichotomous Key

See General Laboratory Supplies list for general supplies

18.2 Use of a Taxonomic Key

A. Some Microscopic Members of the Freshwater Environment

methyl cellulose	Carolina	87-5161
Protoslo Quieting Solution	Carolina	88-5141
Chlamydomonas, living	Carolina	15-2030
Pediastrum, living	Carolina	15-2430
Volvox, living	Carolina	15-2665
Gonium, living	Carolina	15-2264
Spirogyra, living	Carolina	15-2525
Cladophora, living	Carolina	15-2105
Zygnema	Carolina	15-2695
Closterium	Carolina	15-2115

Answers to In-text Questions

18.1 Constructing a Dichotomous Key

PROCEDURE

2. Using the key provided, determine the hypothetical name for each object. Write the name beneath the object and then check with your instructor to see if you have made the correct choices. **Left to right: Elcric, Legnarit, Eraqus, Legnairtosi, Nogatco**

18.2 Using a Taxonomic Key

(To assist the instructor, images of the freshwater algae used are provided below.)

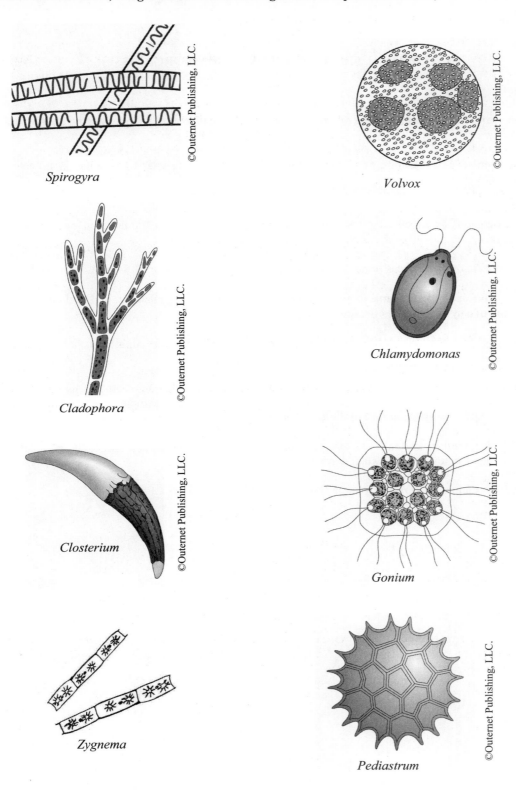

Spirogyra

Volvox

Cladophora

Chlamydomonas

Closterium

Gonium

Zygnema

Pediastrum

©Outernet Publishing, LLC.

Name _____

Section No. _____

TAXONOMY: CLASSIFYING AND NAMING ORGANISMS

Pre-lab Questions

1. The science of classifying and naming organisms is known as: a. taxonomy; b. phylogeny; c. morphology; d. physiology.

2. The name "human" is an example of a: a. common name; b. scientific name; c. binomial; d. polynomial.

3. A binomial is always a: a. genus; b. specific epithet; c. scientific name; d. two-part name.

4. The scientific name for the ruffed grouse is *Bonasa umbellus*. *Bonasa* is: a. the family name; b. the genus; c. the specific epithet; d. all of the above.

5. Current scientific thought places organisms in one of ___ kingdoms: a. two; b. four; c. five; d. six.

6. Phylogeny is the apparent: a. name of an organism; b. ancestry of an organism; c. nomenclature; d. dichotomy of a system of classification.

7. Which scientific name for the wolf is presented correctly? a. Canis lupus; b. canis lupus; c. *Canis lupus*; d. Canis Lupus

8. One objection to common names is that: a. many organisms may have the same common name; b. many common names may exist for the same organism; c. the common name may not be familiar to an individual not speaking the language of the common name; d. all of the above.

9. A road that dichotomizes is a(an): a. intersection of two crossroads; b. road that forks into two roads; c. road that has numerous entrances and exits; d. road that leads nowhere.

10. Most scientific names are derived from: a. English; b. Latin; c. Italian; d. French.

TAXONOMY: CLASSIFYING AND NAMING ORGANISMS

*Answers to Pre-lab Questions
in Lab Manual Order*

1.	a	6.	c
2.	d	7.	b
3.	b	8.	b
4.	d	9.	d
5.	a	10.	b

*Answers to Pre-lab Questions
in Instructor's Manual Order*

1.	a	6.	b
2.	a	7.	c
3.	d	8.	d
4.	b	9.	b
5.	d	10.	b

Answers to Post-lab Questions

1. If you were to use a binomial system to identify the members of your family (mother, father, sisters, brothers), how would you write their names so that your system would most closely approximate that used to designate species? **(Assuming your name is Smith:)** *Smith john, Smith mary, Smith jane, Smith dick.*

2. Describe several advantages of the use of scientific names over common names. **Scientific names are universal, i.e, they are the same despite geopolitical, ethnic, or linguistic differences among people. Each organism has its own specific name, without duplication.**

3. Based upon the following classification scheme, which two organisms are most closely phylogenetically related? Why? *Sitophilus oryzae* and *Sitophilus zeamaize.* **They share the most categories (all the way to genus).**

4. Using the taxonomic key, identify the two plants as either angiosperms or gymnosperms. **Plant A is an angiosperm. Plant B is a gymnosperm.**

5. To what genus does Plant A belong? What is its common name? **Genus:** *Acer.* **Common name: maple.**

6. To what genus does Plant B belong? What is its common name? **Genus:** *Pinus.* **Common name: pine.**

7. As completely as possible, describe the leaf of Plant C. **Oppositely arranged, palmately compound**

8. To what genus does Plant C belong? What is its common name? **Genus:** *Aesculus.* **Common name: buckeye.**

9. Using the taxonomic key in the exercise, identify the genus of the organism below. **Genus:** *Closterium.*

10. If you owned a large, varied music collection, how might you keep track of all your different kinds of music? **Categorize by type of music (rock vs. non-rock); then break other categories into two's; then by artist (Madonna vs. non-Madonna), and finally, by form of recording (CD vs. non-CD, etc.).**

EXERCISE 19

BACTERIA AND PROTISTS I

Materials and Equipment

19.1 Domain Bacteria, Kingdom Bacteria

A. Bacteria: Are Bacteria Present in the Lab?

Per group (4)
- dH$_2$O in dropping bottle
- four nutrient agar culture plates
- bottle of tap water, labeled A
- transparent adhesive tape
- sterile cotton swabs
- china marker
- bottle of 70% ethanol, labeled B
- paper towels

B. Bacteria: Bacterial Shape and Sensitivity to Antibiotics

Per student
- bacteria type slide
- compound microscope

Per lab room:
- demonstration slide - Gram-stained bacteria

C. Cyanobacteria (Blue-Green Algae)

Per student
- microscope slide
- coverslip
- dissecting needle
- compound microscope

Per lab room:
- *Oscillatoria*- living culture; disposable pipet
- *Azolla*-living plants

19.2   Domain Eukarya, Kingdom Protista

A. Phylum Stramenopila

Per student pair
- culture of *Saprolegnia* or A*chlya*
- dissecting needle
- culture of *Phtyophthora cactorum*
- compound microscope
- microscope slides

Per lab bench
- refrigerator or ice bath

B. Phylum Amoebazoa: Slime Molds

Per student
- culture of slime mold (*Physarum*)
- depression slide and coverslip
- compound microscope
- dissecting microscope

Per group (table)
- Carmine, in two screw-cap bottles
- tissue paper

Per lab room
- demonstration of slime mold (*Physarum*) sporangia
- *Amoeba*-living culture on demonstration at dissecting microscope; disposable pipet

C. Phylum Alveolata

Per student pair
- microscope slide
- compound microscope
- coverslip

Per group (table)
- tissue paper
- acetocarmine stain in dropping bottles (2)
- methyl cellulose (or Protoslo) in dropping bottles (2)
- box of toothpicks

Per lab room
- *Paramecium caudatum* , living culture; disposable pipet
- Congo Red–yeast mixture with disposable pipet
- *Plasmodium vivax* , sporozoites, demonstration slide
- *P. vivax* , merozoites, demonstration slide
- *P. vivax* , immature gametocytes, demonstration

D. Phylum Euglenozoa

Per student
- *Trichonympha*, prepared slide
- *Trypanosoma* in blood smear, prepared slide
- compound microscope

Preparation of Materials and Equipment

19.1 Domain Bacteria, Kingdom Bacteria

Nutrient agar (1 L):		
	beef extract	3 g
	peptone	5 g
	agar	15 g
	dH$_2$O	1000 mL

Mix and heat to boiling to dissolve. Dispense into bottles and sterilize in autoclave for 15 minutes at 15 pounds pressure and 121°C. Pour agar while still liquid into sterilized petri dishes, approximately 15 to 20 mL per dish, or enough to cover the bottom about 1/8 inch deep.

Nutrient agar powder may also be purchased. Mix 23 g Difco nutrient agar with 1000 mL dH$_2$O and follow above directions.

Store agar plates in refrigerator in plastic bags until needed.

Yield: 1000 mL agar is adequate for approximately 50 petri dishes.

Sterile cotton swabs: Wrap wooden or paper-sticked cotton swabs in aluminum foil. Autoclave 15 minutes at 15 pounds pressure and 121°C.

Oscillatoria: Oscillatoria cultures may be purchased (see *Ordering Information*) or collected and cultured for future use. This cyanobacterium is commonly found in most greenhouses, growing on the surface of wet soil or flowerpots, especially those kept standing in water.

Culture *Oscillatoria* on the surface of plaster blocks kept constantly moist. Place a 2-cm square chunk of the cyanobacterium in the center of the plaster block and set the culture in a Petri dish containing enough water to keep the block moist. Cover the dish, illuminate indirectly and check daily to ensure an adequate water level to prevent drying. The *Oscillatoria* should begin to spread out on the plaster block surface within 2 days.

Small clumps of *Oscillatoria* may also be placed on culture dishes of water agar. The cyanobacterium will spread out over the agar surface within 2 days.

Yield: Luxurious cyanobacterial growth on 6 bricks or flowerpots from a greenhouse should be sufficient for several laboratory sections. Four plaster blocks should be adequate for approximately 20 students.

Plaster blocks: Prepare quick-setting plaster of Paris according to package directions. Pour it into small cartons (yogurt, milk, etc.) to a depth of about 7 mm. After the plaster has hardened, peel off the carton.

19.2 Domain Eukarya, Kingdom Protista

Saprolegnia, Achlya , and Phytophthora stock cultures: Maintain pure stock cultures of *Saprolegnia, Achlya,* and *Phytophthora* on slants of cornmeal agar. Transfer one or two times a year to maintain and confirm viability. To transfer, cut a small block of mycelium from the lower end of a slant and transfer it to the upper end of a new slant. Hold at room temperature in diffuse light until new mycelium is profuse. Refrigerate cultures in plastic bag to prevent desiccation.

Saprolegnia class cultures: 10 days before class, half-fill a sterile 90 x 50 mm crystallizing dish (with the lid of a 15 x 100 mm petri dish as a cover) or a 20 x 150 mm petri dish with sterile charcoal water or sterile glass-distilled water. Place a 2 mm to 3 mm square agar block of mycelium from a stock culture in the dish with 2 cucumber seeds (freshly boiled until the seed coat splits).

5 to 6 days before class, half-fill sterile 15 x 60 mm petri dishes with sterile charcoal water or glass-distilled water. In each dish place a freshly boiled cucumber seed, and transfer tufts of mycelium from the stock charcoal-water culture to each dish. In many isolates, gametangia will form in cultures about 10 days old and there will probably be some zoosporangia in the 10-day-old cultures.

Maintain all class cultures at room temperature in diffuse light.

Achlya class cultures: For zoosporangia and zoospores, begin cultures 11 days before class. Inoculate cornmeal agar in 1 or more 15 x 100 mm petri dishes with a small square of mycelium from stock culture. After 5 days, place 6 freshly boiled cucumber seeds on the agar in each dish, just beyond the edge of the mycelium. After 2 additional days, remove the cucumber seeds and place these seeds in individual 15 x 60 mm petri dishes of sterile charcoal or glass-distilled water.

For gametangia, repeat the above steps but start cultures 2 days earlier, that is, 13, 8, and 6 days before class.

Maintain all class cultures at room temperature in diffuse light.

Phytophthora cactorum class cultures: Inoculate petri plates of V-8 agar with agar blocks of *P. cactorum* about 10 days before use. Grow colonies to about 5 cm diameter (about 4 or 5 days). Aseptically remove agar margin around colony and flood with enough glass-distilled sterile water to just cover the surface of the colony. This will stimulate sporangial development.

Incubate water colonies for 3 to 10 days. At any time during this period, zoospore release may be stimulated by cooling the colony at 4°C for 15 to 30 minutes. Zoospore release will begin while in the refrigerator and will continue for 20 to 25 minutes after removal.

Release is easily observed at low magnification. Observations at higher magnifications can be accomplished by removing a bit of mycelium from the edge of the colony with forceps and placing on a glass slide in a drop of water. Tease the mycelium apart on the slide and cover with a coverslip.

Different isolates of *P. cactorum* vary in the number of zoospores they will produce by this method.

V-8 agar (1000 mL):		
	V-8 juice	200 mL
	$CaCO_3$	3 g
	agar	15 g
	dH_2O	800 mL

Stir and heat to boiling to dissolve. Dispense into bottles or flasks and sterilize in autoclave for 15 minutes at 15 pounds pressure and 121°C. Pour agar while still liquid into sterilized petri dishes, approximately 15-20 mL per dish, or enough to cover the bottom about 1/8 inch deep.

Store agar plates in refrigerator in sealed plastic bags until needed.

Yield: 1000 mL agar is adequate for approximately fifty to sixty 15 x 100 mm petri dishes.

Cornmeal agar (1000 mL):   Difco cornmeal agar   17 g
                                               dH₂O   1000 mL

      Mix powdered material with water and heat to boiling to dissolve. Dispense into tubes or bottles and sterilize for 15 minutes at 121°C and 15 pounds pressure.

Charcoal water (1000 mL):   Norit (activated charcoal)   3 g
                                               dH₂O   1000 mL

      Mix Norit and water and shake well. Allow to settle for 30 minutes then filter. Dispense into bottles and sterilize for 15 minutes at 121°C and 15 pounds pressure.

Physarum polycephalum *stock culture:* Place the lid or bottom of a 15 x 100 mm petri dish—surface side up—in an 8 in. diameter culture dish. Place a 170 mm circle of filter paper on top of the petri dish. Add enough tap water so that the filter paper overhanging the edges of the petri dish serves as a wick.
      Place a piece of filter paper covered with *Physarum* sclerotia (purchased or prepared as described below) at one edge of the filter paper in the culture dish. Sprinkle rolled oats on the surface of the filter paper adjacent to the sclerotia. Cover the dish with glass and *place the culture in the dark*. The plasmodium will cover the surface of the filter paper and the oat flakes in 4 or 5 days. Replace the water in the culture daily and add more rolled oats 2 days after the initial inoculation. The culture *must* remain in darkness throughout growth; light induces sporangial formation within 24 to 36 hours after illumination.

Physarum sclerotium preparation: Prepare a plasmodial culture like the stock culture described above. Decant the excess water and replace the glass cover with brown wrapping paper. Incubate the culture below 25°C in darkness. After 7 to 10 days of gradual drying, the plasmodium should aggregate into a thick, spongy mass. Test viability by cutting off a small portion and placing it on moistened filter paper or water agar. The plasmodium will begin to spread out if viable. Place the viable sclerotium in an envelope and store it in a refrigerator.

Physarum class cultures: Pour water agar into 15 x 60 mm petri dishes to a depth of about 1 cm. Place a small amount of plasmodium from stock culture into each petri dish. Place 1 or 2 oat flakes adjacent to the plasmodium. Incubate the covered dishes at room temperature in darkness for 1 to 2 days before needed in class.

Physarum sporangial culture: Prepare a plasmodial culture as described for class plate cultures. Place culture in continuous light at least 2 days to induce sporangial formation.

Water agar, 1% (1 L):   Agar   10 g
                                               dH₂O   1000 mL

      Suspend agar in water and heat to boiling to dissolve. Dispense into bottles and autoclave for 15 minutes at 121°C and 15 pounds pressure.

Methyl cellulose (100 mL):   methyl cellulose   10 g
                                               dH₂O   90 mL

      Mix 10 g of methyl cellulose with 45 mL boiling water. Immediately remove from heat and allow mixture to stand for 20 minutes. Add 45 mL of cool water and mix thoroughly. Place at 10°C (top shelf of refrigerator) until solution becomes transparent. Dispense in dropping bottles.
      Yield: 100 mL is sufficient to fill 3 to 4 dropping bottles.

Acetocarmine stain (100 mL): Acetocarmine solution may be purchased (see *Ordering Information*) or may be prepared as follows:

Acetocarmine stain (100 mL):	carmine (alum lake; C. I. Natural Red 4)	1 g
	glacial acetic acid	45 mL
	dH$_2$O	55 mL
	ferric acetate, saturated, aqueous	2 drops

Add acid slowly to distilled water while stirring, then bring to a boil. Dissolve carmine in the boiling 45% acetic acid. Cool and decant. Add 2 drops of a saturated, aqueous solution of ferric acetate and allow to stand for 12 hours. Filter and store in a refrigerator.

Shelf life: indefinite.

Yield: 100 mL is sufficient to fill 3 or 4 dropping bottles.

Ferric acetate: Very insoluble in water. Prepare a saturated solution, filter, and store in an amber bottle or in the dark.

Congo Red–yeast mixture: Place 0.25 ounce of dried commercial yeast pellets in a 500-mL Erlenmeyer flask containing 300 mL of 1 M glucose solution. Add enough Congo Red crystals to turn the solution a light red. (When students place a drop of Congo Red–yeast mixture on a slide and add a drop of *Paramecium* suspension, the resulting color should be pink, not red.) Plug the flask with nonabsorbent cotton and incubate in a warm area (20 to 30°C) for 12 to 24 hours before class. Large numbers of budding yeast cells will be present.

Yield: 300 mL yeast suspension is adequate for many students.

Shelf life: 1 or 2 days. Useful life of the suspension may be increased by incubating the culture on a shaker.

| *1 M glucose* (300 mL): | dextrose (D-glucose) | 54.0 g |
| | dH$_2$O to make | 300 mL |

Notes

19.1 Domain Bacteria, Kingdom Bacteria

Azolla is purchased from Ward's (see *Ordering Information*). One ordering unit (approximately 4 oz.) should be sufficient for several hundred students. Maintain in a shaded aquarium of dechlorinated water with an inch of mud in the bottom.

19.2 Domain Eukarya, Kingdom Protista

No commercial source is known at this time for a preserved specimen of a potato tuber with black wart. Many mycology laboratories or plant pathology departments at land grant institutions may have specimens for loan.

Commercially available cultures of *Amoeba* frequently have few living amoebas. It is best to order cultures that supply nominally more students than you need. *Amoeba* cultures can be maintained several days in indirect light and should be fed paramecia.

Living cultures of protists can be maintained several days in indirect light at room temperature. Generally, cultures provide enough organisms for more students than are listed in the catalogue, for example, a *Paramecium caudatum* culture for a class of 30 is generally adequate for about 50 students. (Note the exception, *Amoeba*, above.)

Microscope slides of *Trichonympha* are no longer available. Therefore, termites can be purchased from Carolina Biological Supply or collected from rotting wood. Check the termite gut to be sure *Trichonympha* are present. Residents of AZ, CA, IA, ME, and OH must apply for a USDA permit to receive this material. Canadian customers must apply for a Canadian Dept. of Agriculture permit.

Ordering Information

See General Laboratory Supplies list on page vii for basic items

19.1 Domain Bacteria, Kingdom Bactria

agar	VWR	90000-760
Azolla, living plants	Ward's	86 V 5400
Bacillus subtilis, Gram stain	Ward's	90 V 0533
beef extract	VWR	90000-718
Difco nutrient agar	VWR	DF0001-17
Escherichia coli, Gram stain	Ward's	90 V 2042
Oscillatoria, live culture	Carolina	15-1866
peptone	VWR	R0118-02
Staphylococcus epidermidis, Gram stain	Ward's	90 V 2076
transparent adhesive tape	purchased locally	
typical bacterial forms, Gram stain	Ward's	90 V 0152

19.2 Domain Eukarya, Kingdom Protista

See General Laboratory Supplies list for general supplies

90 x 50 mm crystallizing dish	Fisher	08-741C
acetic acid, glacial	Fisher	A38-500
acetocarmine stain	Carolina	84-1423
Achlya, living culture	Carolina	15-5901
agar	VWR	90000-760
Amoeba, living culture	Carolina	13-0803
$CaCO_3$	Sigma	C6763
carmine	Fisher	C579-25
Congo Red	Fisher	C580-25
Difco cornmeal agar	VWR	DR0386-17
ferric acetate	Fisher	NC9843546
cucumber seeds, nonviable	Carolina	15-8602
methyl cellulose	Carolina	87-5161
Norit (activated charcoal)	Fisher	S93402
Paramecium caudatum, living culture	Carolina	13-1554
Physarum polycephalum - plasmodium	Carolina	15-6192
Physarum polycephalum - sclerotium	Carolina	15-6190
Phytophthora cactorum, living culture	Ward's	85 V 8250
Plasmodium vivax, smear	Ward's	92 V 4661
Saprolegnia, living culture	Carolina	15-6271
Saprolegnia, living culture	Ward's	85W 5050
Trichonympha, in living termite gut	Carolina	14-3738
Trypanosoma in blood smear, prepared slide	Ward's	92 V 4290
Trypanosoma in blood smear, prepared slide	Triarch	ZA2-73
V-8 juice	local grocery store	

Answers to In-text Questions

19.1 Domain Bacteria, Kingdom Bacteria

A. Bacteria: Are Bacteria Present in the Lab?

7. Make a prediction of what you will find in the culture plates after the next lab period.
Prediction: The control plate will have no bacterial growth. Dishes 2 and 3 will have abundant bacterial growth. Dish 4 will have little or no bacterial growth.
8. Describe what you see.
Source of sample: **Answers will vary.**
Dish 1: Control. **Should have no growth because plate has not been opened to the environment.**
Dish 2: Dry Swab. **Bacterial growth should be present.**
Dish 3: Treatment A. **Bacterial growth should be present, perhaps even more abundant than in dish 2.**
Dish 4: Treatment B. **Little or no bacterial growth should be present because the alcohol should be a disinfectant.**
9. Make a conclusion about the usefulness of tap water and 70% ethyl alcohol as disinfectants. **Tap water does not make a good disinfectant, but 70% ethyl alcohol does.**

B. Bacteria: Bacterial Shape and Sensitivity to Antibiotics

PROCEDURE

TABLE 19-1 Gram Stain Reaction of Various Bacteria	
Bacterial Species	**Gram Reactions (+ or −)**
Escherichia coli	-
Bacillus subtilis	+
Staphylococcus epidermidis	+

C. Cyanobacteria (Blue-Green Algae)

C.1 Oscillatoria

1. Examine the culture provided of *Oscillatoria.* Describe what the culture looks like, including the texture and the color. **The culture looks like a mass of black ooze with a bit of green coloration at the edge of the culture.**
Do all the *Oscillatoria* cells look alike, or is there differentiation of certain cells within the filament? **All of the cells look alike.**

C.2 Anabaena

Is a nucleus present within the cells of *Anabaena?* Explain. **No. These are prokaryotic cells and thus lack nuclei.**

Based upon this electron micrograph, would you hypothesize that the heterocyst is photosynthetic? **No. There are no thylakoids in the heterocyst.**
Which type of symbiosis is the association between *Anabaena* and the water fern? **This would be a mutualistic symbiosis (mutualism).**

19.2 Domain Eukarya, Kingdom Protista

A. Phylum Stramenopila

A.1 Oomycotes: Water molds

A.1.a. Saprolegnia or Achlya

15. … Are humans monoecious or dioecious? **Dioecious**

A.1.b. Phytophthora

B. Phylum Amoebozoa: Slime Molds

B.1 Physarum: A Plasmodial Slime Mold

2. Watch the cytoplasm. The motion that you see within the plasmodium is cytoplasmic streaming (Exercise 6). Is the cytoplasmic streaming unidirectional, or does the flow reverse? **It reverses.**

Because the plasmodium is multinucleate (whereas the spores are uninucleate), what event must occur following spore germination? **Mitosis (but not cytokinesis).**

B.2 Amoeba

4. Which region of the endoplasm appears to stream, the outer or the inner? **Inner**

C. Phylum Alveolata

C.1 Ciliata: Ciliated Protozoans

C.2 Apicomplexans

D. Phylum Euglenozoa

D.1 Trypanosoma

D.2 Trichonympha

BACTERIA AND PROTISTS I

Pre-lab Questions

1. A vector is: a. an organism that causes disease; b. a disease; c. a substance that prevents disease; d. an organism that transmits a disease causing organism.

2. Gram stain would be used to distinguish between different: a. bacteria; b. protistans; c. dinoflagellates; d. all of the above.

3. Most members of the domain Bacteria *lack* all but: a. a nucleus; b. membrane-bound organelles; c. chloroplasts; d. photosynthetic ability.

4. Organisms capable of nitrogen fixation: a. include some bacteria; b. include some cyanobacteria; c. may live as symbionts with other organisms; d. all of the above.

5. A spherical bacterium would be called a: a. bacillus; b. coccus; c. spirillum; d. none of the above.

6. Those organisms that are covered by numerous, tiny locomotory structures belong to the phylum: a. Euglenozoa; b. Stramenopila; c. Amoebozoa; d. Ciliata.

7. A pathogen is a. a disease; b. an organism that causes a disease; c. a substance that kills bacteria; d. the same as a heterocyst.

8. Which of the following is true?: a. All bacteria are autotrophic; b. All protists are heterotrophic; c. *Oscillatoria* is photoautotrophic; d. *Trypanosoma* is photoautotrophic.

9. The organism that causes malaria is: a. a pathogen; b. *Plasmodium vivax*; c. carried by a mosquito; d. all of the above.

10. Which organisms are characterized as decomposers? a. bacteria; b. diatoms; c. amoebas; d. dinoflagellates.

EXERCISE 19

BACTERIA AND PROTISTS I

*Answers to Pre-lab Questions
in Lab Manual Order*

1.	b	6.	b
2.	b	7.	a
3.	c	8.	d
4.	a	9.	d
5.	d	10.	d

*Answers to Pre-lab Questions
in Instructor's Manual Order*

1.	d	6.	d
2.	a	7.	b
3.	b	8.	c
4.	d	9.	d
5.	b	10.	a

Answers to Post-lab Questions

1. What major characteristic distinguishes bacteria from Protists? **Bacteria are prokaryotic while Protists are eukaryotic.**

2. What form of bacterium is shown in this photomicrograph? **Spirilla**

3. Examine the photomicrograph on the right taken using an oil-immersion objective, the highest practical magnification of a light microscope. (The final magnification is 770X.) a. Based upon observation, identify the kingdom to which the organism belongs. **Kingdom Bacteria** b. Justify your answer. **No internal membrane-bound organelles or organized nucleus is present, so the organism is prokaryotic. All prokaryotic organisms are in kingdom Bacteria.**

4. Observe the photomicrograph on the right of an organism that was found growing symbiotically within the leaves of the water fern *Azolla*. a. What is the common name given an organism of this type? **Blue-green alga or cyanobacterium.** b. Give the name and function of the cell depicted by the line. **Heterocyst, functions in nitrogen fixation.**

5. You've never seen the protistan whose sexual structures appear here, but you have seen one very similar to it. What are the circular structures in photo? **Oogonia**

6. While the organism that resulted in the Irish potato famine of 1845–1847 had long been present, environmental conditions that occurred during this period resulted in the destructive explosion in disease. Indicate what those environmental conditions were and why they resulted in a major disease outbreak. **A series of very cool and wet summers occurred in Ireland at this time. The cool temperatures favored the production and release of enormous numbers of zoospores of *Phytophthora*. These zoospores swam in the wet fields from potato plant to potato plant, resulting in explosion of the disease.**

7. This photomicrograph was taken from a prepared slide of a stained specimen. You observed unstained living specimens in lab. Describe the mechanism by which it moves from place to place. **Amoeba moves by use of pseudopodia.**

8. What is phagocytosis? **Phagocytosis is the active engulfing of solid particles or cells by a cell, whereby extensions of the cytoplasm move outward to surround the particle. Phagocytosis is one of two special types of endocytosis, the second being pinocytosis.** What function does it serve? **Phagocytosis is a means to bring particles, particularly food, into the cell.**

9. If you were to travel to a region where rice is grown in paddies, you would see lots of the water fern, *Azolla* growing in the water. A farmer would tell you this is done because *Azolla* is considered a "natural fertilizer." Explain why this is the case. **Because *Azolla* contains the nitrogen-fixing cyanobacterium, *Anabaena*, it accumulates nitrogen containing compounds. When the *Azolla* dies, it degrades and the large amount of nitrogen it has accumulated is released to the rice paddy and thus to the rice plants.**

10. Based upon your knowledge of the life history of *Plasmodium vivax*, suggest two methods for controlling malaria. Explain why each method would work. **a. Kill the mosquito population using insecticides or biological controls. The female mosquito serves as the vector for the disease-causing organism. Without the vector, the organism cannot enter the body. b. Breed and release sterile male mosquitoes. This would prevent the production of offspring, about half of which would be female. c. Destroy the specialized environments in which the mosquitoes breed.**

PROTISTS II

Materials and Equipment

20.1 Phylum Euglenozoa: Euglenoids

Per student
- microscope slides
- compound microscope
- coverslips

Per group (table)
- methyl cellulose in two dropping bottles
- dH$_2$O in two dropping bottles

Per lab room:
- *Euglena* , living culture with disposable pipet

20.2 Phylum Chrysophyta: Diatoms

Per student
- microscope slides
- dissecting needle
- compound microscope
- coverslips
- prepared slide of freshwater diatom

Per group (table)
- diatomaceous earth
- dH$_2$O in two dropping bottles

Per lab room
- diatom, living culture with disposable pipet

20.3 Phylum Dinoflagellata: Dinoflagellates

Per student
- Prepared slide of a dinoflagellate (for example, *Gymnodinium, Ceratium, or Peridinium)*
- compound microscope

Per lab room
- dinoflagellate, living culture with disposable pipet

20.4 Phylum Rhodophyta: Red Algae

Per lab room
- demonstration slide of *Porphyridium*
- culture dish containing dried agar and petri dish of hydrated agar
- demonstration specimen and slide of *Porphyra* (nori)

20.5 Phylum Phaeophyta: Brown Algae

Per lab room
- demonstration specimen of *Laminaria*
- demonstration specimen of *Macrocystis*
- demonstration specimen of *Fucus*

20.6 Phylum Chlorophyta: Green Algae

Per student
- microscope slides
- depression slide
- *Oedogonium*, prepared slide
- Compound microscope
- coverslips
- petri dish, 15 x 60 mm, disposable
- *Spirogyra*, prepared slide
- dissecting needle

Per student pair
- dissecting microscope
- I₂KI in dropping bottle
- tissue paper

Per lab room
- demonstration specimen of *Ulva*
- *Chlamydomonas*, living culture with disposable pipet
- *Volvox*, living culture with disposable pipet or prepared slide of *volvox*
- *Oedogonium*, living culture

20.7 Phylum Charophyta: Desmids and Stoneworts

Per student
- microscope slides
- dissecting needle
- compound and dissecting microscope
- coverslip
- prepared slide of *Spirogyra*
- small culture dish

Per student pair
- diluted India ink in dropping bottle

Per lab room
- living culture of *Spirogyra*
- living or preserved culture of *Chara* or *Nitella*
- demonstration slide of *Chara* with sex organs

Preparation of Materials and Equipment

20.1 Phylum Euglenozoa: Euglenoids

| *Methyl cellulose* (100 mL): | methyl cellulose | 10 g |
| | dH₂O | 90 mL |

Mix 10 g of methyl cellulose with 45 mL boiling water. Immediately remove from heat and allow mixture to stand for 20 minutes. Add 45 mL of cool water and mix thoroughly. Place at 10°C (top shelf of refrigerator) until solution becomes transparent. Dispense in dropping bottles.

Yield: 100 mL is sufficient to fill 3 to 4 dropping bottles.

20.2 Phylum Chrysophyta: Diatoms

None required.

20.3 Phylum Dinoflagellata: Dinoflagellates

None required.

20.4 Phylum Rhodophyta: Red Algae

You will have to make a slide of *Porphyridium* since prepared slides are not available. Ordering information is provided for living *Porphyridium*.

20.5 Phylum Phaeophyta: Brown Algae

None required.

20.6 Phylum Chlorophyta: Green Algae

Iodine (I₂KI) solution (100 mL):	potassium iodide (KI)	7 g
	iodine (I₂)	1 g
	dH₂O	100 mL

Dissolve the potassium iodide in the water. Add the iodine and stir until dissolved. Store in foil-wrapped or brown glass bottle.

20.7 Phylum Charophyta: Desmids and Stoneworts

Dilute India ink: 2 drops ink per 100 mL tap water is suggested.

Notes

Living or preserved specimens of the algae in this exercise may be purchased (see *Ordering Information*), but some may be available fresh in your area. Use discretion in collecting fresh materials; collect only those living materials that are abundant.

When ordering living cultures, be sure to specify a delivery date of a few days before when you actually need the cultures for class. Also keep in mind that cultures that are in transit over a weekend may spend 2 days in uncontrolled temperatures.

Cultures are generally sufficient for nearly twice as many students as stated in the suppliers' catalogues (e.g., a culture for 30 is usually adequate for 50 students).

Following are locations where some of the species used in this exercise may be found:

20.5 Phylum Phaeophyta: Brown Algae

Laminaria and *Fucus* may be found on rocky shores of north temperate regions.
Macrocystis may be found on rocky shores of some regions of the Pacific Ocean basin.
These large brown algae may frequently be found with smaller epiphytes of red, brown, and green algae attached.

20.6 Phylum Chlorophyta: Green Algae

Oedogonium is common in neutral-to-slightly alkaline water. Common epiphyte on aquatic macrophytes, especially *Myriophyllum*.

20.7 Phylum Charophyta: Desmids and Stoneworts

Spirogyra is common in neutral-to-acid ponds, slow-moving streams, and bogs. It is often found with *Mougeotia*, a closely related species with a single plate-like chloroplast that rotates on its long axis in response to light intensity.

Ordering Information

See General Laboratory Supplies list on page vii for basic items

20.1 Phylum Euglenozoa: Euglenoids

| *Euglena,* living culture | Carolina | 15-1351 |
| methyl cellulose | Carolina | 87-5161 |

20.2 Phylum Chrysophyta: Diatoms

diatom, prepared slide	Triarch	2-2o
diatomaceous earth	Carolina	85-7570
diatoms, living culture	Ward's	86 V 0005

20.3 Phylum Dinoflagellata: Dinoflagellates

Ceratium, prepared slide	Triarch	ZA2-55	
Peridinium, prepared slide	Carolina	29-5318	
Dinoflagellate, living culture below:			
Amphidinium	Carolina	15-3240	Ward's 86V1560
Glenodinium	Carolina	15-3250	
Gymnodinium	Carolina	15-3260	
Peridinium	Carolina	15-3290	Ward's 86V 2900
Prorocentrum	Carolina	15-3300	Ward's 86V2905

20.4 Phylum Rhodophyta: Red Algae

Porphyra, "nori," dried	local Asian or health food market	
Porphyra, prepared slide	Carolina	29-6296
Porphyra, preserved	Carolina	15-1425
Porphyridium, prepared slide	Ward's	86 W 2850

20.5 Phylum Phaeophyta: Brown Algae

Fucus, complete plant, preserved	Carolina	22-2125
Fucus, living	Ward's	86 V 3921
Laminaria, preserved	Carolina	22-2130
Macrocystis , life or preserved	sea life supply shop	

20.6 Phylum Chlorophyta: Green Algae

Chara, living (mid-May to Oct. 15 only)	Carolina	15-1241	
Chara, prep. slide, branch with sex organs, w.m	Triarch	2-15A	
Chlamydomonas, living culture	Carolina	15-2030	
iodine, I_2	Fisher	I37-100	
Oedogonium, living culture	Carolina	15-2400	or Ward's 86 V 0355
Oedogonium, prepared slide	Triarch	2-24B	
potassium iodide, KI	Fisher	P410-100	
Ulva, living	Ward's	86 V 0770	
Ulva, preserved	Carolina	22-2085	
Volvox zygotes, prepared slide	Triarch	2-36B	
Volvox, living culture	Carolina	15-2655	or Ward's 86W 0800

20.7 Phylum Charophyta: Desmids and Stoneworts

India ink	Carolina	83-4440	
Nitella, living	Carolina	15-1286	or Ward's 86W 0300
Spirogyra, living culture	Carolina	15-2525	or Ward's 86 V 0650
Spirogyra, prepared slide	Triarch	2-30C	

Answers to In-text Questions

20.1 Phylum Euglenozoa: Euglenoids

7. Notice the direction of motion of the *Euglena* cells. Which type of flagellum does *Euglena* have? **Whiplash**

20.4. Phylum Rhodophyta: Red Algae

Which wavelengths (colors) would be absorbed by a red pigment? **All wavelengths but the red wavelengths.**

20.7 Phylum Charophyta: Desmids and Stoneworts

B. Chara or Nitella—**Stoneworts**

4. Based on your study of previously examined specimens, would you say the egg is motile or nonmotile?
Nonmotile

PROTISTS II

Pre-lab Questions

1.   Agar is derived from: a. red algae; b. brown algae; c. green algae; d. all of the above.

2.   Red tides are caused by: a. dinoflagellates; b. red algae; c. brown algae; d. diatoms.

3.   A reagent that stains the stored food of a green alga black is: a. India ink; b. I_2KI; c. methylene blue; d. both a and b.

4.   Which of these organisms (or parts of the organisms) might you find as an ingredient in toothpaste? a. euglenoids; b. diatoms; c. dinoflagellates; d. stoneworts.

5.   The starch production center within many algal cells is the: a. nucleus; b. cytoplasm; c. stipe; d. pyrenoid.

6.   The phylum of organisms most closely linked to the evolution of land plants is the: a. chlorophyta; b. charophyta; c. phaeophyta; d. euglenophyta.

7.   Which is the correct plural word for the organisms studied in this exercise? a. alga; b. algae; c. algas; d. algaes

8.   Phycobilins are: a. photosynthetic pigments; b. found in the red algae; c. blue and red pigments; d. all of the above.

9.   Specifically, female sex organs are known as: a. oogonia; b. gametangia; c. antheridia; d. zygotes.

10.   The cell wall component algin is: a. found in the brown algae; b. used in the production of ice cream; c. used as a medium on which microorganisms are grown; d. a and b above.

EXERCISE 20

PROTISTS II

Answers to Pre-lab Questions
in Lab Manual Order

1.	b	6.	d
2.	a	7.	a
3.	a	8.	b
4.	b	9.	d
5.	d	10.	a

Answers to Pre-lab Questions
in Instructor's Manual Order

1.	a	6.	a
2.	a	7.	b
3.	b	8.	d
4.	b	9.	a
5.	d	10.	d

Answers to Post-lab Questions

1. The protistan *Euglena* is often studied in plant-related courses because it is photosynthetic. What characteristic of the pellicle makes *Euglena* different from true plants? **The pellicle is non-rigid and is composed largely of protein, unlike the rigid cellulosic walls of true plants. The pellicle is inside the cell membrane. Plant cell walls are outside the cell membrane.**

2. On a field trip to a stream, you collect a leaf that has fallen into the water and scrape some of the material from its surface, and prepare a wet mount. You examine your preparation with the high-dry objective of your compound microscope, finding the organism pictured at the right. What substance makes up a significant portion of the cell wall? **Opaline *Silica* ($SiO_2 \cdot nH_2O$)**

3. While wading in the warm salt water off the beaches of the Florida Keys on spring break, you stoop down to look at the feathery alga shown here.

   a. What pigment gives this organism its coloration? **Phycobillins**
   b. What commercial products are derived from this phylum? **Agar (a solidifying agent in microbiological media) and carageenan (a thickener used in ice cream)**

4. While walking along the beach at Point Lobos, California, the fellow pictured below walks up to you with alga in hand. Figuring you to be a college student who has probably had a good introductory biology course, he asks if you know what it is. a. What is the cell wall component of the organism that has commercial value? **Algin** b. Name three uses for the cell wall component. **Makes ice cream smooth, cosmetics soft, and paint uniform in consistency.**

5. Your class takes a field trip to a freshwater stream, where you collect the organism shown microscopically here. a. what is the genus name of this organism? ***Spirogyra.*** b. Identify and give the function of the structure within the chloroplast at the end of the leader (line). **Pyrenoid, functions in starch synthesis.**

6. Some botanists consider the stoneworts to be a link between the higher plants and the algae. As you will learn in future exercises, higher plants, such as the mosses, have both haploid and diploid stages that are *multicellular*. a. Describe the multicellular organism in the charophytes. **Consists of nodes, internodes, with gametangia borne at the nodes.** b. Is this organism haploid or diploid? **Haploid.** c. Is the zygote haploid or diploid? **Diploid.** d. Is the zygote unicellular or multicellular? **Unicellular.**

7.   a. What color are the marker lights at the edge of an airport taxiway? **Blue**. b. Are the wavelengths of this color long or short, relative to the other visible wavelengths? **Short**. c. Which wavelengths penetrate deepest into water, long or short? **Short**. d. Make a statement regarding why phycobilin pigments are present in deep-growing red algae. **Phycobilin pigments are red and blue. The red pigment (phycoerythrin) absorbs the short wavelengths that penetrate the deepest. The energy captured from these wavelengths is passed on to chlorophyll to be used in photosynthesis.** e. What benefit is there to the color of airport taxiway lights for a pilot attempting to taxi during foggy weather? **Fog is water vapor condensed as fine particles suspended in the air near ground level. Blue wavelengths "penetrate" fog best, making blue the most visible color to a pilot attempting to maneuver in fog.**

8.   a. How is an algal holdfast similar to a root? **It anchors the alga to the substrate.** b. How is it different? **It lacks vascular tissue and does not serve a specialized absorptive function.**

9.   Why do you suppose the Swedish automobile manufacturer, Volvo, chose this company name? **Volvo is derived from the Latin word "*volvere*" which means "to roll." The auto manufacturer wishes to give the image of a long lasting automobile that "keeps on rolling."**

10.   List three reasons why algae are important to life. **a. Phytoplankton are the base of the aquatic food chain. b. Algae evolve oxygen through photosynthesis. c. Algae are a source of food in many cultures. d. Algal derivatives have many commercial uses.**

EXERCISE 21

FUNGI

Materials and Equipment

21.1 Phylum Chytridiomycota

Per lab room
- preserved specimen of potato tuber with black wart disease

21.2 Phylum Zygomycota: Zygosporangium-Forming Fungi

Per student
- culture of *Rhizopus*
- coverslip
- prepared slide of *Rhizopus*
- dissecting needle
- compound microscope
- glass microscope slide

Per student pair
- dH$_2$O in dropping bottle

Per lab room
- demonstration culture of *Rhizopus* zygosporangia, on dissecting microscope

21.3 Bread Mold and Food Preservatives

Per student group
- one slice of bread without preservatives
- one slice of bread with preservatives
- two large culture bowls
- pipet and bulb
- suspension culture of *Rhizopus* (+) strain spores
- 15-cm metric ruler
- sterile dH$_2$O in dropping bottle
- plastic film
- china marker

21.4 Phylum Ascomycota: Sac Fungi

Per student
- compound microscope
- glass microscope slide
- dissecting needle
- prepared slide of *Peziza*
- coverslip

Per student pair
- culture of *Eurotium*
- large preserved specimen of *Peziza* or another cup fungus
- dH$_2$O in dropping bottle

21.5 Class Basidiomycota: Club Fungi

Per student
- commercial mushroom
- prepared slide of mushroom pileus (cap), c.s. (*Coprinus*)
- compound microscope

Per lab room
- demonstration of various club fungi specimens

21.6 "Imperfect Fungi"

Per student
- dissecting needle
- coverslip
- prepared slide of *Penicillium* conidia (optional)
- compound microscope
- microscope slide

Per student pair
- dH$_2$O in dropping bottle
- culture of *Alternaria*

Per lab room
- demonstration of *Penicillium* covered food stuff ***and/or*** plate cultures

21.7 Mutualistic Fungi

Per student
- compound microscope
- ectomyccorhizal pine root, prep. slide, c.s.
- endomyccorhizal root, prep. slide, c.s.

Per lab room
- demonstration specimens of crustose, foliose, and frutocose lichens
- demonstration slide of lichen, c.s. on compound microscope
- demonstration slide of mycorrhizal root, c.s. on compound microscope

21.8 Experiment: Environmental Factors and Fungal Growth

A. Light and Darkness

Per student pair
- transfer loop
- matches or striker
- three petri plates containing potato dextrose agar (PDA)
- bunsen burner
- china marker

Per lab bench
- test tubes with spore suspensions of *Trichoderma viride, Penicillium claviforme,* and A*pergilllus ornatus*

B. Directional Illumination

Per student pair
- transfer loop
- bunsen burner
- two petri plates containing either potato dextrose agar (PDA) or cornmeal (CM) agar
- china marker
- matches or striker

Per lab bench
- test tubes with spore suspensions of *Phycomyces blakesleeanus* (inoculate onto PDA), *Penicillium isariforme* (inoculate onto PDA), *Aspergillus giganteus*(inoculate onto CM)

Preparation of Materials and Equipment

21.1 Phylum Chytridiomycota

None Required

21.2 Phylum Zygomycota: Zygosporangium-Forming Fungi

Rhizopus stock culture: Maintain pure cultures of + and - strains on cornmeal agar slants. Add 5 mL sterile dH_2O to a sporulating culture to form a spore suspension. Using a transfer loop, aseptically transfer a loopful of spore suspension to a new slant. Incubate at room temperature until the surface of each slant is covered with sporangia-bearing hyphae (usually 3 to 5 days). Refrigerate and transfer twice a year to maintain viability.

Rhizopus vegetative class cultures: Use + strain stock cultures to inoculate cultures for production of sporangia. Make "spot plates" of cornmeal agar in which only a small amount of agar is used to cover the central region of a 15 x 100 mm petri dish. Five days before class, inoculate the agar spot aseptically with a loopful of spore suspension. Rhizoids will grow from the agar onto the bare surface of the plate, allowing easier observation with a dissecting microscope.

Also, use the + strain to inoculate slices of preservative-free bread. Four to five days before class, place a slice of bread in a large culture dish with enough sterile water to just cover the bottom of the dish. Pour spore suspension over the surface of the bread, cover and incubate at 30°C. Hyphae and black sporangia will completely cover the surface of the bread.

Rhizopus sexual stage demonstration cultures: Make spore suspensions on one stock culture slant for + and – strains. Aseptically *dab* one loopful of + strain suspension near one edge of a 15 x 100 mm petri dish of cornmeal agar. *Streak* a loopful of spores of the – strain in a line about 2 cm from the edge of the petri dish *opposite* the dab of + strain. Cover and incubate at room temperature.

Mature zygosporangia should appear first in a relatively distinct line where the two strains of hyphae meet in about 10 days. Eventually zygosporangia will be found throughout the dish. Zygosporangia are produced on the agar surface and may be more visible by looking at the bottom of the dish.

Optional: You may want to use the above method with *Mucor hiemalis* or *Phycomyces blakesleeanus* for production of zygosporangia since the line formed where the + and – strains meet is much more dramatic than with *Rhizopus*.

| *Cornmeal agar* (1000 mL): | Difco cornmeal agar | 17 g |
| | dH_2O | 1000 mL |

Mix powdered material with water and heat to boiling to dissolve. Dispense into tubes or bottles and sterilize for 15 minutes at 121°C and 15 pounds pressure.

21.3 Experiment: Bread Mold and Food Preservatives

Rhizopus stock culture: See above. Use + strain for this experiment.

Rhizopus spore suspension: Add approximately 10 mL sterile dH_2O to a slant or plate culture of sporulating *Rhizopus* + strain. With a sterile microbiological transfer loop or rubber policeman, gently brush the spores from the mycelium into the water. Decant the resulting spore suspension into sterile, capped culture tubes. Dense suspensions may be diluted with additional sterile dH_2O.

21.4 Phylum Ascomycota: Sac Fungi

Eurotium stock cultures: Maintain pure stock cultures of *E. chevalieri* on slants of honey-peptone agar. Transfer twice a year to maintain viability. To transfer, cover slant with a small quantity of sterile distilled water. Aseptically scrape spores from culture surface into water with a bacteriological transfer loop. Streak a loopful of spore suspension onto a fresh slant. Hold at room temperature until growth is profuse. Store in sealed plastic bags in refrigerator to prevent desiccation.

Eurotium class cultures: 10 to 14 days before use, streak a spore suspension of *E. chevalieri* onto plates of honey-peptone agar. Incubate at room temperature. Cleistothecia and conidia will be produced.

Honey-peptone agar (1000 mL):	Honey	60 g
	Peptone	10 g
	agar	20 g
	dH$_2$O	1000 mL

Stir and heat to boiling to dissolve. Dispense into bottles or flasks and sterilize by autoclaving tubes for 10 minutes at 121°C and flasks or bottles for 15 minutes. Honey-peptone agar may also be purchased (see *Ordering Information*).

21.5 Phylum Basidiomycota: Club Fungi

Various club fungi can be collected in the summer and autumn in temperate zones. Many of these fungi may be preserved by drying ("shelf" fungi, rusts, smuts, puffballs, earthstars, etc.), while more fleshy forms may be preserved in FAA for future use.

Commercial mushrooms (*Agaricus bisporus*) are commonly available at grocery stores. Alternatively, many members of the Basidiomycota may be purchased in preserved form (see catalogues of Carolina Biological Supply and Ward's).

F.A.A. (100 mL):	ethanol, 95%	50 mL
	glacial acetic acid	5 mL
	formalin (37% formaldehyde)	10 mL
	dH$_2$O	35 mL

21.6 "Imperfect Fungi"

Penicillium stock culture: Maintain *Penicillium* on slants of potato dextrose agar by aseptically streaking a loopful of spore suspension from an old culture onto a new slant. Transfer twice a year to maintain viability and store in a refrigerator.

Penicillium class culture: *Penicillium* plate cultures can be grown on cornmeal or potato dextrose agar. Inoculate plates 5 days before needed in class.

Many grocery store produce departments will save moldy citrus fruits upon request. Mold can be induced upon healthy fruit by making a small cut in the rind and inoculating with *Penicillium* mycelium about a week before class. Place the orange in a culture dish, add a small amount of water, cover, and set aside in a warm place.

Alternaria alternata stock culture: Maintain on slants of cornmeal agar. Transfer once or twice a year to maintain viability. To transfer, aseptically cut a small block of mycelium from the margin of a colony on a slant and transfer it to a new slant. Hold at room temperature until new mycelium is profuse. Refrigerate stock cultures in sealed plastic bag to prevent desiccation.

Alternaria alternata class cultures: 14 to 28 days before use, transfer small blocks of agar from the margin of a colony to the center of water agar plates. Incubate at room temperature. Conidia will be produced profusely.

| *Water agar, 2%* (1000 mL): | agar | 20 g |
| | dH$_2$O | 1000 mL |

Suspend agar in water and heat to boiling to dissolve. Dispense into bottles or flasks and autoclave for 15 minutes at 121°C and 15 pounds pressure. Pour into petri dishes while still molten, approximately 20 mL per 15 x 100-mm dish.

Yield: 1000 mL agar should be sufficient for about 50 to 60 plates.

Cornmeal agar: See above.

| *Potato dextrose agar* (1 L): | Difco potato dextrose agar | 39 g |
| | dH$_2$O | 1000 mL |

Suspend dehydrated agar in water and heat to boiling. Dispense into tubes or bottles and autoclave for 15 minutes at 121°C and 15 pounds pressure.

21.7 Mutualistic Fungi

None Required

21.8 Experiment: Experimental Factors and Fungal Growth

Potato dextrose agar: See above.

Cornmeal agar: See above.

Spore suspensions of the various cultures: Prepare spore suspensions as described above for *Rhizopus*.

Notes

21.3 Phylum Ascomycota: Sac Fungi

At the time of publication no commercial source existed for preserved *Morchella*.

21.5 "Imperfect Fungi"

Alternaria alternata is listed as a plant pathogen. As such, its shipment to some states is restricted because of plant quarantine regulations. Institutions located in Alabama, Alaska, California, Florida, Georgia, Hawaii, Michigan, Puerto Rico, Tennessee, and Wisconsin must obtain a permit from the state Plant Quarantine Office. Contact the supplier, Ward's (800-962-2660), for information and application forms.

Ordering Information

See General Laboratory Supplies list on page vii for basic items

21.1 Phylum Chytridiomycota

preserved specimen of potato tuber with black wart disease   Check local grocery store

21.2 Phylum Zygomycota: Zygosporangium-Forming Fungi

Difco cornmeal agar	VWR	DF038617		
Rhizopus, - strain, living culture	Carolina	15-6224	Ward's	85 V 4901
Rhizopus, + strain, living culture	Carolina	15-6222	Ward's	85 V 4900
Rhizopus, prepared slide	Triarch	4-2c		

21.3 Experiment: Bread Mold and Food Preservatives

bread with preservatives	local grocery			
bread without preservatives	local grocery			
plastic film	local grocery			
Rhizopus, + strain, living culture	Carolina	15-6222	Ward's	85 V 4900

21.4 Phylum Ascomycota: Sac Fungi

Agar	VWR	DF014001
Eurotium chevalieri, living culture	Carolina	15-6032
honey-peptone agar, 125 mL, sterile	Carolina	15-6364
Peptone	VWR	DF0118-17
Peziza, cup with asci, l.s., prepared slide	Triarch	4-12
Peziza, preserved specimen	Carolina	22-2450
Morchella, preserved specimen—see *Notes*		

21.5 Phylum Basidiomycota: Club Fungi

basidiomycete set	Carolina	15-5819
Coprinus pileus, c.s., prepared slide	Triarch	4-16a
Various individual genera of preserved	See Carolina catalogue	

21.6 "Imperfect Fungi"

Alternaria alternata, freeze-dried culture	Ward's	85 V 4133
Difco cornmeal agar	VWR	DR0386-17
Penicillium, mycelium with conidia, prepared slide	Triarch	4-10A
potato dextrose agar	Ward's	88 V 1610
Penicillium italicum, living culture	Carolina	15-6152

21.7 Mutualistic Fungi

crustose, foliose and fruticose lichens	Carolina	15-6400	
ectomycorrhizal pine root, c.s.	Ward's	91 W 9810	Triarch 10-245
endomyccorhizal root, c.s.	Ward's	91 V 9812	
lichen, prepared slide, c.s.	Carolina	29-8476	

21.8 Experiment: Environmental Factors and Fungal Growth

cornmeal agar	VWR	DF 0386-17
inoculating needle	Ward's	14 V 0957
laboratory burner	Fisher	03-917
Phycomyces blakesleeanus	Ward's	85 V 1198
potato dextrose agar	Ward's	88 V 1610
*Trichoderma viride****		
*Aspergillus giganteus***		
*Aspergillus ornatus***		
*Penicillium claviforme***		
*Penicillium isariforme***		

** Currently available through the American Type Culture Collection; *** at the time of printing this manual, *Trichoderma viride* was not being offered for sale.

Answers to In-Text Questions

21.2 Phylum Zygomycota: Zygosporangium-Forming Fungi

5. It's likely that when you added the coverslip, you crushed the sporangia, liberating the spores. Are there many or few spores within a single sporangium? **Many**

21.3 Experiment: Bread Mold and Food Preservatives

TABLE 21-2 Growth of Bread Mold			
Ingredients **(These will vary but below is a sample.)**			
Bread without preservatives: **filtered water, untreated high gluten wheat flour, stone ground whole wheat flour, wheat bran, ground flaxseed, crystalline corn fructose, vital wheat gluten, oats, wheat germ, wheat fiber, sorghum flour, inulin, yeast, salt, pea fiber, barley malt, sunflower oil, potato flour, sesame seed**			
Bread with preservatives: **Enriched wheat flour (wheat flour, barley malt, , niacin, iron, thiamine mononitrate, riboflavin, folic acid), water, high fructose corn syrup, soybean oil, yeast, salt, dough conditioners (monoglycerides, sodium stearoyl lactylate, polysorbate 60, calcium peroxide, enzymes, calcium phosphate, dicalcium phosphate, ascorbic acid), yeast nutrients (calcium sulfate, monocalcium phosphate, ammonium sulfate) calcium propionate (a preservative).**			
Prediction: **There will be more fungal growth on the bread without preservatives than with preservatives.**			
	Mycelial Diameter (cm)		
Culture	Day 1	Day 2	Day 3
With preservatives			
No preservatives			
Conclusion: **The preservatives used in bread retard or inhibit growth of fungi.**			

Design an experiment that would allow you to identify the substance that has the effect you observed.
The different ingredients in the bread could be isolated and each incorporated into sterile culture media. Because calcium propionate is specifically listed as a preservative, this would be the best ingredient to start with. One of the media would incorporate calcium propionate and the other would not and serve as a control. Then the cultures could be inoculated with bread mold fungal spores and the growth of the fungi could be determined.

21.7 Mutualistic Fungi

A. Lichens

1. Examine the demonstration specimen of a crustose lichen. 2. What is it growing on? **Rock**

3. Write a sentence describing the crustose lichen. **A crutsose lichen appears as a mostly flat growth.**

4. Observe the demonstration specimen of a foliose lichen (Figure 21-22).

5. What is it growing on? **On the bark of a woody plant.**

6. Write a sentence describing the foliose lichen. **A foliose lichen appears as a leaf-like growth rising from the surface of a branch or the bark of a woody plant. It reminds one somewhat of a coral**.

7. Examine the demonstration specimen of a fruticose lichen (Figure 21-23).

8. What is it growing on? **On the ground, among mosses or on a branch of a woody plant.**

9. Write a sentence describing the fruticose lichen. **It appears more or less "shrubby," like a tiny shrub.**

21.8 Experiment: Environmental Factors and Fungal Growth

A. Light and Darkness

TABLE 21-3 Effect of Light on Fungal Sporulation in   (insert the fungus name)
Prediction: **Variable answers, but a reasonable one might be that because fungi are not green, they will not react to directional illumination.**
Conditions Continuous light **Trichoderma: plate covered with spores; Penicillium: plate has rod-like growths with blue-green spores; Aspergillus: plate has mass of brown spores.** Continuous darkness **Trichoderma: plate devoid of spores; Penicillium: plate has rod-like growths with blue-green spores; Aspergillus: plate is devoid of spores.** Alternating light and darkness **Trichoderma: spores exist in concentric bands, correlating with light periods when spores were produced and spore-free zones due to vegetative growth in the dark; Penicillium: plate has rod-like growths with blue-green spores; Aspergillus: plate has mass of brown spores with no particular pattern.**
Conclusions: *Trichoderma viride* **Light is required for sporulation.** *Penicillium claviforme* **Light serves neither as a stimulus or inhibitor of sporulation.** *Aspergillus ornatus* **Light stimulates sporulation, but does not seem to be necessary as there is no pattern related to light and dark periods.**

B. Directional Illumination

TABLE 21-4 Effect of Directional Illumination on Growth of the Fungus   (insert fungus name)
Prediction: **Answers will vary, but expect students to say that light has no effect on fungal sporulation, or that light is necessary for sporulation or inhibits sporulation.**
Conditions Unilateral illumination Illumination from above
Conclusions: *Phycomyces blakesleeanus* **Conidiophores bend toward the light source.** *Penicillium isariiforme* **Conidiophores bend toward the light source.** *Aspergillus giganteus* **Conidiophores bend toward the light source.**

FUNGI

Pre-lab Questions

1. Which structures would you find in a sac fungus? a. ascogonium, antheridium, zygospores; b. ascospores, oogonia, asci, ascocarps; c. basidia, basidiospores, basidiocarps; d. ascogonia, asci, ascocarps, ascospores.

2. A mutualistic association between a plant root and a fungus is known as a: a. sac fungus; b. lichen; c. mycorrhizal root; d. club fungus.

3. An organism that is made up of a fungus and an associated green alga or cyanobacterium is known as a: a. sac fungus; b. lichen; c. mycorrhizal root; d. club fungus.

4. The club fungi are placed in the class Basidiomycota: a. because of their social nature; b. because they form basidia; c. because of the presence of an ascocarp; d. because they are dikaryotic.

5. A relationship between two organisms in which both members benefit is said to be: a. parasitic; b. saprotrophic; c. mutualistic; d. heterotrophic.

6. Which statement is *not* true of the zygospore-forming fungi? a. they are in the phylum Zygomycota; b. Ascospores are found in an ascus; c. *Rhizopus* is a representative genus; d. A zygospore is formed after fertilization.

7. Which statement is *not* true of the imperfect fungi? a. they reproduce sexually by means of conidia; b. they form an ascocarp; c. sex organs are present in the form of oogonia and antheridia; d. all of the above are false.

8. An organism that grows specifically on non-living organic material is called: a. an autotroph; b. a heterotroph; c. a parasite; d. a saprophyte.

9. Fungi is to fungus as _____ is to _____. a. mycelium, mycelia; b. hypha, hyphae; c. sporangia, sporangium; d. ascus, asci.

10. Taxonomic separation into fungal phyla is based upon: a. sexual reproduction, or lack thereof; b. whether or not the fungus is a parasite or saprophyte; c. the production of certain metabolites, such as citric acid; d. the edibility of the fungus.

FUNGI

Answers to Post-lab Questions

1. Observe this photo at the right of a portion of a fungus you examined in lab. a. What is structure a? **sporangium** b. To which fungal phylum does it belong? **Phylum Zygomycota**

2. Distinguish between a *hypha* and a *mycelium*. **A hypha is one threadlike portion of the fungal body, while the mycelium is the totality of all the hyphae.**

3. Examine the below photomicrographs of a fungal structure you studied in lab. Is this structure labeled b in the photomicrograph below the product of sexual or asexual reproduction? **Sexual**

4. Distinguish among *ascus,* an *ascospore,* and an *ascocarp.* An ascus is a sac-like cell of the Ascomycetes in which meiosis gives rise to ascospores. An ascospore is the meiotic product which is formed in an ascus. An ascocarp is a fruiting body of the Ascomycetes in which asci are formed.

5. Walking in the woods, you find a cup-shaped fungus. Back in the lab, you remove a small portion from what appears to be its fertile surface and crush it on a microscope slide, preparing the wet mount that appears at the right. Identify the fingerlike structures present on the slide. **Asci containing ascospores**

6. What type of spores are produced by the fungus pictured at the right? **Basidiospores**

7. The photo below shows a fungus growing on a dead hemlock tree. What is the common name of a fungus of this sort? Be specific. **Shelf fungus or Bracket fungus**

8. Explain the name "imperfect fungi." **Someone decided that an organism without sexual reproduction was "imperfect." Those fungi, for which sexual reproduction is absent or unknown, are called the "imperfect fungi."**

9. Give the correct singular or plural form of the following words in the blanks provided.

	Singular	*Plural*
a.	hypha	**hyphae**
b.	**mycelium**	mycelia
c.	zygospore	**zygospores**
d.	**ascus**	asci
e.	basidium	**basidia**
f.	**conidium**	conidia

10. Lichens are frequently the first colonizers of hostile growing sites, including sun-baked or frozen rock, recently hardened lava and even gravestones. How can lichens survive in habitats so seemingly devoid of nutrients and under such harsh physical conditions? **Lichens have the ability to go into a state of "suspended animation" when environmental conditions do not favor growth. They reduce their respiration rates and cease most cellular activities, but resume these functions when water becomes available.**

BRYOPHYTES—LIVERWORTS AND MOSSES

Materials and Equipment

22.1 Phylum Charophyta—Ancestors of True Plants

Per student
- small culture dish

dissecting microscope

Per lab room
- living culture (or preserved) *Chara* or *Nitella*
- demonstration slide of *Chara* with sex organs

22.2 Phylum Hepatophyta: Liverworts

Per student
- dissecting microscope
- living or preserved *Marchantia* thalli with gemma cups, antheridiophores, archegoniophores and mature sporophytes

22.3 Experiment: Effect of Photoperiod

Per student group
- china or other marker
- pot label
- vigorously growing colony of *Marchantia polymorpha*

Per lab room
- growth chambers set to long day (16 hr. light, 8 hr. darkness) and to short day (8 hr. light, 16 hr. darkness) conditions

22.4 Phylum Bryophyta: Mosses

Per student
- glass microscope slide
- coverslip
- dissecting needle
- prepared slide of moss antheridial head, l.s.
- prepared slide of moss archegonial head, l.s.
- prepared slide of moss sporangium (capsule), l.s
- *Polytrichum*, male and female gametophytes, the latter with attached sporophytes
- dissecting microscope
- compound microscope

Per student pair
- dH_2O in dropping bottle

Per student group (table)
- moss protonemata growing on culture medium

22.5 Experiment: Effect of Light Quality on Moss Spore Germination and Growth

Per student group

- culture plate with moss agar
- china or other marker
- 1-mL pipet
- compound microscope

- water suspension of moss spores
- Pipette pump (2 mL or 10 mL)
- 8-cm strip of Parafilm
- glass microscope slide and coverslip

Per lab room

- four incubation chambers (one each for white, blue, green, and red light)

Preparation of Materials and Equipment

22.1 Phylum Charophyta—Ancestors of True Plants

None required.

22.2 Phylum Hepatophyta: Liverworts

Marchantia growth and maintenance: Living *Marchantia* may be purchased (see *Ordering Information*) or may be collected from the field where it grows primarily on damp, shaded, limestone cliffs.

  To prepare a terrarium for growth of liverworts, place a 3-cm layer of coarse gravel or pebbles on the bottom of a container and add a few pieces of charcoal or coal "clinkers" (obtainable from a coal-fired stove or power plant). Over this, spread a 2-cm layer of sand and then add a 3-cm deep cover of garden loam. Plant the liverworts on this bed.

  Maintain water level halfway up the gravel layer and cover the tank with glass. Keep the terrarium in medium, non-direct light. If fungi grows, reduce the amount of water and remove the glass cover until they disappear.

  Many liverworts and mosses can be maintained in this manner.

22.3 Experiment: Effect of Photoperiod

None required.

22.4 Phylum Bryophyta: Mosses

Moss and fern agar (*Modified Beijerinck's Agar*; 1 L): May be purchased as C-FERN® Medium, Basic (see *Ordering Information*) or prepared as follows:

Stock solution:		
	ammonium nitrate (NH_4NO_3)	5 g
	magnesium sulfate ($MgSO_4$)	2 g
	monobasic potassium phosphate (KH_2PO_4)	2 g
	calcium chloride ($CaCl_2$)	1 g
	dH_2O	1000 mL
Ferric chloride, 1%:	ferric chloride ($FeCL_3$)	1 g
	dH_2O to make	100 mL

  Dilute 10 mL stock solution in 990 mL dH_2O. Add 1 mL of 1% ferric chloride solution per liter of diluted stock solution just before use. Add 16 g agar per liter, heat to boiling to dissolve. Dispense into bottles (appr. 125 mL per 8-oz. wide-mouth bottle) and autoclave 15 minutes at 121°C and 15 pounds pressure. Store in refrigerator until needed.

  Shelf life: stock solution shelf life is indefinite when refrigerated.

Moss protonemata culture: Obtain protonemata and/or moss spores from biological supply company (see *Ordering Information*) or collect them from the field from nearly mature sporophytes. Capsules of the hairy cap moss, *Polytrichum*, are a good source and may be collected in summer and then frozen until needed.

Make an agar slant by placing an 8-oz. bottle of molten moss agar at a 30° angle until solidified. Use forceps to squeeze spores from a sporangium and transfer the spores to the agar surface. Screw cap on loosely and incubate culture at room temperature with a 16-hour photoperiod of artificial or indirect natural illumination. Protonemata should cover the surface of the agar in 4 to 6 weeks.

The culture can be maintained indefinitely by periodically transferring a 1-cm square chunk of moss-covered agar to a fresh slant. "Leafy" gametophytes will be produced from the protonemata several months after spore inoculation.

22.5 Experiment: Effect of Light Quality on Moss Spore Germination and Growth

Moss and fern agar (Modified Beijerinck's Agar): See above. Pour moss agar while molten into sterile petri dishes, about 20 mL per 15 x 100 mm petri dish. Store petri dishes of agar in sealed plastic bags in refrigerator until use to prevent contamination and desiccation.

Moss spore suspension: Add one vial of spores to 50 mL sterile distilled water. Shake to disperse.

Growth chambers: Growth chambers can be constructed from cardboard boxes, with the size of the box determined by the number of petri dish cultures for each light regime. Cut part of the top of the box out and tape the appropriate light filter in place over the opening. Transparency films can be sandwiched between thin plates of glass to make them more sturdy. Place chambers under a bank of fluorescent cool white lights.

Notes

22.4 Phylum Bryophyta: Mosses

Collect *Polytrichum* if possible in summer with male and female gametophytes visible. Female gametophytes should have attached sporophytes. If this is impossible, a generic "fruiting moss," gametophyte with sporophyte may be purchased (see *Ordering Information*).

22.5 Experiment: Effect of Light Quality on Moss Spore Germination and Growth

Colored transparency films can be purchased from Rosco Laboratories (http://www.rosco.com). Roscolux filters (20 in. x 24 in. sheets) are much cheaper. Rosco Laboratories, Inc., however, sells only through designated retail outlets across the country. Phone them for the outlet nearest you or visit online at www.rosco.com/us/retail.

Ordering Information

See General Laboratory Supplies list on page vii for basic items

22.1 Phylum Charophyta—Ancestors of True Plants

Nitella, living	Ward's	86 V 0300	
Chara, living (mid-May to October 15 only)	Carolina	15-1241	
Chara, prepared slide, branch with sex organs, w.m.	Triarch	2-15a	

22.2 Phylum Hepatophyta: Liverworts

Marchantia thalli, preserved, life cycle set	Carolina	22-3001	Ward's 63 V 1030
Marchantia, living, antheridia (seasonal)	Carolina	15-6544	
Marchantia, living, archegonia (seasonal)	Carolina	15-6546	
Marchantia, living, vegetative	Carolina	15-6540	Ward's 86 V 4200

22.3 Experiment: Effect of Photoperiod

clay saucers	local garden supply		
Marchantia, living, vegetative	Carolina	15-6540	Ward's 86 W 4200
pot labels, 4 in.	Carolina	66-5951	66-5951

22.4 Phylum Bryophyta: Mosses

agar	VWR	90000-760
ammonium nitrate	Fisher	A676-500
calcium chloride	Fisher	C77-500
C-FERN® Medium, Basic	Carolina	15-6780
ferric chloride	Fisher	I88-100
magnesium sulfate	Fisher	S93295
Mnium, archegonial head, l.s., prepared slide	Triarch	6-4E
Mnium, fruiting stem, l.s., prepared slide	Triarch	6-4A
monobasic potassium phosphate	Fisher	P382-500
moss protonemata	Carolina	15-6881
moss, fruiting	Carolina	15-6695
Polytrichum spores	Carolina	15-6666
Polytrichum, antheridial head, l.s., slide	Triarch	6-2B

22.5 Experiment: Effect of Light Quality on Moss Spore Germination and Growth

Parafilm, 4 in. x 125 ft. roll	Carolina	21-5600	Fisher 13-374-10
Roscolux #26 (Light Red)	http://www.rosco.com		
Roscolux #69 (Brilliant Blue)	http://www.rosco.com		
Roscolux #89 (Moss Green)	http://www.rosco.com		

Answers to In-Text Questions

22.1 Phylum Charophyta—Ancestors of True Plants

4. Based on your study of previously examined specimens, would you say the egg is motile or non-motile? **Nonmotile**

22.2 Phylum Hepatophyta: Liverworts

2. The thallus is the gametophyte portion of the life cycle. Is it haploid or diploid? **Haploid**
6. Are gemmae haploid or diploid? **Haploid**

22.3 Experiment: Effect of Photoperiod

Write a prediction about the effect of day length on *Marchantia* reproduction

TABLE 22-1 Effect of Photoperiod on the Reproduction of the Liverwort, *Marchantia polymorpha*
Prediction: Variable answers, but a reasonable one would be "Long day (>X hours) is required to stimulate gametangiophore production. (Sexual reproduction is stimulated when gametophytes are exposed to uninterrupted light periods of 12 or more hours.)"
Week   Observation of the effect of _____ (long or short) Day illumination
1
2
3
4
5
6

TABLE 22-2 Summary of Results: The Effect of Photoperiod on the Reproduction of the Liverwort, *Marchantia polymorpha*	
Photoperiod	**Results**
Long day	**Gametophytes have antheridial and archegonial branches.**
Short day	**Gametophytes lack antheridial and archegonial branches.**
Conclusions:	**Sexual reproduction, as evidenced by the production of archegonial and antheridial branches (archegoniophores and antheridiophores, respectively), is stimulated when gametophytes are exposed to uninterrupted light periods of 12 or more hours.**

Did the experimental results support your hypothesis? **Answer depends on what the prediction is.**

Can you suggest any reasons why it might be beneficial to the liverwort to display the results that the different experimental groups found? **In a temperate environment, short days are typically associated with decreasing temperatures and winter. Winter conditions are not conducive to growth of liverworts. Thus, it would not be useful to produce structures at a time when they would be killed (or not grow).**

22.4 Phylum Bryophyta: Mosses

2. Identify the root-like rhizoids at the base of the plant. What function do you think rhizoids perform? **Anchorage**
3. Notice that the leaf-like organs are arranged more or less radially about the stemlike axis. You are examining the gametophyte generation of the moss. In terms of the life cycle of the organism, what function does the gametophyte serve? **The gametophyte is the part of the life cycle that is photosynthetic and also reproduces sexually.**
9…Numerous mitotic divisions produce an embryo (embryo sporophyte, Figure 22-15f), which differentiates into the mature sporophyte (Figure 22-15g) that protrudes from the tip of the gametophyte. What is the function of the sporophyte (that is, what does it do, or what reproductive structures does it produce)? **The sporophyte is the portion of the life cycle that produces spores, one form of asexual reproduction.**
10. Is the sporophyte green? **Yes**
What can you conclude about its ability to produce at least a portion of its own food? **Because it is green, this suggests that it is photosynthetic, and thus produces its own food.**
15. What type of nuclear division must take place for the sporogenous tissue to become spores? **Meiosis**

Is the protonema part of the gametophyte or sporophyte generation? **Gametophyte**

22.5 Experiment: Effect of Light Quality on Moss Spore Germination and Growth

TABLE 22-3 Effect of Light Quality on Moss Spore Germination and the Growth of Protonemata	
Prediction: Variable answers, but a reasonable one would be "Spores will not germinate in green light."	
Week	**Observation of the Dependent variables (list them here)**
1	
2	

11. Was your hypothesis supported by the experimental results? **The answer depends upon prediction.**

BRYOPHYTES—LIVERWORTS AND MOSSES

Pre-lab Questions

1. In the bryophytes, the sporophyte is: a. the dominant generation; b. dependent upon the gametophyte generation; c. able to produce all of its own nutritional requirements; d. a and c above.

2. Gemmae function for: a. sexual reproduction; b. water retention; c. anchorage of a liverwort thallus to the substrate; d. asexual reproduction.

3. Which statement *best* describes the concept of alternation of generations? a. one generation of plants is skipped every other year; b. there are two phases, a sporophyte and a gametophyte; c. the parental generation alternates with a juvenile generation; d. a green sporophyte phase produces food for a non-green gametophyte.

4. Liverworts and mosses utilize which of the following pigments for photosynthesis? a. chlorophylls a and b; b. carotenes; c. xanthophylls; d. all of the above.

5. The suffix *-phore* derives from a Greek word meaning: a. branch; b. moss; c. liverwort; d. male.

6. Land plants are believed to have evolved from: a. mosses; b. ferns; c. charophytes; d. fungi.

7. Alternation of heteromorphic generations: a. is found only in the bryophytes; b. is common to all land plants; c. is typical of most green algae; d. occurs in the liverworts but not mosses.

8. A protonema: a. is part of the sporophyte generation of a moss; b. is the product of spore germination of a moss; c. looks very much like a filamentous brown alga; d. produces the sporophyte when a bud grows from it.

9. An organ that is hygroscopic is: a. sensitive to changes in moisture; b. exemplified by the peristomal teeth in the sporophyte of mosses; c. may aid in spore dispersal in mosses; d. all of the above.

10. Sperm find their way to the archegonium: a. by swimming; b. due to a chemical gradient diffusing from the archegonium; c. as a result of sucrose being released during the breakdown of the neck canal cells of the archegonium; d. all of the above.

EXERCISE 22

BRYOPHYTES—LIVERWORTS AND MOSSES

*Answers to Pre-lab Questions
in Lab Manual Order*

1.	c	6.	d
2.	b	7.	d
3.	d	8.	d
4.	b	9.	b
5.	b	10.	a

*Answers to Pre-lab Questions
in Instructor's Manual Order*

1.	b	6.	c
2.	d	7.	b
3.	b	8.	b
4.	d	9.	d
5.	a	10.	d

Answers to Post-lab Questions

1. Explain why water must be present for the bryophytes to complete the sexual portion of their life cycle. **The bryophytes have flagellated sperm that must swim to the female organ to effect fertilization.**

2. Green algae are believed to be the ancestors of the bryophytes. Cite four distinct lines of evidence to support this belief. **a. same photosynthetic pigments; b. same stored carbohydrate (starch); c. water necessary for fertilization; d. similar structural features of their flagella.**

3. Complete this diagram of a "generic" alternation of generations. **Refer to figures 22-1 and 22-2.**

4. Describe in your own words the difference between a sporophyte and a gametophyte. **Sporophytes produce spores, gametophytes produce gametes. Sporophytes are diploid, gametophytes are haploid.**

5. While the plant shown here is one that you did not study specifically in lab, you should be able to identify it. Is this gametophyte or the sporophyte of the plant? **Gametophyte**

6. In what structure does meiosis occur in the bryophytes? **Meiosis occurs in the sporangium, a specialized organ.**

7. Identify the type of gametangium shown here. **Archegonium**

8. Walking along a stream in a damp forest, you see the plants shown at right. Is this the sporophyte or the gametophyte? **Gametophyte**

9. a. What are the golden stalks seen in this photo? **Moss sporophytes.** b. Are they the products of meiosis or fertilization? **Fertilization**

10. Identify the plants in the photo at the right as male or female, gametophyte or sporophyte, moss or liverwort. **Male gametophyte of a moss.**

SEEDLESS VASCULAR PLANTS: CLUB MOSSES AND FERNS

Materials and Equipment

23.1 Phylum Lycophyta: Club Mosses

Per lab room

- culture bowl containing water
- *Lycopodium* gametophyte, preserved (optional)
- *Lycopodium*, living, preserved, or herbarium specimens with strobili
- *Selaginella*, living, preserved, or herbarium specimens
- *Selaginella lepidophylla,* resurrection plant, two dried specimens

23.2 Phylum Moniliophyta, Subphylum Psilophyta: Whisk Ferns

Per lab room

- *Psilotum*, living plant
- *Psilogum*, herbarium specimen showing sporangia and rhizome
- *Psilotum*, gametophyte, living or preserved
- dissecting microscope

23.3 Phylum Moniliophyta, Subphylum Sphenophyta: Horsetails

Per lab room

- *Equisetum*, living, preserved, or herbarium specimens with strobili
- *Equisetum* gametophytes, living or preserved

23.4 Phylum Moniliophyta, Subphylum Pterophyta: Ferns

Per student

- dissecting microscope
- compound microscope
- fern sporophytes, fresh, preserved, or herbarium specimens
- fern gametophytes, living, preserved, or whole mount preserved slides
- fern gametophyte with young sporophyte, living or preserved
- microscope slide
- prepared slide of fern rhizome, c.s.

Per lab room

- squares of fern sori, in moist chamber (*Polypodium aureum* recommended)
- demonstration slide of fern archegonium, median l.s
- other fern sporophytes, as available

23.5 Experiment: Fern Sperm Chemotaxis

Per student group (pair)

- six sharpened toothpicks
- dissecting microscope
- depression slide
- petri dish culture containing *C-Fern*®gametophytes
- five test solutions
- dissecting needle

- petri dish, sterile, 60 x 15 mm
- marking pen
- sterile spore spreader
- fluorescent light bank
- pre-sterilized *C-fern*® Spores of an F_1 Hybrid (Wild Type x Polka Dot)

- Basic *C-fern*®Medium
- sterile dH_2O
- sterile pipet
- culture dome

Preparation of Materials and Equipment

23.1 Phylum Lycophyta: Club Mosses

None required.

23.2 Phylum Moniliophyta, Subphylum Psilophyta: Whisk Ferns

Psilotum gametophyte: Search soil in pots of greenhouse plants in which young sporophytes are just becoming visible. Sift the soil through a series of soil sieves and look for small, separate pieces that look like rhizome. Gametophytes will be approximately 3 to 5 mm in length and are brown in color with white tips. Examine each piece with a dissecting microscope and look for gametangia.
Preserve in FAA.

FAA (100 mL):		
	ethyl alcohol, 95%	50 mL
	glacial acetic acid	5 mL
	formalin (37% formaldehyde)	10 mL
	dH_2O	35 mL

23.3 Phylum Moniliophyta, subphylum Sphenophyta: Horsetails

None required.

23.4 Phylum Moniliophyta, Subphylum Pterophyta: Ferns

Moss and fern agar (*Modified Beijerinck's Agar*; 1 L): May be prepared as follows:

Stock solution:		
	ammonium nitrate (NH_4NO_3)	5 g
	magnesium sulfate ($MgSO_4$)	2 g
	monobasic potassium phosphate (KH_2PO_4)	2 g
	calcium chloride ($CaCl_2$)	1 g
	dH_2O	1000 mL

Ferric chloride, 1%:		
	ferric chloride ($FeCL_3$)	1 g
	dH_2O to make	100 mL

Dilute 10 mL stock solution in 990 mL dH_2O. Add 1 mL of 1% ferric chloride solution per liter of diluted stock solution just before use. Add 16 g agar per liter, heat to boiling to dissolve. Dispense into bottles (approx. 125 mL per 8-oz. wide-mouth bottle) and autoclave 15 minutes at 121°C and 15 pounds pressure. Pour fern agar while molten into sterile petri dishes, about 20 mL per dish. Store in refrigerator until needed.
Shelf life: stock solution shelf life is indefinite when refrigerated.

Fern gametophytes and young sporophytes: Fern spores and/or prothallia may be purchased (see *Ordering Information*) or spores may be collected from fertile fronds bearing nearly mature sporangia. Collect spores by placing a detached frond (*Osmunda claytonia*, interrupted fern, or *O. cinnamomea*, cinnamon fern are very satisfactory) on a clean piece of smooth paper or in an envelope. Spores will be shed as the frond dries. Collect the spores into #1 gelatin capsules or small screw-cap vials for storage. *Osmunda* spores maintain viability for about 3 months at room temperature and for more than 2 1/2 years at 0°C. One gelatin capsule of spores is enough for a very large number of cultures.

Empty the contents of a capsule into a flask of 100 mL sterile dH₂O. Agitate and remove 1 mL of this suspension to another flask of 100 mL sterile dH₂O. Agitate again. Remove 1 mL of this suspension and spread on the surface of a petri dish of fern agar. Try to spread the spores as evenly as possible on the agar surface to avoid abnormal morphology that might result from crowding of prothallia. Illuminate at room temperature with a 16-hour photoperiod of indirect natural or fluorescent light.

Prothallia will be visible in about 2 weeks. If they are very dense at this stage, thin out extras with forceps. At 6 weeks, begin to look microscopically for gametangia. When gametangia have been observed, periodically spray the cultures with sterile dH₂O to allow fertilization to occur.

Remove prothallia with attached sporophytes from the growing medium and preserve in FAA plus cupric acetate in a screw-cap vial.

FAA plus cupric acetate: Dilute 9 parts FAA with one part cupric acetate stock.

Cupric acetate stock:		
cupric acetate [Cu(CH₃COO)₂•H₂O]	about 5 g
glacial acetic acid	50 mL
dH₂O	50 mL

Mix acid and water. Add cupric acetate until a saturated solution is obtained. Filter solution.

23.5 Experiment: Fern Sperm Chemotaxis

A similar experiment can be purchased as a kit from Carolina Biological Supply Company. (See *Ordering Information* below.)

Melt Basic *C-fern®* medium in boiling water bath or microwave oven. The 160 mL bottle of media will require approximately 15 minutes to melt. Aseptically pour the media into sterile 60 x 15 mm petri dishes. Fill the dishes about ¾ full with about 15 mL/60 mm dish. One bottle of media (160 mL) will prepare approximately 10 petri dishes. Allow the dishes to cool undisturbed. The dishes of media may be stored at room temperature.

Suspend the pre-sterilized spores in 4 mL sterile distilled water. Invert the vial several times to wet the spores, and then dispense and spread three drops per dish. Yield: Over 30 petri dishes. Plan to inoculate the cultures and place under lights at least 10 days prior to the first class period. Fully mature gametophytes require approximately 10 days from starting to reach maturity at the optimal 28°C.

Notes

23.1 Phylum Lycophyta: Club Mosses

Preserved *Lycopodium* gametophytes may be available for loan from local botanists or plant morphologists.

Various species of *Lycopodium* may be found in mostly moist, acid soils, predominantly in Midwestern, Northeastern, and Mid-Atlantic states. Collect *Lycopodium* twice yearly, if possible, for demonstration of fresh material, since it is often difficult to maintain in good condition, even in a greenhouse, for more than a few months.

At the time of publication no commercial source existed for *Lycopodium* or *Selginella* herbarium mounts.

23.2 Phylum Moniliophyta, Subphylum Psilophyta: Whisk Ferns

Preserved *Psilotum* gametophytes may be available for loan from local botanists or plant morphologists. At the time of publication no commercial source existed for *Psilotum* herbarium mounts.

23.3 Phylum Moniliophyta, Subphylum Sphenophyta: Horsetails

Equisetum species may be collected from moist woodlands, streambanks, roadside ditches, and meadows. *Equisetum* may also be successfully maintained in a greenhouse.

At the time of publication no commercial source existed for *Equisetum* herbarium mounts or preserved gametophytes.

23.4 Phylum Moniliophyta, Subphylum Pterophyta: Ferns

Include as many living species of ferns as possible, especially some with conspicuous sporangia. Ferns such as *Polypodium virginianum* with discrete sori are also valuable for student observation and may be collected and pressed for herbarium specimens in the summer.

Hare's foot fern, *Polypodium aureum*, is greenhouse grown and should be in mature condition to provide sori for classroom observation of spore discharge. Keep sori-containing squares of fronds in a covered bowl with moist filter paper to prevent drying.

23.5 Experiment: Fern Sperm Chemotaxis

An excellent resource, "Culture Instructions for *C-fern*® Investigations,," is available from Carolina Biological.

Ordering Information

See General Laboratory Supplies list on page vii for basic items

23.1 Phylum Lycophyta: Club Mosses

Lycopodium gametophyte, preserved	See *Notes*	
Lycopodium, herbarium mount	See *Notes*	
Lycopodium, living plant	Carolina	15-6980
Lycopodium, preserved	See *Notes*	
Selaginella apoda preserved	See *Notes*	
Selaginella lepidophylla, dried	Carolina	15-7010
Selaginella, herbarium mount	See *Notes*	
Selaginella, living plant	Carolina	15-7016
Fern allies set *(Selaginella, Lycopodium,* and *Equisetum)*, living	Carolina	15-6950

23.2 Phylum Moniliophyta, Subphylum Psilophyta: Whisk Ferns

Psilotum gametophyte	see *Notes*	
Psilotum herbarium specimen	see *Notes*	
Psilotum nudum, living plant	Carolina	15-7000

23.3 Phylum Moniliophyta, Subphylum Sphenophyta: Horsetails

Equisetum gametophytes, preserved	See *Notes*	
Equisetum herbarium mount	See *Notes*	
Equisetum, living plant	Ward's	86 V 5300
Equisetum, preserved fertile shoots	Ward's	63 V 0545

23.4 Phylum Moniliophyta, Subphylum Pterophyta: Ferns

acetic acid, glacial	Fisher	A38-500
agar	VWR	90000-760
ammonium nitrate	Fisher	A676-500
calcium chloride	Fisher	C77-500
cupric acetate	Fisher	C437-500
fern prothallia living with young sporophyte	Carolina	15-6881
fern prothallia, living, filamentous stage	Carolina	15-6873
fern prothallium with archegonium, l.s. slide	Triarch	7-16H
fern prothallium, monoecious, w.m., slide	Triarch	7-16E
fern spores	Carolina	15-6860
fern, fruiting	Carolina	15-6902
ferric chloride	Fisher	I89-500
formaldehyde	Carolina	86-3553
magnesium sulfate	Fisher	S93295
monobasic potassium phosphate	Fisher	P382-500
Dennstaedtia punctilobula rhizome, c.s.	Triarch	7-3
Polypodium virginianum, rhizome, c.s. slide	Triarch	7-12A

23.5 Experiment: Fern Sperm Chemotaxis

C-fern® kit	Carolina	15-6714
toothpicks	purchase locally	

If ordered separately:

Basic C-fern® Medium	Carolina	15-6780
pre-sterilized C-fern® Spores(Wild Type)	Carolina	15-6728
L-malic acid	Fisher	AC15059-0250
fumaric acid	Fisher	A120-500
succinic acid	Fisher	A294-500
D-malic acid	Sigma	M0750
maleic acid	Fisher	O3417-500
culture dome	Carolina	15-6792
lighting system	Carolina	97-1944
sterile spore spreader	Carolina	70-3414

Answers to In-Text Questions

23.1 Phylum Lycophyta: Club Mosses

A. Lycopodium

Is the sporophyte haploid (n) or diploid (2n)? **Diploid**
Since the spores are haploid, what process must have taken place within the sporangium? **Meiosis**

B. Selaginella

4. Describe the color and appearance of the dried specimen. **Looks like a wrapped up brown ball.**
5. Now place a dried specimen in a culture bowl containing water. Observe what happens in the next hour or so and describe the change in appearance of the plant. **Over time (minutes), the ball unfurls and becomes bright green.**

23.2 Phylum Moniliophyta, Subphylum Psilophyta: Whisk Ferns

2. If the pot contains a number of stems, you can see how it got its common name, the whisk fern, because it looks a bit like a whisk broom. Closely examine a single aerial stem. What color is it? **Green**

3. From this observation, make a conclusion regarding one function of this stem. **This is the photosynthetic organ of the plant.**

10. The male sex organs are antheridia (Figure 23-6b; singular, antheridium); the female sex organs are archegonia (singular, archegonium). Both antheridia and archegonia are on the same gametophyte. Is the gametophyte dioecious or monoecious? **Monoecious**

23.3 Phylum Moniliophyta, Subphylum Sphenophyta: Horsetails

4. Examine both the aerial stem and rhizome closely.

Do both have nodes? **Yes**

Do both have leaves? **Yes**

Which portion of Equisetum is primarily concerned with photosynthesis? **The stem (as opposed to the leaves)**

5. Find the strobilus (Figure 23-7). Where on the plant is it located? **At the tip**

Based on the knowledge you've acquired in your study of Lycopodium, what would you expect to find within the strobilus? **Spores**

When spores fall to the ground, what would you expect them to grow into after germination? **Gametophytes**

6. Now observe the horsetail gametophytes (Figure 23-8). What color are they? **Green**

Would you expect them to be found on or below the soil surface? Why? **On the surface. It would make no sense for them to grow beneath the surface if they were green because the green color indicates the presence of chlorophyll and chlorophyll, being the photosynthetic pigment, would be active only in the light.**

23.4 Phylum Moniliophyta, Subphylum Pterophyta: Ferns

5. What process occurred within the sporangium to produce the haploid spores? **Meiosis**

7. Using your dissecting microscope, examine a living, preserved, or prepared slide whole mount of the gametophyte (Figures 23-12, 23-16f). What color is the gametophyte? **Green**

What does the color indicate relative to the ability of the gametophyte to produce its own carbohydrates? **It suggests that the gametophyte is photosynthetic and thus produces its own carbohydrates.**

23.5 Experiment: Fern Sperm Chemotaxis

4. Repeat step 3 with the four remaining toothpicks and four other test solutions. Leave the unmarked toothpick dry. Which toothpick serves as the control? **The unmarked toothpick**

TABLE 23-1 My Data: Chemotactic Response of C-Fern™ Sperm				
Prediction: Answer variable, but a reasonable one would be that there are some substances that serve as chemical attractants to the sperm.				
	Swarming Response			
	Intensity (low, medium, high)		**Duration (short, medium, long)**	
Test Substance	**My data**	**Pooled Data**	**My data**	**Pooled Data**
0	None			
1	Low			
2	High			
3	Medium			
4	Low			
5	High			
Conclusion:				

Note: Malic acid is known to be an intermediate of the Kreb's cycle and would be released by the archegonia. While succinic and fumaric acids are also Kreb's cycle intermediates, their structure is very distinct compared with L-malic; they are not attractants. Maleic acid is not naturally produced but should serve as a strong attractant nonetheless.

17. Examine the chemical structures of each test solution (Figure 23-19). Relate the biological (chemotactic) response you observed to any of the chemical structural differences of the test substances. **L-malic acid serves as a strong attractant. But a minor change in chemical structure alters the response to the chemicals. Interestingly, while maleic acid is a strong attractant, fumaric acid, with a very similar chemical structure, has no similar activity.**

What is the advantage to using the pooled data to draw your conclusion? **The more replicates used during experimentation, the less likely an error will be made in the conclusion.**

What do you hypothesize the naturally occurring chemical produced by mature archegonia to be? **L-malic acid. (Students will need some assistance coming to this conclusion. If you have a very complete description of the Kreb's cycle, the students could be asked to search for the chemicals used in this experiment and draw their conclusions from that.)**

Name _____

Section No. _____

SEEDLESS VASCULAR PLANTS: CLUB MOSSES AND FERNS

Pre-lab Questions

1. In ferns: a. xylem and phloem are present in the sporophyte; b. the sporophyte is the dominant generation; c. the leaf is called a frond; d. all of the above are true.

2. Which phrase *best* describes a plant that is an epiphyte? a. a plant that grows upon another plant; b. a parasite; c. a plant with the gametophyte generation dominant and conspicuous; d. a plant that has a mutually beneficial relationship with another plant.

3. Which statement is *not* true? a. nodes are present on horsetails; b. the rhizome on horsetails bears roots; c. the internode of a horsetail is the region where the leaves are attached; d. horsetails are members of the subphylum Sphenophyta.

4. The resurrection plant: a. is a species of *Selaginella* ; b. grows in the desert Southwest of the United States; c. is a member of the division Lycophyta; d. all of the above.

5. *Psilotum* lacks: a. roots; b. a mechanism to take up water and minerals; c. vascular tissue; d. alternation of generations.

6. Club mosses: a. are placed in the subphylum Pterophyta; b. are so called because of the social nature of the plants; c. do not produce gametophytes; d. are so called because most produce strobili.

7. Spore germination followed by cell divisions results in the production of: a. a sporophyte; b. an antheridium; c. a zygote; d. a gametophyte.

8. A tracheophyte is a plant that has: a. xylem and phloem; b. a windpipe; c. a trachea; d. the gametophyte as its dominant generation.

9. The spores of a fern are: a. produced by mitosis within the sporangium; b. diploid cells; c. the first cells of the gametophyte generation; d. a and b above.

10. The sporophyte is the dominant and conspicuous generation in the: a. fern allies and ferns; b. gymnosperms; c. flowering plants; d. all of the above.

SEEDLESS VASCULAR PLANTS: CLUB MOSSES AND FERNS

Answers to Pre-lab Questions
in Lab Manual Order

1.	d	6.	d
2.	a	7.	d
3.	a	8.	c
4.	d	9.	d
5.	a	10.	c

Answers to Pre-lab Questions
in Instructor's Manual Order

1.	d	6.	d
2.	a	7.	d
3.	c	8.	a
4.	d	9.	c
5.	a	10.	d

Answers to Post-lab Questions

1. List two features that distinguish the seedless vascular plants from the bryophytes. **a. Dominant portion of the life cycle is the gametophyte in bryophytes, the sporophyte in the seedless vascular plants. b. Seedless vascular plants have vascular tissue and bryophytes don't.**

2. After consulting a biological or scientific dictionary, explain the derivation from the Greek of the word *symbiosis*. **Sym means "with, together" and bios means "life." Thus, symbiosis means "living together" and is a mutually beneficial relationship between two closely associated organisms.**

3. Using a biological or scientific dictionary or a reference in your textbook, determine the meaning of the root word *psilo*, relating it to the appearance of *Psilotum*. **Psilo is derived from Greek, meaning "bare, naked" and refers to the bare appearance of the stems of *Psilotum*, which bear only tiny scale-like growths instead of leaves.**

4. Both *Lycopodium* and *Equisetum* have strobili, roots, and rhizomes. What did you learn in this exercise that would allow you to distinguish these two plants? **Lycopodium is covered with leaves and has strobili made up of tightly packed specialized fertile leaves. *Equisetum* stems have leaves in whorls only at nodes with distinct internodes. *Equisetum* stems are highly ridged, *Lycopodium* stems are round. *Equisetum* strobili are not associated with specialized leaves as are those of *Lycopodium*.**

5. Examine the photo at the right. a. Give the genus of this plant. **Lycopodium** b. Label the structure indicated. **Strobilus**

6. Some species of *Lycopodium* produce gametophytes that grow beneath the surface of the soil while others grow on the soil surface. Basing your answer upon what you have learned from other plants in this exercise, make a prediction concerning how each respective type of *Lycopodium* gametophyte would obtain its nutritional needs. **Subterranean gametophytes rely on a symbiotic association with a fungus while above-ground gametophytes are green and photosynthetic.**

7. Examine the photo on the right. You studied this genus in lab, but this is a different species. This species has two separate stems produced at different times in the growing season. The stem on the left is a reproductive branch, while that on the right is strictly vegetative. Based on the characteristics obvious in this photo, identify the plant, give its scientific name then identify the labeled structures. **Common name: Horsetail, Scientific name: Equisetum.** A: **strobilus or cone** B. **leaves** C. **branches**

8. Explain the distinction between a *node* and an *internode*. **A node is a place on a stem where leaves arise. An internode is the region on a stem between the nodes and bears no leaves.**

9. While rock climbing, you encounter this plant at the right growing out of a crevice. a. Is this the sporophyte or the gametophyte? **Sporophyte** b. What special name is given to the leaf of this plant? **Frond**

10. The environments in which ferns grow range from standing water to very dry areas. Nonetheless, all ferns are dependent upon free water in order to complete their life cycles. Explain why this is the case. **The flagellated sperm need a film of free water to swim down the archegonia to fertilize the egg cells.**

SEED PLANTS I: GYMNOSPERMS

Materials and Equipment

24.1 Phylum Coniferophyta: Conifers

Per student
- cluster of *Pinus* male cones
- dissecting microscope
- prepared slide of pine seed, l.s.
- prepared slide of male strobilus, l.s., with microspores
- prepared slide of female strobilus, l.s., with megaspore mother cell
- single-edged razor blade
- compound microscope
- young female cone

Per student group (table)
- young *Pinus* sporophyte, living or herbarium specimen

Per lab room
- pine seeds, soaking in water
- demonstration slide of fertilization
- demonstration slide of female strobilus with archegonium
- pine seedlings, 12 weeks old
- pine seedlings, 36 weeks old

24.2 Phylum Cycadophyta: Cycads

Per lab room
- demonstration specimens of *Zamia* and/or *Cycas*

24.3 Phylum Ginkgophyta: Ginko

Per lab room
- demonstration specimens of *Ginkgo* (living plant or herbarium specimen)

24.4 Phylum Gnetophyta: Gnetophytes (Vessel-Containing Gymnosperms)

Per lab room
- demonstration specimens of *Ephedra* and/or *Gnetum* (living plant or herbarium specimen)

Preparation of Materials and Equipment

Pinus edulis seedlings: Plant seeds in sand-filled saucers or pots at 12 weeks and at 36 weeks before use for laboratory demonstration of cotyledons and later elongation and leaf production.

Notes

Collect male cones of *Pinus* in summer prior to pollen shed. The strobili may be frozen until use. Female cones may also be stored frozen.

Ordering Information

See General Laboratory Supplies list on page vii for basic items

24.1 Phylum Coniferophyta: Conifers

Pine seeds (from grocery or specialty food store or)	Ward's	86 V 8260
Pinus seed, l.s., prepared slide	Triarch	10-6W
Pinus, archegonium, l.s., showing fertilization, slide	Triarch	10-6Z
Pinus, archegonium, l.s., prepared slide	Triarch	10-6RR
Pinus, mature male strobilus, l.s., prepared slide	Triarch	10-6HL
Pinus, megaspore mother cell in strobilus, l.s., slide	Triarch	10-6M

24.2 Phylum Cycadophyta: Cycads

Cycas revoluta, living plant	local greenhouse	
Zamia, living plant	Ward's	86 V 5510

24.3 Phylum Ginkgophyta: Ginko

Ginkgo, living plant - If living specimens are not available from local greenhouse, herbarium specimens may be substituted. (*Ginkgo* set, preserved from Ward's 63V 0560)

24.4 Phylum Gnetophyta: Gnetophytes (Vessel-Containing Gymnosperms)

Ephedra, and *Gnetum* living plants. If living specimens are not available from local greenhouse, herbarium specimens may be substituted.

Answers to In-Text Questions

24.1 Phylum Coniferophyta: Conifers

B. Female Reproductive Structures and Events

4....The female gametophyte of pine is produced **within** the megasporangium.
10. Identify the papery remnant of the megasporangium, the white female gametophyte, and embryo (embryo sporophyte). How many cotyledons are present? **Many (more than three)**

24.2 Phylum Cycadophyta: Cycads

1. Examine the demonstration specimen of *Zamia* and/or *Cycas* (Figure 24-13). Both have the common name cycad. Do these plants resemble any of the conifers you know? **(Most students would say "no.")**

Name _____

Section No. _____

SEED PLANTS I: GYMNOSPERMS

Pre-lab Questions

1. Which statement is *not* true about conifers? a. conifers are gymnosperms; b. all conifers belong to the genus *Pinus* ; c. all conifers have naked seeds; d. conifers are heterosporous

2. A pine tree is: a. a sporophyte; b. a gametophyte; c. diploid; d. a and c above.

3. Which of these are produced *directly* by meiosis in pine? a. sperm cells; b. pollen grains; c. microspores; d. microspore mother cells.

4. The male pine cone: a. produces pollen; b. contains a female gametophyte; c. bears a megasporangium containing a megaspore mother cell; d. gives rise to a seed.

5. The process by which pollen is transferred to the ovule is called: a. transmigration; b. fertilization; c. pollination; d. all of the above.

6. The male gametophyte of a pine tree: a. is produced within a pollen grain; b. produces sperm; c. is diploid; d. a and b above.

7. An ovule: a. is the structure which develops into a seed; b. contains the microsporophyll; c. is produced on the surface of a male cone; d. all of the above.

8. Which statement is true of the female gametophyte of pine? a. it's a product of repeated cell divisions of the functional megaspore; b. it's haploid; c. it serves as the stored food to be used by the embryo sporophyte upon germination; d. all of the above are true.

9. Seed plants: a. have alternation of generations; b. are heterosporous; c. develop a seed coat; d. all of the above.

10. The seed coat of a pine seed: a. is derived from the integuments; b. was produced by the micropyle; c. surrounds the male gametophyte; d. is divided into the hypocotyl-root axis and epicotyl.

EXERCISE 24

SEED PLANTS I: GYMNOSPERMS

Answers to Pre-lab Questions
in Lab Manual Order

1.	b	6.	c
2.	d	7.	a
3.	d	8.	c
4.	a	9.	d
5.	d	10.	a

Answers to Pre-lab Questions
in Instructor's Manual Order

1.	b	6.	d
2.	d	7.	a
3.	c	8.	d
4.	a	9.	d
5.	c	10.	a

Answers to Post-lab Questions

1. What survival advantage does a seed have that has allowed the seed plants to be the most successful of all plants? **Seeds contain immature sporophytes surrounded by a protective seed coat. They also contain stored food material. A seed can remain dormant until environmental conditions are such that the embryo stands a better chance for survival as compared with immediate germination. The stored food gets the seedling off to a "head start" so that growth and development of roots and shoots, the organs used to absorb and produce nutrients, take place rapidly.**

2. In the diagram below of a seed, give the ploidy level (n or 2n) of each part listed. Seed coat: **2n**; Megasporangium: **2n**; Female gametophyte: **n**; Embryo sporophyte: **2n**.

3. Distinguish between a homosporous and a heterosporous type of life cycle. **In a homosporous life cycle, only one type of spore is produced by meiosis, and thus, the gametophyte produced from divisions of that spore is usually bisexual. By contrast, heterosporous plants produce two spore types: microspores and megaspores. The microspore develops into a male gametophyte and the megaspore develops into a female gametophyte.**

4. List four uses for conifers. **a. Christmas trees; b. ornamental landscape specimens; c. lumber; d. paper; e. source of turpentine; f. windbreaks; g. wildlife food and cover; h. firewood.**

5. While snowshoeing through the winter woods, you stop to look at the tree branch pictured at the right. Specifically, what are the brown structures hanging from the branch? **Female (seed) cones**

6. Distinguish between *pollination and fertilization.* **Pollination is the transfer of pollen grains to the female reproductive structure. Fertilization is the fusion of sperm nuclei (produced within the pollen grain in seed plants) with the egg nucleus.**

7. Are antheridia present in conifers? **No** Archegonia? **Yes**

8. Suppose you saw the seedling pictured at the right while walking in the woods. a. To which gymnosperm phylum does the plant belong? **Coniferophyta.** b. Identify structures A and B. **A is the seed coat; B is the cotyledon.**

9. On spring break, you are strolling through a tropical garden in Florida and encounter the plant pictured at the right. Would the xylem of this plant contain tracheids, vessels, or both? **Tracheids**

10. A friend of yours picks up a branch like the one pictured at the right. Knowing that you have taken a biology course and studied plants, she asks you what the plant is: Identify this branch, giving your friend the full scientific name for the plant. ***Ginkgo biloba***

EXERCISE 25

SEED PLANTS II: ANGIOSPERMS

Materials and Equipment

25.1 External Structure of the Flower

Per student
- dissecting microscope
- flower for dissection, gladiolus or hybrid lily
- single-edged razor blade

25.2 The Life Cycle of a Flowering Plant

A. Male Gametophyte (Pollen Grain) Formation in the Microsporangia

Per student
- prepared slide of young lily anther, c.s.
- glass microscope slide and coverslip
- prepared slide of mature lily anther (pollen grains), c.s.
- *Impatiens* flower with mature pollen
- compound microscope

Per student pair
- 0.5% sucrose in dropping bottle

B. Female Gametophyte Formation in the Megasporangia

Per student
- compound microscope
- prepared slide of lily ovary, c.s., megaspore mother cell

Per lab room
- demonstration slide of lily ovary, c.s., 7 celled, 8 nucleate gametophyte
- demonstration slide of lily ovary, c.s. double fertilization

C. Embryogeny

Per lab room
- demonstration slides of *Capsella* embryogeny: globular embryo, emerging cotyledons, torpedo-shaped embryo, mature embryo

D. Fruit and Seed

Per student
- bean fruits
- iodine solution (I_2KI), in dropping bottle
- soaked bean seeds

Per lab room
- herbarium specimen of *Capsella*, with fruits
- demonstration slide of *Capsella* fruit, c.s

E. Seedling

Per student
- germinating bean seeds, 6 days old
- bean seedlings, 10 days old

Per table
- dishpan of water

25.3 Experiment: An Investigative Study of the Life Cycle of Flowering Plants

A. Germination

Day 0

Per student
- one RCBr seed pod
- metric ruler
- transparent adhesive tape
- model seed
- forceps
- paper towel or filter paper disk to fit petri dish
- 3 x 5 in. index card
- 600-mL beaker
- petri dish
- disposable pipet with bulb
- marker

Option A: Polystyrene Growth Quad Method
- polystyrene growing quad
- four paper wicks
- twelve N-P-K fertilizer pellets
- pot label

Option B: Film Canister Method
- two 35-mm film canisters
- two cotton string wicks
- wide-mouth bottles
- twenty-four N-P-K fertilizer pellets
- two pot labels

Per student group (4)
- 2-L soda bottle bottom or tray
- water mat
- moistened soil mix
- watertight tray

Per lab room
- light bank

Day 1

Per student pair
- dissecting microscope
- source of tap water
- disposable pipet with bulb
- metric ruler

Day 2
- germination experiment from Day 0
- metric ruler and forceps
- dissecting microscope
- two petri dishes
- paper towel or filter paper disks to fit petri dishes
- disposable pipet with bulb
- source of tap water
- two RCBr seed pods
- 2-L soda bottle bottom or tray

Day 3
- disposable pipet with bulb
- gravitropism experiment from Day 2
- source of tap water
- germination experiment from Day 0

B. Growth

Day 4 or 5
- germination experiment from Day 0
- dissecting microscope
- metric ruler
- forceps

Day 7
- metric ruler

C. The Pollinator and Pollination

Day 10
- metric ruler
- three toothpicks
- (provide tube of glue and scissors *per student group*)
- dissecting microscope
- three dried honeybees

Day 12
(*Pollination*)
- beestick prepared on Day 10
- dissecting microscope
- compound microscope
- prepared slide of *Brassica* flower, l.s
- forceps
- metric ruler
- marker
- index card divider

Day 14
- metric ruler
- bee stick prepared on Day 10

Day 17
- metric ruler
- bee stick prepared on Day 10

E. Fertilization and Seed Development

Day 26
- dissecting microscope
- iodine solution (I_2KI) in dropper bottle
- glass microscope slide
- dH_2O in dropping bottle
- two dissecting needles

Day 29
- dissecting microscope
- two dissecting needles
- dH_2O in dropping bottle
- glass microscope slide

Day 31
- dissecting microscope
- two dissecting needles
- dH_2O in dropping bottle
- glass microscope slide

Days 35 to 37
- dissecting microscope
- two dissecting needles

Preparation of Materials and Equipment

25.1 External Structure of the Flower

Flowers for dissection: Supply gladiolus or hybrid lily flowers to students in a covered glass bowl lined with moist paper. Flowers can usually be held for several days in tightly closed plastic bags in a refrigerator.

25.2 The Life Cycle of a Flowering Plant

A. Male Gametophyte (Pollen Grain) Formation in the Microsporangia

Impatiens flowers: Grow *Impatiens* continuously in a greenhouse in order to ensure an adequate supply of flowers for this exercise. Flowers may be stored for several days in tightly closed plastic bags in a refrigerator.
  Students may share flowers, using one anther apiece, if supplies are short.

| *0.5% sucrose* (100 mL): | sucrose ($C_{12}H_{22}O_{11}$) | 0.5 g |
| | distilled water (dH_2O) to make | 100 mL |

Shelf life: 2 to 3 weeks. Refrigerate to prevent bacterial and fungal contamination.
Yield: 100 mL is enough for several hundred students.

B. Female Gametophyte Formation in the Megasporangia

None required.

C. Embryogeny

None required.

D. Fruit and Seed

Soaked bean seeds: Soak beans overnight in water to soften them.

Iodine (I_2KI) solution (100 mL):	potassium iodide (KI)	7 g
	iodine (I_2)	1 g
	dH_2O	100 mL

Dissolve the potassium iodide in the water. Add the iodine and stir until dissolved. Store in foil-wrapped or brown glass bottle.

Shelf life: months, if stored in dark.

Yield: 100 mL is enough for several hundred students.

E. Seedling

Germinating bean seeds: Plant bean seeds in flats of moist vermiculite 6 days before needed and keep in warm place.

Bean seedlings: Plant bean seeds in flats of moist vermiculite 10 days before needed and keep in warm place. Exact number of days to germination may vary depending upon your conditions. The optimum soil temperature for germination of bean seeds is 30°C.

25.3 Experiment: An Investigative Study of the Life Cycle of Flowering Plants

For complete information regarding preparation of materials and equipment for growth of rapid-cycling *Brassica* (RCBr) plants, refer to Appendix A of this manual.

RCBr seed pods: Grow sufficient quantities of RCBr plants to provide three RCBr seed pods per student for the life cycle study, and growth and gravitropism experiments. Each RCBr seedling may be expected to produce approximately four to six seedpods.

Plant RCBr seeds well in advance of when seedpods and seeds are needed in class (*at least* 40 days). The exact time RCBr plants require to complete a life cycle depends upon the temperature and light intensity of your conditions.

Paper wicks (Option A): Cut wicks from white household paper towels or rough filter paper. Wicks should be diamond-shaped, approximately 3.5 cm in length and 0.5 cm across base. Quad wicks may also be purchased (see *Ordering Information*).

*String wicks (*Option B): Cut 8-cm lengths of ordinary *cotton* household string to wick moisture from the water tray into the film canister growing containers. It is important that the wick be of absorbent fiber.

*Film canisters (*Option B): Punch a single hole in the center bottom of each film canister with a small drill press or heated dissecting needle. The hole should be large enough to easily admit the string wick.

Iodine (I_2KI) solution: See above.

Model seed: Model seeds are cut from ordinary synthetic household sponges (4 3/4 in. x 3 in. x 11/16 in.) following the illustrations below. The cotyledon section is split lengthwise to form the two cotyledons, after which the sponge model is thoroughly wetted and rolled into a tiny ball. Wrap tightly with string and let dry completely, approximately 2 days. Remove string and wrap the model with tissue to simulate a seed coat. Secure with a small piece of tape. The seeds "germinate" and expand when placed in a container of water and may be re-rolled, dried, and used again.

(For reference, please see Figure 25-16, page 382 of Lab Manual.)

Notes

25.1 External Structure of the Flower

Check availability and order gladiolus or hybrid lily flowers from a local florist well ahead of the time they're needed. If necessary, substitute another simple flower, such as *Ranunculus, Iris,* or *Azalea.* Avoid doubled or complex flower types such as zinnia, many roses, or orchids.

B. Female Gametophyte Formation in the Megasporangia and
C. Embryogeny

Instructors may want to tape a card next to each demonstration slide on which they've drawn and labeled an outline of the important structures illustrated. Students often find this helpful in orienting themselves and identifying the stages of megasporogenesis and embryogeny.

D. Fruit and Seed

At the time of publication, no commercial source existed for *Capsella* herbarium mounts.

25.3 Experiment: An Investigative Study of the Life Cycle of Flowering Plants

Extra RCBr seed may be stored for up to several years if refrigerated in a sealed container containing a small amount of silica gel desiccant or powdered milk to absorb moisture.

Many film processing outlets or camera stores discard great quantities of empty film canisters and will save them for you upon request.

Wide-mouthed bottles (32 mm diameter) to be used as water reservoirs for film canisters may be purchased but various small household bottles, such as empty pill bottles, may also be appropriate.

Ordering Information

See General Laboratory Supplies list on page vii for basic items

25.1 External Structure of the Flower

Flowers for dissection from local florist

25.2 The Life Cycle of a Flowering Plant

A. Male Gametophyte (Pollen Grain) Formation in the Microsporangia

See General Laboratory Supplies list for general supplies

Lilium, mature anther, c.s., prepared slide	Triarch	18-9
Lilium, young anther, c.s., prepared slide	Triarch	18-5 or 18-8
Sucrose	Fisher	S5-500

B. Female Gametophyte Formation in the Megasporangia

Lilium ovary, double fertilization, c.s., prepared slide	Triarch	19-12A
Lilium ovary, megasporangium with integuments, slide	Triarch	19-2C
Lilium, ovule with mature embryo sac, c.s., slide	Triarch	19-11A

C. Embryogeny

Capsella, early cotyledons, l.s., prepared slide	Triarch	20-2B
Capsella, globular embryo, l.s., prepared slide	Triarch	20-2A
Capsella, mature embryo, l.s., prepared slide	Triarch	20-2D
Capsella, torpedo-shaped embryo, l.s., pre pared slide	Triarch	20-2C

D. Fruit and Seed

bean seeds	local garden supply	
Capsella, fruit, c.s., prepared slide	Triarch	20-2G
Capsella, herbarium mount	See *Notes*	
iodine, I_2	Fisher	I37-100
potassium iodide, KI	Fisher	P410-100

E. Seedling

Viable bean seeds purchased from local garden supply

25.3 Experiment: An Investigative Study of the Life Cycle of Flowering Plants

Brassica flower bud, median l.s., prepared slide	Triarch	17-289-2
dried honeybees*	Carolina	15-8985
Fast Plants™ Watering System	Carolina	15-8974
film canisters	local photo processing outlet	
growing quad	Carolina	15-8960
iodine, I_2	Fisher	I37-100
light system	Carolina	15-8998
pot labels	Carolina	15-8982
potassium iodide, KI	Fisher	P410-100
quad wicks	Carolina	15-8978
RCBr (Wisconsin Fast Plants™) seeds(200)	Carolina	15-8811
Soil-less growing mix	local garden supply	
Time-release fertilizer pellets**	Carolina	15-8970
water mat	Carolina	15-8977
watertight tray	Carolina	15-8975

*dried honeybees can be obtained from local apiarist
**time-release fertilizer pellets can also be purchased from local garden supply

Answers to In-Text Questions

25.1 External Structure of the Flower

7. How many carpels does your flower contain? **Three (assuming using gladiolus or hybrid lily)**
12. Count the number of petals or sepals in the flower you have been examining. Are you studying a monocot or dicot? **Monocot**

25.2 The Life Cycle of a Flowering Plant

B. Female Gametophyte Formation in the Megasporangia

6. …The zygote is a **diploid** (haploid, diploid) cell.
    The other sperm nucleus enters the central cell and fuses with the two polar nuclei, forming the primary endosperm nucleus (Figure 25-15q). Thus, the primary endosperm nucleus is **pentaploid** (haploid, diploid, triploid, tetraploid, pentaploid).

C. Embryogeny

How many cotyledon were there in the slides you examined? **Two**
Thus, is *Capsella* a monocot or dicot? **Dicot**

D. Fruit and Seed

3. Obtain a bean pod and carefully split it open along one seam. The pod is a matured ovary and thus is a **fruit**.

7. What is this tiny opening? (Hint: The pollen tube grew through it.) **Micropyle**

8. What substance is located in the cotyledon? **Starch**

E. Seedling

6. Knowing what you do about the prefix *hypo-*, speculate on what the prefix *epi-* means. **Above**

As noted earlier, the seedling has true leaves. Contrast the function of the cotyledons ("seed leaves") with the true leaves. **Cotyledons contain stored carbohydrates that are exported to the developing seedling before the photosynthetic (true) leaves are fully functional as photosynthetic, exporting organs.**

SEED PLANTS II: ANGIOSPERMS

Pre-lab Questions

1.   Double fertilization refers to: a. fusion of two sperm nuclei and two egg cells; b. fusion of one sperm nucleus with two polar nuclei and fusion of another with the egg cell nucleus; c. maturation of the ovary into a fruit; d. none of the above.

2.   Where does germination of a pollen grain occur in a flowering plant? a. in the anther; b. in the micropyle; c. on the surface of the corolla; d. on the stigma.

3.   Ovules mature into _____, while ovaries mature into _____. a. seeds, fruits; b. stamens, seeds; c. seeds, carpels; d. fruits, seeds.

4.   Which group of terms is in the correct developmental sequence? a. microspore mother cell, meiosis, megaspore, female gametophyte; b. microspore mother cell, meiosis, microspore, pollen grain; c. megaspore, mitosis, female gametophyte, meiosis, endosperm mother cell; d. all of the above.

5.   Which group of terms refers to the microsporophyll, the male portion of a flower? a. ovary, stamens, pistil; b. stigma, style, ovary; c. anther, stamen, filament; d. megasporangium, microsporangium, ovule.

6.   Plants that produce flowers are: a. members of the Anthophyta; b. angiosperms; c. seed-producers; d. all of the above.

7.   All of the petals of a flower are collectively called the: a. corolla; b. stamens; c. receptacles; d. calyx.

8.   A bean pod is a: a. seed container; b. fruit; c. part of the stamen; d. a and b above.

9.   A carpel is the: a. same as a megasporophyll; b. structure producing pollen grains; c. component making up the anther; d. synonym for microsporophyll.

10.   The portion of the flower containing pollen grains is the: a. pollen sac; b. microsporangium; c. anther; d. all of the above.

EXERCISE 25

SEED PLANTS II: ANGIOSPERMS

*Answers to Pre-lab Questions
in Lab Manual Order*

1. d	6. b
2. a	7. d
3. c	8. b
4. a	9. a
5. d	10. d

*Answers to Pre-lab Questions
in Instructor's Manual Order*

1. b	6. d
2. d	7. a
3. a	8. d
4. b	9. a
5. c	10. d

Answers to Post-lab Questions

1. There are two major groups of seed plants, gymnosperms (Exercise 24) and angiosperms. Compare these two groups of seed plants with respect to the following features:

Feature	Gymnosperms	Angiosperms
a. type of reproductive structure	**cones (no flowers)**	**Flowers**
b. source of nutrition for the developing embryo	**female gametophyte**	**Endosperm**
c. enclosure of mature seed	**none**	**Within fruit**

2. What *event*, critical to the production of seeds, is shown at the right? **Pollination**

3. Distinguish between *pollination* and *fertilization*. **Pollination is the transfer of pollen grains from the male portion of the plant to the female gametophyte. Fertilization is the fusion of sperm nuclei, produced within the pollen grain, and the egg nucleus, produced within the female gametophyte.**

4. Identify the parts of the trumpet creeper flower shown at the right. **a. calyx; b. corolla; c. ovary; d. style; e. stigma.**

5. Examine the photo of the *Trillium* flower pictured at the right. a. Is *Trillium* a monocotyledon or dicotyledon? **Monocotyledon** b. Justify your answer. **The flower parts are in three's.**

6. Based on your observation of the stigma of the daylily flower in the photo at the right, how many carpels would you expect to comprise the ovary? **Three**

7. The photo is a cross section of an **anther**. The numerous circles within the four cavities are **pollen grains.**

8. The photo shows a flower of the pomegranate some time after fertilization. Identify the parts shown. **a. sepal; b. stamens; c. seeds; d. fruit.**

9. Some biologists contend that the term *double fertilization* is a misnomer and that the process should be called *fertilization* and *triple fusion*. Why do they argue that the fusion of the one sperm nucleus and the two polar nuclei is *not* fertilization? **Strictly defined, fertilization is the fusion of a sperm nucleus with an egg nucleus. The two polar nuclei with which the sperm nucleus fuses are components of the central cell, *not* egg cells.**

10. Your roommate says that you need vegetables, and asks you to pick up tomatoes at the store. To your roommate's surprise, you say a tomato is not a vegetable, but a fruit. Explain. **A fruit is a "ripened" (mature) ovary containing seeds. Fertilization of a tomato flower causes the ovary to mature into a fruit. Botanically speaking, many "vegetables" are really fruits.**

SPONGES AND CNIDARIANS

Materials and Equipment

26.1 Sponges (Phylum Porifera)

Per student
- dissecting microscope
- microscope slides
- hand lens
- compound microscope
- coverslip
- safety goggles (optional)

Per student pair
- preserved specimen of *Scypha*
- slide of teased commercial sponge fibers
- slide of *Leucosolenia*, w.m
- slide of *Scypha* spicules (optional)
- slide of sponge gemmules
- slide of *Scypha*, l.s.
- slide of *Spongilla* spicules, w.m

Per student group (4)
- 100-mL heat-proof glass beaker
- wash bottle of dH$_2$O (optional)
- 5% sodium hydroxide (NaOH) or 5% potassium hydroxide (KOH)
- hot plate (optional)

Per lab room
- demonstration of living or dried freshwater sponges wash bottle of 50% vinegar and water
- demonstration collection of commercial sponges

26.2 Cnidarians (Phylum Cnidaria)

Per student
- dissecting microscope
- compound microscope
- microscope slide
- coverslip

Per student pair
- prepared slide of *Hydra*, c.s
- prepared slide of *Obelia* (showing colonial polyps and medusa), w.m.
- prepared slide of *Hydra* (showing testes, ovaries, buds, and embryos), w.m.
- prepared slide of *Obelia*, medusa, w.m

Per student group (4)
- small finger bowl
- slide of *Aurelia*, strobila, w.m.
- scalpel or single-edged razor blade
- slide of *Aurelia*, ephyra (medusa), w.m.
- preserved specimen of *Gonionemus*
- slide of *Aurelia*, scyphistoma, w.m.
- slide of *Aurelia*, planula larva, w.m.

Per lab room
- demonstration specimen of *Physalia*
- demonstration specimen of *Metridium*
- demonstration collection of corals

Per lab section
- culture of live copepods or cladocerans
- dropping bottle of glutathione
- dropping bottle of vinegar
- culture of live *Hydra*
- container of fresh stream water

Preparation of Materials and Equipment

26.1 Sponges (Phylum Porifera)

| *5% NaOH or KOH* (100 mL): | NaOH or KOH pellets | 5.0 g |
| | dH$_2$O | 100.0 mL |

    Yield: 100 mL hydroxide solution should supply 4 or 5 student groups.

| *50% vinegar and water* (1000 mL): | vinegar | 500 mL |
| | water | 500 mL |

    Yield: 1000 mL 50% vinegar-water solution should fill two wash bottles.

26.2 Cnidarians (Phylum Cnidaria)

| *glutathione* (100 mL): | Glutathione | 3 mg |
| | distilled water | 100 mL |

    Shelf life: about one week.

Notes

Provide plastic gloves, especially when students work with preserved specimens. Students who wear contact lenses should also have access to safety goggles for the entire exercise, and *all* students should wear the goggles when working with hot 5% hydroxide solution (26.1 Phylum Porifera).

Dispose of hydroxide solutions and preservatives in non-glass, labeled waste bottles according to your institution's guidelines.

Much helpful information about culturing invertebrates can be found in the following manual: R. H. Whitten and W. R. Pendergrass. 1980. *Carolina Protozoa and Invertebrates Manual*. Carolina Biological Supply Company, Burlington, NC/Gladstone, OR. (See *Ordering Information*.)

Many institutions offer courses in invertebrate biology and have extensive collections of specimens that might be borrowed for demonstration in this exercise.

26.1 Sponges (Phylum Porifera)

Any sponges of the class Calcarea may be used to extract spicules. Alcohol-preserved specimens may be used for this preparation if the alcohol is first allowed to evaporate completely. Rinse the dried sponges in water and re-dry before boiling in hydroxide solutions.

26.2 Cnidarians (Phylum Cnidaria)

Order *Hydra* to arrive just before needed. They will survive in their shipping containers with the lids ajar for a few days at room temperature.

Hydra may be transferred with a dropper to individual small dishes for study. Pond or other dechlorinated water should be deep enough to allow the *Hydra* to extend its tentacles without encountering the surface of the water.

Ordering Information

See General Laboratory Supplies list on page vii for basic items

26.1 Sponges (Phylum Porifera)

commercial sponge set, dry	Carolina	22-4070
KOH pellets	Fisher	P250-500
Leucosolenia, w.m., prepared slide	Triarch	ZB2-1
NaOH pellets	Fisher	S318-100
Scypha, l.s., prepared slide	Triarch	ZB1-12
Scypha, preserved, medium	Ward's	68 V 0142
Spongilla, freshwater sponge, living	Carolina	13-2735
Spongilla gemmules, w.m., prepared slide	Ward's	92W 0580
vinegar	purchase locally	

26.2 Cnidarians (Phylum Cnidaria)

Aurelia, ephyra (medusa), w.m., prepared slide	Triarch	ZC2-2
Aurelia, planula larva, w.m., prepared slide	Triarch	ZC3-1
Aurelia, scyphistoma, w.m., prepared slide	Ward's	92 V O783
Aurelia, strobila, w.m., prepared slide	Ward's	92 V O784
coral collection, nine different species	Carolina	26-1282
culture dish, 2 1/2 in. diam.	Carolina	74-1000
Daphnia, living (hydra food)	Carolina	14-2314
Glutathione	Fisher	AC120000250
Gonionemus, preserved	Carolina	22-4138
green hydra, living	Carolina	13-2810
Hydra, budding, living	Carolina	13-2804
Hydra, c.s., prepared slide	Triarch	ZC1-5
Hydra, living	Carolina	13-2800
Hydra, w.m., ovaries, prepared slide	Ward's	92 V O660
Hydra, w.m., , prepared slide	Ward's	92 V O654
Metridium, preserved	Carolina	22-4228
Obelia, colony, w.m., vegetative and reproductive, prepared slide	Triarch	ZC2-1
Obelia, medusa stage, w.m., prepared slide	Triarch	ZC2-2
Physalia, preserved	Carolina	POM829
vinegar	purchase locally	

Answers to In-Text Questions

26.1 Sponges (Phylum Porifera)

TABLE 26-2 Circulation of Water Through the Syconoid Sponge *Scypha*	
Structure	**Order of water circulation**
Spongocoel	4
Incurrent canals	2
Radial canals	3
Incurrent pores	1
Osculum	5

26.2 Cnidarians (Phylum Cnidaria)

A. Class Hydrozoa: Hydrozoans

1.

(c) …Is *Hydra* monoecious or dioecious? ***Hydra* is potentially monoecious.**

(e) …How might two layers of epitheliomuscular cells function to maintain and change the body shape of a Cnidarian? **Contracting the longitudinal fibers causes the hydra to shorten and relaxing them allows Cniderians to lengthen. Contracting the circular fibers causes a decrease its diameter and vice versa. Changes in body shape also depend on water pressure in the gastrovascular cavity.**

What additional function can you suggest for the epitheliomuscular cells of the gastrodermis? (*Hint:* What happens to partially digested food?) **Contraction of the muscle fibers in general increases the pressure in the gastrovascular cavity and, upon opening the osculum, food remnants are ejected from the Cniderian.**

(f) …Describe what you observe. **Stinging cells release their nematocysts.**

(g) …Can you explain the green color of your *Hydra*? **Green *Hydra* have symbiotic green algae.**

C. Class Anthozoa: Corals and Sea Anemones.

2. What do you think is the function of the pedal disk? **The function of the pedal disk is adherence to the underlying substrate.**

Name _____

Section No. _____

SPONGES AND CNIDARIANS

Pre-lab Questions

1. Many sponges produce both eggs and sperm and thus are: a. monoecious; b. dioecious; c. hermaphroditic; d. a and c.

2. Freshwater sponges reproduce asexually by forming resistant internal buds called: a. spicules; b. larvae; c. ovaries; d. gemmules.

3. Cnidarians capture their prey with the use of: a. poison claws; b. nematocysts; c. oral teeth; d. pedal disks.

4. Cnidarians evolved from an ancestral group of: a. sponges; b. protists; c. fungi; d. plants.

5. Coral reefs, atolls, and islands are the result of the buildup of coral: a. polyps; b. medusae; c. exoskeletons; d. wastes.

6. The "skeleton" of a typical sponge is composed of: a. bones; b. cartilages; c. spicules; d. scales.

7. Which statement is true for scyphozoan medusae? a. they are the dominant body form; b. they are generally smaller than hydrozoan medusae; c. most live in fresh water; d. they are scavengers.

8. A free-swimming jellyfish has a body form known as a: a. polyp; b. strobila; c. medusa; d. hydra.

9. Sponges are atypical animals because they: a. reproduce sexually; b. are sessile as adults; c. lack definite tissues; d. lack a "head."

10. Which of the following is characteristic of animals? a. heterotrophy; b. autotrophy; c. photosynthesis; d. b and c.

SPONGES AND CNIDARIANS

*Answers to Pre-lab Questions
in Lab Manual Order*

1.	a	6.	b
2.	c	7.	c
3.	c	8.	b
4.	d	9.	a
5.	d	10.	c

*Answers to Pre-lab Questions
in Instructor's Manual Order*

1.	d	6.	c
2.	d	7.	a
3.	b	8.	c
4.	b	9.	c
5.	c	10.	a

Answers to Post-lab Questions

1. List 6 characteristics of members of the animal kingdom. **1. Multicellular; 2. Heterotrophic; 3. Oxygen consumers; 4. Usually motile; 5. Mostly diploid with sexual reproduction, although asexual reproduction is also common; 6. Usually develop through a series of embryonic stages that often include a larval stage.**

2. Define asymmetry and radial symmetry. **Asymmetry is the condition where an animal or other object cannot be divided into tow like haves. Radial symmetry is the form of symmetry where the body is shaped like a cylinder or wheel. There is one axis (longitudinal) around which there are numerous planes of section that will divide the body into almost identical halves.**

3. Identify the symmetry (asymmetry, radial symmetry, or bilateral symmetry) of the following objects: a. fork-**bilateral symmetry**, b. jagged piece of rock-**asymmetry**, c. rubber ball-**radial symmetry**.

4. Define *cell specialization* and indicate how sponges exhibit this phenomenon. **Cell specialization involves changes during the development of an organism that lead to cells of different types with different, specialized functions. Sponges have choanocytes (collar cells), pinacocytes, amoebocytes, etc.**

5. Describe three ways that sponges reproduce. **1. Sexually; 2. Asexually by budding; 3. Asexually by gemmules.**

6. Identify this photo; it is magnified 186x. **Spicules of calcium carbonate.**

7. Define the *tissue level of organization* and indicate how Cnidarians exhibit this phenomenon. **Animals with this level of organization have identifiable tissues. The body wall of cnidarians has two tissue layers: the epidermis and gastrodermis, which are derived from ectoderm and endoderm, respectively. These tissue layers are separated from each other by a thin acellular layer called the mesoglea.**

8. Name and draw the two body forms of cnidarians. **a. Polypoid (polyp); b. Medusoid. See Figure 26-17 for illustrations.**

9. Describe the means by which the cnidarians seize and eat organisms that are faster than they are. **The tentacles contain stinging cells that contain stinging elements, the nematocysts. The nematocysts are discharged in response to mechanical or chemical stimuli and either pierce or entangle the prey, which is then pulled toward the mouth by the tentacles.**

10. What adaptations of sponges and cnidarians have helped them to endure for so long on the earth? **Sponges and cnidarians occupy relatively stable aquatic, mostly marine, habitats. They posses both sexual and asexual reproductive strategies. Both groups have larvae and many cnidarians, a motile body form. Freshwater sponges exhibit resistant gemmules to carry them through harsh winters.**

FLATWORMS AND ROTIFERS

Materials and Equipment

27.1 Flatworms (Phylum Platyhelminthes)

Per student
- dissecting microscope
- compound microscope
- scalpel
- blunt probe

Per student pair
- slide of *Dugesia* (planaria), w.m.
- slide of *Dugesia* pharyngeal region c.s.
- slide of *Fasciola hepatica*, w.m.
- slide of *Dugesia* with digestive system stained, w.m.
- slide of bladder worm stage of *Taenia*, section
- slide of *Taenia pisiformis*, w.m.
- slide of *Clonorchis sinensis*, w.m.
-

Per student group (4)
- penlight or microscope light source
- glass petri dish

Per lab room
- chunk of beef liver
- container of live planaria
- container of fresh stream water
- collection of preserved tapeworms
- single-edged razor blades

27.2 Rotifers (Phylum Rotifera)

Per student
- microscope slide
- compound microscope
- coverslip

Per lab room
- live culture of rotifers
- disposable transfer pipet and bulb

Preparation of Materials and Equipment

27.1 Flatworms (Phylum Platyhelminthes)

Beef liver: Dice fresh beef liver into small cubes, approximately 2 to 3 mm square with a single-edged razor blade. Planaria that have been fed should be kept separate from those that are unfed. "Fed" planaria can be used again to demonstrate feeding behavior after 1or 2 days.

27.2 Rotifers (Phylum Rotifera)

None required.

Notes

Much helpful information about culturing invertebrates can be found in the following manual: R. H. Whitten and W. R. Pendergrass. 1980. *Carolina Protozoa and Invertebrates Manual*. Carolina Biological Supply Company, Burlington, NC/Gladstone.

Many institutions offer courses in invertebrate biology and have extensive collections of specimens that might be borrowed for demonstration in this exercise.

27.1 Flatworms (Phylum Platyhelminthes)

Use only fresh stream or pond water to maintain planarians. The water must be kept clean and changed daily. Feed planarians about once a week with a pea-sized piece of hard-boiled egg yolk or beef liver for 50 planarians in an 8-in. culture dish. Planarians will do best in a wide, shallow container, rather than a narrow, deep one. Move with droppers or transfer pipettes.

Ordering Information

See General Laboratory Supplies list on page vii for basic items

27.1 Flatworms (Phylum Platyhelminthes)

Clonorchis sinensis, w.m., prepared slide collection of preserved tapeworms*	Ward's	92 W 4904
Fasciola hepatica, preserved	Carolina	22-4335
Fasciola hepatica, w.m.,prepared slide	Triarch	ZD 3-1
Huber Mall Probe	Carolina	62-7405
planaria, c.s., pharyngeal region, prepared slide	Triarch	ZD1-121
planaria, living	Carolina	13-2950
planaria, w.m., stained and unstained on same slide	Triarch	ZD1-12
pond water	Carolina	16-3380
Taenia, in pork muscle, section, prepared slide	Carolina	30-6784
Taenia, w.m., prepared slide	Triarch	ZD4-11

* Many different genera available. See Ward's and Carolina catalogues.

27.2 Rotifers (Phylum Rotifera)

rotifers, mixed culture*	Carolina	L30868

*Call Carolina Biological Supply to order.

Answers to In-Text Questions

27.1 Flatworms (Phylum Platyhelminthes)

A. Class Turbellaria: Planarians

2. …What function does the extensive branching of the intestine facilitate? **It increases the surface area for food processing, including absorption.**

3. …Describe what you see with a dissection microscope. **A planarian protrudes its pharynx from its belly side and sucks up bits of beef liver.**

…If you do, describe what you see; if not, state the route by which this must occur. **As the incomplete gut only has one opening, undigested food remnants are eliminated by propelling them through opening to the pharynx.**

4. …What is the function of these cilia? **Cilia are motile hairs that propel the planarian when it is attached to a surface.**

5. …Note its general size and shape. Touch the animal with a probe. What is its reaction? How does its shape change? Which muscle layers likely contract to produce this shape change? **Planarians are long and flat with distinctive heads. The initial reaction to being touched is to withdraw by shortening the body. Contraction of the longitudinal muscle fibers accomplishes this movement.**

B. Class Trematoda: Flukes

What is a likely explanation for the presence of this tough, resistant cuticle? **The cuticle protects the flukes from their hosts' digestive juices, antibodies, etc.**

2. …What is the infectious stage (for humans) of this parasite? **Encysted larvae (metacercaria) in fish muscle.** What two main precautions can humans take to reduce exposure to this parasite? **The two main precautions are to fully cook the fish and to improve sanitation procedures. The latter approach minimizes infection of water snails and thus blocks the life cycle of the parasite.**

C. Class Cestoda: Tapeworms

3. …For what task does the tapeworm use these **hooks** and **suckers**? **These structures are used to firmly attach the scolex of the tapeworm to the intestinal wall.**

6. …Which mammal is the host? **Humans** Which mammal is the intermediate host? **Pigs**

Examine the bladder worm stage of *Taenia solium* with the dissection microscope. Draw what you see in Figure 27-12. **See Figure 27-11.**

27.2 Rotifers (Phylum Rotifera)

…what is the likely function of the mastax? **The mastax is used to capture and to chew up food.**

Name _____

Section No. _____

FLATWORMS AND ROTIFERS

Pre-lab Questions

1. The life cycle of the human liver fluke has _____ intermediate hosts: a. one; b. two; c. three; d. four.

2. Cephalization is: a. the division of the trunk into a scolex, neck, and body; b. the presence of a head with sense organs; c. sexual reproduction involving self-fertilization; d. the ability to replace lost body parts.

3. Rotifers obtain their food by the action of: a. tentacles; b. cilia on the wheel organ; c. a muscular pharynx; d. pseudopodia.

4. Free-living flatworms (planaria) move by using: a. cilia; b. flagella; c. pseudopodia; d. a muscular foot.

5. The oldest proglottid of a tapeworm is a: a. the scolex; b. the one nearest the neck; c. the one in its middle; d. the one at its end.

6. Bladder worms are found in: a. proglottids in human feces; b. proglottids in the human intestine; c. improperly cooked pork; d. none of the above.

7. The flukes and tapeworms are covered by a protective: a. cuticle; b. shell; c. scale; d. slime layer.

8. Nematodes and rotifers have a body cavity that is: a. called a coelom; b. called a pseudocoelom; c. completely lined by tissues derived from mesoderm; d. a and c.

9. Flatworms: a. are radially symmetrical; b. possess a body cavity; c. reproduce by parthenogenesis; d. have tissues derived from all three primary germ layers.

10. Tapeworms do not have a: a. reproductive system; b. head; c. excretory system; d. digestive system.

FLATWORMS AND ROTIFERS

*Answers to Pre-lab Questions
in Lab Manual Order*

1.	b	6.	d	
2.	d	7.	d	
3.	a	8.	c	
4.	a	9.	b	
5.	b	10.	b	

*Answers to Pre-lab Questions
in Instructor's Manual Order*

1.	c	6.	c	
2.	b	7.	a	
3.	b	8.	b	
4.	a	9.	d	
5.	d	10.	d	

Answers to Post-lab Questions:

1. How is bilateral symmetry different from radial symmetry? **While an animal with radial symmetry can be divided into almost identical halves by numerous planes, only one plane parallel to the main axis will divide the body of an animal with bilateral symmetry into almost identical right and left sides—the sagittal plane of section.**

2. List the characteristics of flatworms. **Flatworms comprise a phylum of animals that have soft, flat, worm-like bodies. Characteristics include the lack of a body cavity (acoelomate) and the presence of a head, bilateral symmetry (right and left halves), and systems with organs. Other characteristics include sexual reproduction (mostly monoecious with internal fertilization), and possibly complicated life cycles. Some are capable of asexual reproduction by transverse fission. They are found in aquatic, moist terrestrial or parasitic habitats.**

3. Distinguish between a host and an intermediate host. *Intermediate host*—**an organism that contains a sexually immature form of a parasite.** *Host*-**the adult form of the parasite resides in the host.**

4. Identify and label this illustration. It is magnified 9x. **a. intestine; b. ventral sucker; c. ovary; d. yolk glands; e. testes.**

5. Describe several adaptations of parasitic flatworms to their external environment. **The parasitic flatworms have much reduced nervous connections and no cephalization, though the anterior end carries hooks and/or suckers for attachment to the host. Their bodies are covered with an acellular cuticle that is resistant to the digestive enzymes and acids of the host. Extensive development of the reproductive system, with the production of millions of eggs per individual, may be associated with difficulties in dispersing the species. They are dorsoventrally flattened for maximum absorption of nutrients or gaseous exchange. Digestive organs are absent or greatly reduced as some species absorb nutrients from the host directly across their body walls. Also, these parasites utilize intermediate hosts to transport the species from primary host to primary host.**

6. Pseudocoel means "false body cavity." Why is this term applied to the body cavity of rotifers? **Because their body cavity is incompletely lined by a derivative of the mesoderm.**

7. Contrast the digestive systems of free-living and parasitic flatworms. **Most flatworms have an incomplete gastrovacular type digestive system with a mouth but no separate exit. Tapeworms, which are surrounded by the nutrient rich contents of the intestinal tract, have secondarily lost their digestive system.**

8.   Explain the relationship between the tremendous numbers of eggs produced by flukes and tapeworms and the complexity of their life cycles. **It is likely that those individuals that produced more eggs in the past had a greater number of progeny survive. Because of the complexity of the life cycle, mortality is high and those individuals that produce more eggs (and thus, more young) have a greater chance of genetic representation in future generations.**

9.   The relatively simple animals *Hydra* and *Dugesia* can regenerate lost body parts, but humans generally cannot. Discuss this in terms of tissue differentiation and the comparative levels of structural complexity of these organisms. ***Hydra* and *Dugesia* are structurally relatively simple animals with less complex body plans (i.e., less overall tissue differentiation and cellular specialization) than humans. Although humans can regenerate some tissues (e.g., skin, some bone), lost body parts cannot be regenerated presumably because of the inability to coordinate the growth of the specialized tissues.**

10. Search the World Wide Web for sites that include references to flatworms or rotifers. List two addresses and briefly describe their contents. **Answers will vary.**

EXERCISE 28

SEGMENTED WORMS AND MOLLUSKS

Materials and Equipment

28.1 Annelids (Phylum Annelida)

Per student

- blunt probe or dissecting needle
- dissecting pins

Per student pair

- dissecting microscope
- dissection pan
- *Eisenia foetida* cocoons
- preserved earthworm
- fine dissecting scissors

Per lab room

- live freshwater leeches in an aquarium
- large plastic bag for wastes
- labeled demonstration dissection of the internal anatomy of the earthworm (optional)
- demonstration collection of living and preserved polychaetes
- several preserved leeches
- boxes of different sizes of latex gloves

28.2 Mollusks (Phylum Mollusca)

Per student

- scalpel
- blunt probe or dissecting needle
- compound microscope, lens paper
- lens cleaning solution (optional)

Per student pair

- dissection microscope
- prepared slide of glochidia
- preserved freshwater clam
- glass petri dish
- dissection pan
- prepared slide of section of clam gill

Per lab room

- freshwater aquarium with snails (for example, *Physa*)
- collection of gastropod shells, living and preserved specimens
- labeled demonstration dissection of a freshwater clam (optional)
- demonstration collection of bivalve shells, living and preserved specimens
- demonstration collection of gastropod shells, and living and preserved specimens
- several preserved squids, octopuses, and chambered nautiluses
- labeled demonstration dissection of internal anatomy of the squid
- large plastic bags for disposal of dissected specimens
- boxes of different sizes of latex gloves
- box of safety goggles

Preparation of Materials and Equipment

28.1 Annelids (Phylum Annelida)

Demonstration dissection of earthworm: Pin each end of an earthworm to a dissecting pan. Make an incision with fine scissors just to the right of the black dorsal blood vessel, 10 segments anterior to the anus. Cut superficially to the mouth and pin both sides of the body wall to the pan at 10-segment intervals. Cover the specimen with 0.5–1.0 cm tap water. Label body parts listed in lab exercise with a dissecting pin to which a label is attached. (See Figure 28-3 and Figure 28-4 in the Lab Manual.)

Instructors may wish to dissect a living earthworm to demonstrate the beating of the 5 pairs of aortic arches. Drop the earthworm into a container of water and add 0.5% chloroform or alcohol (0.5 mL chloroform or ethanol in 99.5 mL water) slowly. Dissect as above after the worm has stopped moving, keeping the worm moist or under water during the dissection.

28.2 Mollusks (Phylum Mollusca)

Demonstration dissection of freshwater clam or mussel: Open the shell by cutting through the adductor muscles. Cut through the foot and into and through the middle of the visceral mass. Peel back both halves to reveal the viscera. A short esophagus leads from the mouth to the stomach, which is surrounded by the gray or green digestive gland (liver). The intestine loops from the stomach through the visceral mass and ends at the anus, which empties into the excurrent siphon.

The nephridium (kidney) is a mass of brown or green tissue ventral to the heart and embedded in the mantle. The cream-colored mass that surrounds the intestine in the upper part of the foot is the gonad (ovary or testis).

Label the above mentioned structures with dissecting pins to which labels are attached. (See Figure 28-9 and Figure 28-10 in the Lab Manual.) Keep the dissected mollusca moist with water or preservative.

Notes

Provide plastic gloves for the students. In addition, students who wear contact lenses should to wear safety goggles when dissecting preserved specimens.

Dispose of excess preservatives in non-glass, labeled waste bottles according to your institution's guidelines.

Provide non-leaking large plastic bags for disposal of waste tissue. Discard and then replace these bags after each laboratory session. Be sure that dissecting trays and instruments are washed at the end of each session and that trays are stacked to dry. Clean all tissue from the sink and discard in the plastic bags.

Freshly collected specimens (living, if possible) are a desirable alternative to preserved collections. A day of collecting in nearby woods, beach, or grasslands can often provide diverse specimens for demonstrations. Many can be held alive for short periods in terraria or aquaria and then returned to their natural habitat.

Many institutions offer courses in invertebrate biology and have extensive collections of specimens that perhaps could be borrowed for demonstration in this exercise.

28.1 Annelids (Phylum Annelida)

Live leeches are very sensitive to metallic ions, so keep them only in non-metallic containers of pond or spring water that is changed daily. Do not crowd the leeches and cover the containers securely to prevent escapes.

28.2 Mollusks (Phylum Mollusca)

Maintain live freshwater snails in aquaria of pond or dechlorinated tap water provided with aquatic plants for them to crawl on. Snails can be fed pelleted or flaked fish food plus boiled spinach or lettuce.

Ordering Information

See General Laboratory Supplies list on page vii for basic items

28.1 Annelids (Phylum Annelida)

earthworm, preserved, large	Carolina	22-5012
Eisenia foetida cocoons	Carolina	14-1640
leech, live	Carolina	14-1764
leech, preserved	Carolina	22-5060
polychaetes, preserved*		
pond water	Carolina	16-3380

    * Many genera available. See Carolina catalogue.

28.2 Mollusks (Phylum Mollusca)

clam gill, section, prepared slide	Triarch	ZI1-12
freshwater mussel, large, preserved	Carolina	14-1276
freshwater snails, living	Carolina	16-2955
glochidia, mussel, w.m., slide	Wards	92 V 8135
large nautilus shell	Carolina	26-1856
mollusk shell collection, identified	Carolina	26-1788
octopus, preserved	Carolina	22-4876
pelecypods and gastropods, preserved*	Carolina	
split nautilus shell	Carolina	26-1854
squids, preserved	Carolina	22-4872

    *Many genera available. See Carolina catalogue.

Answers to In-Text Questions

28.1 Annelids (Phylum Annelida)

A. Oligochaetes (Class Oligochaeta)

1. …Recalling past experiences with this organism, list as many features of the earthworm as you can.
Earthworm characteristics include a cylindrical shaped body that tapers at the very ends, a segmented body, a ring-like structure around the body (clitellum), earthtone color, moist body surface, and perhaps a bristly feeling when the lower surface is touched (setae).
2. …Is its body bilaterally or radially symmetrical? **Bilaterally symmetrical**
3. …Count them and record the number: **100 or more**
(b) What is their likely function? **They are extended during longitudinal contraction for locomotion.**

C. Leeches (Class Hirudinea)

2. …Explain their movements in terms of the contraction and relaxation of circular and longitudinal layers of muscle that comprise part of their body wall. **After the posterior sucker is attached to the substrate, the circular muscles contract and the longitudinal muscle relaxes. This causes the body to lengthen in a forward direction. Then the anterior sucker is attached and the posterior sucker releases. Now, the longitudinal muscles contract and the circular muscle relaxes, pulling the body behind the anterior sucker forward. This cycle is repeated to produce forward motion.**

28.2 Mollusks (Phylum Mollusca)

A. Bivalves (Class Bivalvia)

1. (b) …Age of mussel: **Insert the number of ridges in the growth rings.**

5. …List the features they have in common. **Common characteristics of bivalves include flat bodies (laterally compressed), a shell consisting of two dorsally hinged valves, dorsal protuberance on each valve (umbro) surrounded by growth ridges), no obvious head, muscular foot, and gills.**
List some of the differences. **Common differences between bivalves include body size, shell shape and its size relative to body size, the presence and absence of teeth at the edge of the valves, cutting teeth, and other abrasive modifications on surface of valve (borers) and siphons.**
How can you tell which live on sandy bottoms? **One valve, the upper one, is sand colored.**

B. Snails, Slugs, and Nudibranchs (Class Gastropoda)

1. …A *slime gland* in the front of the foot secretes mucus. Briefly describe the muscular contractions of the foot that allow the animal to glide over this mucus. **Waves of contraction sweeping usually in a posterior to anterior direction. Small snails and larger snails moving slowly can glide over the mucous trail using ciliary action.**
Looking at the foot through the glass you can see the mouth. Describe its location. **The mouth is located on the head and opens just in front of the anterior margin of the foot.**
2. …Which way does your snail's shell spiral? **Dextral (clockwise, right-handed) or sinestral (anticlockwise, left-handed).**

Name _____

Section No. _____

SEGMENTED WORMS AND MOLLUSKS

Pre-lab Questions

1. One of the two major distinguishing characteristics of mollusks is: a. the presence of three body regions; b. the mantle; c. segmentation of the body; d. jointed appendages.

2. Functions of the mantle include: a. secreting the shell; b. forming pearls around irritating grains of sand; c. forming the incurrent and excurrent siphons; d. all of the above.

3. Which of the following is a gastropod? a. clam; b. snail; c. squid; d. octopus

4. Which of the following is a cephalopod? a. clam; b. snail; c. slug; d. octopus

5. The protostomes are animals whose: a. stomach is in front of the crop; b. mouth is covered by a fleshy lip; c. blastopore becomes a mouth; d. digestive tract is lined by mesoderm.

6. The deuterostomes are animals whose: a. stomach is in the front of the crop; b. mouth is covered by a fleshy lip; c. blastopore becomes the anus; d. digestive track is lined mesoderm.

7. Further evolution of the protostomes changed the coelom by: a. losing it; b. reducing it; c. it becoming a pseudocoel; d. all of the above.

8. Earthworms exhibit segmentation defined as the: a. division of the body into a series of similar segments; b. presence of a true coelom; c. difference in size of the male and female; d. presence of a "head" equipped with sensory organs.

9. The copulatory organ of the earthworm is the: a. penis: b. clitellum; c. gonopodium; d. vestibule.

10. Leeches belong to the phylum: a. Arthropoda; b. Mollusca; c. Annelida; d. Cnidaria.

SEGMENTED WORMS AND MOLLUSKS

Answers to Pre-lab Questions
in Lab Manual Order

1.	c	6.	c
2.	c	7.	b
3.	d	8.	d
4.	a	9.	b
5.	b	10.	d

Answers to Pre-lab Questions
in Instructor's Manual Order

1.	b	6.	c
2.	d	7.	d
3.	b	8.	a
4.	d	9.	b
5.	c	10.	c

Answers to Post-lab Questions

1. Indicate the differences between protostomes and deuterostomes. **Protostomes are animals whose blastopore in the gastrula stage of development becomes a mouth; the anus develops later. In deuterostomes, the blastopore becomes the anus. Other differences in development and the formation of the coelom exist.**

2. List the animal phyla that are protostomes and those that are deuterostomes. **Protostomes— Platyhelminthes, Rotifera, Annelida, Mollusca, Nematoda, Arthropoda; Deuterostomes— Echinodermata, Chordata.**

3. What happens to the coelom as each phyla of protostomes evolve? **Protostome ancestors evolved a coelom- - a body cavity lined with mesodermally derived tissue. This coelom is thought to be lost in flatworms, reduced in mollusks and joint-legged animals, and modified so that it is incompletely lined with mesoderm in rotifers and roundworms.**

4. Briefly describe the life cycle of an earthworm. **Copulation occurs between two earthworms that have both male and female reproductive tracts. They face belly to belly in opposite directions and are held together at their sticky clitellums. Sperm are transferred between them and are stored temporarily in their seminal receptacles. A few days after the individuals separate, each worm secretes a cocoon. The cocoon contains eggs and stored sperm. The eggs are fertilized and the cocoon slips off the front end of the worm and is deposited in the soil. In *Lumbricus terrestris*, a single young earthworm eats the other fertilized eggs. Late in development, it breaks free of the cocoon, becoming an adult in several weeks. As long as the stored sperm lasts, an earthworm will continue to form new cocoons.**

5. Label this diagram of an annelid and identify its class (Oligochaeta, Polychaeta, or Hirudinea) **Head, Parapodia; Class-Polychaeta.**

6. Explain what causes the growth ridges found on the shells of bivalves. **Growth ridges result from the deposition of material during periods of restricted winter growth. Since successive layers of materials are deposited between periods of little growth, these layers build up to form an annual ridge similar to the dark growth rings representing restricted winter or dry season growth in trees.**

7. List some structures that distinguish bivalves from the other molluscan classes **Valves, laterally flattened body**

8. List some structures that distinguish slugs from nudibranchs? **Slugs are neither brightly colored nor have fleshy projections.**

9. Is it possible that some of the monsters reportedly by ancient mariners were giant squid or octopi? Search the internet before giving and explaining your answer. **Throughout history specimens caught in fishermen's nets along with those washed up on shores have stirred the imagination and led to tall tales. Moreover, harvested sperm whales often bear sucker scars that are inflicted by giant squid, their favorite prey.**

10. Define *segmentation* and indicate how the annelids, arthropods, and *your* body exhibit this phenomenon.
Segmentation is the division of the trunk into a series of similar segments. Annelids are composed of a series of segments that represent partitioning of the animal externally and internally. Arthropods are segmented, with generally one pair of jointed appendages per body segment. Humans are fundamentally segmented. This is reflected internally by the series of similar ribs, intercostal muscles, vertebrae, and so on.

ROUNDWORMS AND JOINT-LEGGED ANIMALS

Materials and Equipment

29.1 Roundworms (Phylum Nematoda)

Per student
- dissecting microscope
- sharp probe or dissecting needle

Per student pair
- finger bowl

Per lab room
- tray of moist soil
- collection of free-living roundworms
- container of fresh stream water
- demonstration microscope of cross section female and male *Ascaris*
- demonstration dissections of female and male *Ascaris*

29.2 Joint-Legged Animals (Phylum Arthropoda)

Per student
- dissecting scissors
- blunt probe or dissecting needle
- scalpel
- compound microscope

Per student pair
- dissecting microscope
- preserved crayfish
- preserved grasshopper (*Romalea*)
- dissection pan
- prepared slide, w.m. of grasshopper mouthparts

Per lab room
- collection of preserved centipedes
- collection of preserved millipedes
- collection of preserved and mounted crustaceans
- collection of preserved and mounted insects
- collection of preserved and mounted spiders, horseshoe crabs, scorpions, ticks, and mites
- living specimens when possible of the above
- large plastic bags for wastes

Preparation of Materials and Equipment

29.1 Roundworms (Phylum Nematoda)

Demonstration dissections of Ascaris: Select large preserved specimens for dissection. Pin each end of the worm in a dissecting pan and make a longitudinal incision with fine scissors the length of the worm. Add water to keep the specimen moist. Pull much of the packed reproductive organs out of the body so that the other structures are visible. Label organs with dissecting pins to which labels are attached (see Lab Manual Figures 29-4 and 29-5).

29.2 Joint-Legged Animals (Phylum Arthropoda)

None Required.

Notes

Provide plastic gloves for the students. Students who wear contact lenses should also have access to safety goggles.

Dispose of excess preservative in non-glass, labeled waste bottles according to your institution's guidelines.

Provide non-leaking large plastic bags for disposal of waste tissue. Discard and then replace these bags after each laboratory session. Be sure that dissecting trays and instruments are washed at the end of each laboratory period and that trays are stacked to dry. Clean all tissue from the sink and discard in the plastic bags.

Freshly collected specimens (living, if possible) are a desirable alternative to preserved collections. A day of collecting in nearby woods, beach, or grasslands can often provide diverse specimens for demonstrations. Many can be held alive for short periods in terraria or aquaria and then returned to their natural habitat.

Many institutions that offer courses in invertebrate and/or vertebrate biology have extensive collections of specimens that might be borrowed for demonstration in this exercise.

29.1 Roundworms (Phylum Nematoda)

Do not collect soil from areas that may have been treated with insecticides or nematicides (i.e., agricultural lands or "well-maintained" turf).

Ordering Information

See General Laboratory Supplies list on page vii for basic items

29.1 Roundworms (Phylum Nematoda)

Ascaris, c.s., prepared slide, male and female	Carolina	30-6918
Ascaris, males and females, preserved	Ward's	68 V 0802
Nematodes,, mixed, living	Ward's	87 V 2800

29.2 Joint-Legged Animals (Phylum Arthropoda)

pond water	Carolina	16-3380
arachnid collection, mounted	Carolina	26-2251
arachnid collection, preserved	Carolina	22-5430
crayfish, live	Carolina	14-2520
crayfish, preserved	Carolina	22-5302
crustacean collection, mounted	Carolina	26-2156
crustacean collection, preserved	Carolina	22-5204
grasshopper (Romalea), preserved	Carolina	22-5555
grasshopper mouthparts, w.m., prepared slide	Triarch	ZK3-141
insect collection, mounted	Department resource	
insect collection, preserved	Ward's	68 V 4008
millipedes, live	Carolina	14-3118
myriapod collection, preserved	Carolina	P 648

Answers to In-Text Questions

29.1 Roundworms (Phylum Nematoda)

A. Free-Living Roundworms

2. …Describe the behavior of any roundworms you find and make a note of any visible anatomical features they possess. **When suspended in water, they show whipping and thrashing movements of their bodies. When directed against a substrate, the locomotor function of these movements is more apparent. Their bodies are round and cylindrical, tapering towards each end.**

29.2 Phylum Arthropoda: Arthropods

A. Crustaceans (Subphylum Crustacea)

3. (c) …What is the function of these two sets of muscles? **They are contracted in an organized fashion to produce the up and strongly down movements of abdomen that allow lobsters to rapidly swim backwards to escape predators.**

(e) …What role in digestion do you think this structure plays? **It grinds up pieces of food to reduce the size of particles and increases the efficiency of digestion.**

B. Insects (Subphylum Hexapoda)

3. Figure 29-14 Isolated grasshopper mouthparts, w.m. (7x) (Photo courtesy Biodisc, Inc.)
From top to bottom, the mouthparts are: labrum, left mandible, left maxilla, and labium.

D. Subphylum Chelicerata: Spiders, Horseshoe Crabs, Scorpions, Ticks, and Mites

How many pairs of walking legs do insects have? **Three pairs.**

Name _____

Section No. _____

ROUNDWORMS AND JOINT-LEGGED ANIMALS

Pre-lab Questions

1. Sexual dimorphism, as seen in the crayfish, is: a. the presence of male and female individuals; b. the production of eggs and sperm by the same individual; c. another term for copulation; d. the presence of observable differences between males and females.

2. The grinding apparatus of the digestive system of the crayfish is the: a. oral teeth; b. gizzard; c. pharyngeal jaw; d. gastric mill.

3. The insects were the first organisms to: a. show bilateral symmetry; b. exhibit segmentation; c. fly; d. develop lungs.

4. Like the insects, the arachnids (spiders and so on) have: a. three pairs of walking legs; b. one pair of antennae; c. true mandibles; d. an abdomen.

5. Structures that are shed in one piece include: a. the cuticle of roundworm; b. the exoskeleton of arthropods; c. human hair; d. all of the above.

6. Nematodes and rotifers have a body cavity that is: a. called a coelom; b. called a pseudocoelom; c. completely lined by tissues derived from mesoderm; d. a and c.

7. Filarial roundworms cause elephantiasis by: a. encysting in muscle tissue; b. promoting the growth of fatty tumors; c. obstructing lymphatic vessels; d. laying numerous eggs in the joints of their hosts.

8. Digestive wastes of the male *Ascaris* roundworm exit the body through the: a. anus; b. cloaca; c. mouth; d. excretory pore.

9. The animal phylum with the most species is: a. Mollusca; b. Annelida; c. Arthropoda; d. Platyhelminthes.

10. The body of arthropods includes: a. a head; b. a thorax; c. an abdomen; d. all of the above.

ROUNDWORMS AND JOINT-LEGGED ANIMALS

Answers to Pre-lab Questions
in Lab Manual Order

1.	d	6.	d
2.	b	7.	d
3.	c	8.	d
4.	b	9.	c
5.	c	10.	d

Answers to Pre-lab Questions
in Instructor's Manual Order

1.	d	6.	b
2.	d	7.	c
3.	c	8.	b
4.	d	9.	c
5.	d	10.	d

Answers to Post-lab Questions

1. Indicate the differences between protostomes and deuterostomes, and list the phyla of animals in each group. **Protostomes are animals whose blastopore in the gastrula stage of development becomes a mouth; the anus develops later. In deuterostomes, the blastopore becomes the anus. Other differences in development and the formation of the coelom exist. Protostomes—mollusks, annelids, arthropods. Deuterostomes—echinoderms, chordates.**

2. Describe ecdysis in roundworms and joint-legged animals. **Both roundworms and joint-legged animals loose the outer covering of the integument during growth in a process know as ecadysis. The cuticle of the roundworms and the exoskeleton of joint-legged animals are all shed at once.**

3. Pseudocoel means "false body cavity." Why is this term applied to the body cavity of roundworms? **Because their body cavity is not lined by a derivative of the mesoderm.**

4. Define *sexual dimorphism*, describe it in the crayfish, and list two other animals that exhibit this phenomenon. ***Sexual dimorphism* is the condition whereby males and females of a species differ morphologically. In the crayfish, males have a narrower abdomen than females, and the anterior two pairs of swimmerets are enlarged for clasping the female and transferring sperm. In small migrating birds, the male is often more brightly colored than the female. In humans, males are larger, on average, than females.**

5. Identify and label the following structures. **a. cephalothorax; b. abdomen; c. cheliped; d. antennule; e. antenna; f. walking legs; g. third maxilliped; h. swimmeretes; i. uropod; j. telson.**

6. How has flight been at least partly responsible for the success of the insects? **Because of flight, insects were able to exploit a variety of opportunities (niches) that were previously unexploited by other animals. Flight increased their mobility and allowed them to occupy habitats and forage at great heights above the substrate.**

7. List several differences between insects and spiders. **1. Insects have three pairs of walking legs, spiders have four. 2. Insects have one pair of antennae, spiders have none. 3. Insects have a pair of mandibles, spiders have no true mandibles. 4. Insects have compound eyes, spiders do not. 5. The insect body is divided into a head, thorax, and abdomen. The spider's body consists of a cephalothorax and abdomen.**

8. List the roundworm parasites and use the Internet to learn how they gain entry into the body. Describe that process. ***Ascaris* (ingesting eggs from contaminated food or water); hook worms (larvae penetrate skin such as the soles of the feet); Trichinella (eating improperly cooked meat); pin worms (ingestion of eggs dislodged from the skin around the anus of infected individuals, e.g., children); and filarial worms that cause lymphatic filariasis, also known as elephantiasis (mosquito bite).**

9. Write the phylum and choose the appropriate description for each animal (or group of animals) listed in the following table.

Symmetry:	none, radial, or bilateral
Level of Organization:	cell-specialization, tissue, or organ-system
Body Cavity:	none, pseudocoelomate, or coelomate
Gut:	none, incomplete, complete.

Animal	Phylum	Symmetry	Level of Organization	Body Cavity	Gut
Sponge	Porifera	none	cell-specialization	none	none
Hydra and jellyfish	Cnidaria	radial	tissue	none	incomplete
Flatworm	Platyhelminthes	bilateral	organ-system	none	incomplete
Rotifer	Rotifera	bilateral	organ-system	pseudocoelomate	complete
Segmented worm	Annelida	bilateral	organ-system	coelomate	complete
Clam, snail, and octopus	Mollusca	bilateral	organ-system	coelomate	complete
Roundworm	Nematoda	bilateral	organ-system	pseudocoelomate	complete
Crayfish, insect and spider	Arthropoda	bilateral	organ-system	coelomate	complete

10. Define *segmentation* and indicate how the annelids, arthropods, and *your* body exhibit this phenomenon.
Segmentation is the division of the trunk into a series of similar segments. Annelids are composed of a series of segments that represent partitioning of the animal externally and internally. Arthropods are segmented, with generally one pair of jointed appendages per body segment. Humans are fundamentally segmented. This is reflected internally by the series of similar ribs, intercostal muscles, vertebrae, and so on.

EXERCISE 30

ECHINODERMS AND INVERTEBRATE CHORDATES

Materials and Equipment

30.1 Echinoderms (Phylum Echinodermata)

Per student
- dissecting scissors
- blunt probe or dissecting needle

Per student pair
- dissecting microscope
- dissecting pan
- preserved sea star
- dissecting pins
- prepared slide of sea star arm (ray), c.s.
- compound microscope
- prepared slide of bipinnaria larvae, w.m.

Per lab room
- large plastic bags for waste
- live specimens of above (optional)
- collection of preserved or mounted brittle stars
- collection of preserved sea cucumbers
- collection of sea urchins and sand dollars (preserved specimens and skeletons)
- collection of preserved or mounted feather stars and sea lilies

30.2 Chordates (Phylum Chordata)

Per student
- blunt probe

Per student pair
- compound and dissecting microscope
- dissecting pan
- plastic mount of *Amphioxus*
- preserved sea tunicates (sea squirts)
- preserved *Amphioxus* specimens
- plastic mount of sea tunicate
- prepared slide of *Amphioxus*, pharyngeal region, c.s.

Preparation of Materials and Equipment

None required.

Notes

Provide plastic gloves for the students. Students who wear contact lenses should also have access to safety goggles.

Dispose of excess preservative in non-glass, labeled waste bottles according to your institution's guidelines.

Provide non-leaking large plastic bags for disposal of waste tissue. Discard and then replace these bags after each laboratory session. Be sure that dissecting trays and instruments are washed at the end of each laboratory period and that trays are stacked to dry. Clean all tissue from the sink and discard in the plastic bags.

Many institutions that offer courses in invertebrate biology have extensive collections of specimens that might be borrowed for demonstration in this exercise.

Ordering Information

See General Laboratory Supplies list on page vii for basic items

30.1 Echinoderms (Phylum Echinodermata)

echinoderm collection, 5 genera, preserved	Carolina	22-6000
echinoderm collection, 7 genera, mounted	Carolina	26-1540
sea star, preserved	Carolina	22-6010
starfish ray, c.s., prepared slide	Triarch	ZJ1-2

30.2 Chordates (Phylum Chordata)

Amphioxus, plastic mount, adult	Wards	55 V 8100
Amphioxus, preserved	Wards	69 V 0052
Amphioxus, through pharynx, mouth, intestine, tail, c.s., prepared slide	Triarch	ZL1-21
Amphioxus, w.m., prepared slide	Triarch	ZL 1-1
sea squirt, preserved	Wards	69 V 0032

Answers to In-Text Questions

30.2 Chordates (Phylum Chordata)

B. Lancelets (Subphylum Cephalochordata)

2. Now describe the capture of food and the path it takes through the digestive system, as was done previously for the tunicates. Unlike the tunicates, the *anus* in a lancelet opens externally. **Wheel organ → in vestibule, which is surrounded by oral hood, buccal tentacles, and velum → pharynx → midgut → intestine (and intestinal ceca) → anus.**

Name _____

Section No. _____

ECHINODERMS AND INVERTEBRATE CHORDATES

Pre-lab Questions

1. The skin gills of sea stars are organs: a. for exchange of gases and excretion of ammonia; b. of defense; c. for movement; d. that produce the skeletal elements.

2. Aristotle's lantern is a tooth-bearing structure of the: a. sea stars; b. tunicates; c. acorn worms; d. sea urchins.

3. Which structure is *not* a major diagnostic feature of the chordates? a. dorsal hollow nerve cord; b. notochord; c. pharyngeal gill slits; d. vertebral column.

4. The dermal endoskeleton of echinoderms is made of: a. cartilage; b. bone; c. calcium carbonate; d. chitin.

5. Echinoderms and chordates are: a. deutersomes; b. protostomes; c. animals whose blastopore becomes a mouth; d. both b and c.

6. Invertebrates: a. do not have a vertebral column; b. have a vertebral column; c. are all members of the phylum Chordata; d. do not include animals that are members of the phylum Chordata.

7. The tube feet of a sea star: a. bear tiny toes; b. are located only at the tips of the arms; c. function in movement; d. protect the organism from predatory fish.

8. Which animal is a chordate? a. sea star; b. sea cucumber; c. acorn worm; d. lancelet.

9. The sea squirts and lancelets have an inner chamber that expels water. This chamber is called the: a. intestine; b. bladder; c. atrium; d. nephridium.

10. The sieve plate, stone canal, circular canal, and radial canals of a sea star are structures of the: a. nervous system; b. water-vascular system; c. digestive system; d. excretory system.

EXERCISE 30

ECHINODERMS AND INVERTEBRATE CHORDATES

Answers to Post-lab Questions

1. Describe the various structures on the aboral "spiny skin" of a sea star and discuss their function.
   a. Pedicellaria—the valves of these pincer-like structures grasp objects that land on the surface of the body, such as potential parasites. b. Skin gills—the thin surface of these soft, hollow conical structures allows for the exchange of gases and waste ammonia between the sea water and coelomic fluid.

2. Describe the various functions of tube feet. **Functions of tube feet include locomotion, food handling (prying open bivalves), and increasing surface area for the diffusion of respiratory gasses and ammonia between the water-vascular system and sea water.**

3. Identify the following structures on this aboral view of the tip of a sea star arm. **a. skin gills; b. pedicellaria; c. tube feet.**

4. Describe reproduction in the sea star. **Separate sexes release sperm and eggs into the sea water. After fertilization, eggs develop into bipinnaria larvae, which in turn develop into new sea stars.**

5. List the structures that comprise the water-vascular system of a sea star. **madreporite → stone canal → circular canal → radial canals → tube feet.**

6. List the four major characteristics of chordates. **All chordates have a dorsal hollow nerve cord, gill slits, a postanal tail, and a notochord at some point in their life span.**

7. Why are sea squirts and lancelets referred to as invertebrate chordates? **Because they possess all of the characteristics of chordates, but do not have a vertebral column.**

8. Compare the presence or absence of the four chordate characters in adult sea squirts and lancelets. **Adult sea squirts do not have a notochord or postanal tail. A nerve ganglion develops in the adult. The number of pharyngeal gill slits increase in the adult sea squirt. The adult lancelets have a notochord present, a dorsal nerve cord, postanal tail, and pharyngeal gill slits.**

9. Compare arthropods, echinoderms, and chordates in terms of their similarities and differences. **Like arthropods, echinoderms and chordates have a true body cavity and an organ-system level of organization. Differences between the phyla include the skeleton (exoskeleton of chitin for arthropods, a calcareous endoskeleton for echinoderms, and a endoskeleton of cartilage or bone for chordates) and body symmetry (bilateral for arthropods, radial for echinoderms, and bilateral for chordates).**

10. Hypothesize an evolutionary relationship between the bipinnaria larva of echinoderms, larval and adult tunicates, and lancelets. **Bipinnaria larvae → larval tunicates → lancelets**

    ↓   ↓

    adult echinoderms   adult tunicates

VERTEBRATES

Materials and Equipment

Per student
- scalpel
- blunt probe or dissecting needle
- compound microscope
- dH$_2$O in dropping bottle

- dissecting scissors
- dissecting pins
- microscope slide
- forceps

Per student pair
- dissecting microscope and dissecting pan

- preserved leopard frog

Per student group
- prepared slide of lamprey ammocoete, w.m.
- preserved sea lamprey

- preserved yellow perch
- preserved dogfish

Per lab room
- collection of preserved bony fishes
- collection of preserved amphibians
- assortment of feathers
- several field guides to birds
- collection of stuffed mammals
- prepared skeleton of a frog
- skeleton of a snake
- collection of preserved cartilaginous fishes
- collection of mammalian placentas and embryos (*in utero*)

- skeleton of human
- collection of preserved reptiles
- turtle shell or skeleton
- collection of stuffed birds
- large plastic bags for waste tissue
- shark jaw with teeth

Preparation of Materials and Equipment

None required.

Notes

Provide plastic gloves for the students. Students who wear contact lenses should also have access to safety goggles.

Dispose of excess preservative in non-glass, labeled waste bottles according to your institution's guidelines.

Provide non-leaking large plastic bags for disposal of waste tissue. Discard and then replace these bags after each laboratory session. Be sure that dissecting trays and instruments are washed at the end of each laboratory period and that trays are stacked to dry. Clean all tissue from the sink and discard in the plastic bags.

Many institutions that offer courses in vertebrate biology have extensive collections of specimens that might be borrowed for demonstration in this exercise.

A day of collecting in nearby woods, beach, or grasslands might provide diverse specimens for demonstration. Many can be held unharmed for short periods in terraria or aquaria and then returned to nature.

Many individual genera of specimens preserved in various ways are offered in the catalogues of Carolina Biological Supply and Ward's. Consult the catalogues for details.

Human skeletons, even those of plastic, are very fragile and very expensive. Because of this, you may wish to consider purchase of miniature human skeletons (Schlossberg, 18 in.), which are useful for small student groups to examine, rather than an adult human size skeleton.

Ordering Information

See General Laboratory Supplies list on page vii for basic items

ammocoete, w.m., prepared slide	Triarch	ZL4-11	
amphibian collection, Biosmount	Ward's	69 V 2099	
articulated adult human skeleton, with stand, plastic	Carolina	24-6909	Ward's 82 V 3010
bird feathers,	Carolina	26-4038	
bony fishes collection, Biosmount	Carolina	26-3226	
comparative placentas, mounted	Carolina	26-4342	
dogfish, preserved	Ward's	69 V 1191	
frog skeleton, prepared	Carolina	24-3720	
leopard frog, preserved	Carolina	22-7460	
mixed fishes set, preserved	Carolina	22-6555	
reptile collection,	Ward's	69 V 3359	
sea lamprey, preserved	Ward's	69 V 1001	
snake skeleton, mounted	Carolina	POM3640	
turtle skeleton,	Ward's	65 V 3330	
yellow perch, preserved	Carolina	22-6940	

Answers to In-Text Questions

31.1 Lampreys (Class Cephalaspidomorphi)

2. …Count and record below the number of pairs of external **gill slits. There are seven pairs of gill slits.**

31.2 Cartilaginous Fishes (Class Chondrichthyes)

2. (a) …How many dorsal fins are there? **Two not including the dorsal lobe of the tail fin.**
(g) … How does it feel? **Smooth**
Now run your hand in the opposite direction along the animal. How does it feel this time? **Rough**

31.3 Bony Fishes (Class Osteichthyes)

2. (d) How are the annual rings of the fish scale analogous to the annual ridges of the mussel or clam shell? **Each ring represents a period of rapid growth followed by a period of slow growth or a year.**

31.4 Amphibians (Class Amphibia)

2. (a) …Is your frog a male or female? **"Insert sex of frog."**
3. (c) …Are the bronchi dorsal or ventral to the esophagus? **The bronchi are ventral to the esophagus.**
4. (b) …List some reasons for the differences in the girdles, appendages, and cranium of the frog and human skeletons. **The primary mode of locomotion is different—humans walk/run, frogs jump. The brain of humans is relatively larger and more complex, especially the fore- and hindbrain.**

31.5 Reptiles (Class Reptilia)

2. Describe any differences you see. **Snakes do not have appendicular skeletons (except for vestigial girdles in pythons) or a sternum. Also both jaws are loosely articulated with the rest of the skull.**
3. …What portions of the skeleton are incorporated into the shell? **During development the ribs and thoracic vertebrae fuse with the dorsal shell (carapace).**

31.6 Birds (Class Aves)

Why is this circulatory arrangement an advantage for birds, as opposed to that found in amphibians and reptiles? (*Hint:* Recall that birds are endothermic and most can fly.) **Complete separation of the pulmonary and systemic circuits increases the efficiency of blood circulation in concert with the higher metabolic demands of endothermy and flight.**

1. What else do birds use their feathers for besides flight? **Feathers are excellent insulation against both heat and cold. Also, feather coloration can be cryptic or used to facilitate behavioral interactions, especially for reproduction.**

31.7 Mammals (Class Mammalia)

1. …Study the assortment of mammals on display and list as many functions for hair as you can. **Hair functions include insulation from heat and cold (dense), sensory detection, and evaporation of pheromones. Hair coloration can be cryptic or used to facilitate behavioral interactions.**

2. Can you suggest a relationship between the early development of mammals and the comparative sophistication of the nervous system and behavior of adult mammals? **The placenta is an adaptation for feeding an embryo internally. It provides a level of nutrition much higher than that available in an externally incubated egg. Thus the possible time of development is lengthened and the possible size of offspring released to the external environment is increased. Coupled with extended parental care this allows more time for a more complex brain to develop and therefore more sophisticated behavior.**

Name _____

Section No. _____

VERTEBRATES

Pre-lab Questions

1.   The bones that surround and protect the brain are collectively called the: a. spinal cord; b. vertebral column; c. pelvic girdle; d. cranium.

2.   The amniotic egg of reptiles, birds, and mammals is an adaptation to: a. carnivorous predators; b. a life on land; c. compensate for the short period of development of the young; d. protect the young from the nitrogenous wastes of the mother during the formation of the embryo.

3.   The ammocoete is the larva of: a. lampreys; b. sharks; c. bony fishes; d. amphibians.

4.   The structure of the cartilaginous and bony fishes that detects vibrations in the water is the: a. anal fin; b. operculum; c. nostrils; d. lateral line.

5.   The bony movable flap that covers the gills and gill slits is called the: a. operculum; b. cranium; c. tympanum; d. colon.

6.   The lampreys are unusual vertebrates in that they have no: a. eyes; b. jaws; c. gill slits; d. mouth.

7.   Placoid scales are characteristic of class: a. Cephalaspidomorphi b. Chondrichthyes; c. Osteichthyes; d. Reptilia.

8.   Amphibians have: a. a two-chambered heart; b. a three-chambered heart; c. a four-chambered heart; d. none of the above.

9.   Which group of animals is endothermic? a. fishes; b. mammals; c. reptiles; d. amphibians.

10. Animals that have the four basic characteristics of chordates plus a vertebral column are: a. invertebrates; b. hemichordates; c. cephalocordates; d. vertebrates.

EXERCISE 31

VERTEBRATES

Answers to Post-lab Questions

1. What characteristic of vertebrates is missing in all invertebrates? **The vertebral column.**

2. List the basic characteristics of vertebrates. **Along with their chordate characteristics, vertebrates have a vertebral column that protects the structures that develop from the dorsal hollow nerve cord—the brain and spinal cord.**

3. What is an ammocoete? What is its possible significance to the evolution of vertebrates? **An ammocoete is the larval stage of the lamprey. Because basic chordate as well as many vertebrate characteristics are present, many consider it the closest living form to ancestral chordates.**

4. How do lampreys differ from other vertebrates? **They lack jaws and paired appendages. The notochord persists in the adult.**

5. Explain how the adaptations of cartilaginous fishes make them better predators. **The evolution of jaws and paired appendages along with more efficient respiration and a better developed nervous system, including sensory structures allows cartilaginous fishes to chase, catch and eat larger and more active prey.**

6. Identify this vertebrate structure. What do the rings represent? **This is a typical scale of a bony fish. The rings are indicators of annual growth.**

7. Describe an amniotic egg. What is its evolutionary significance? **The shelled egg of amniotes contains the developing embryo along with its accompanying fetal membranes. It provides an aquatic environment for development that is independent of environmental water and is an adaptation for life entirely on land.**

8. List the unique characteristics of mammals. **Endothermic; skin glands (e.g., mammary glands); 4-chambered heart; hair; pinna of ear; relatively large brain.** Describe the difference between ectothermic and endothermic animals. **Endotherms are capable of maintaining a relatively high body temperature physiologically by using metabolic heat. Ectotherms cannot do this.**

9. Describe the evolution of the heart in vertebrates. **The structure of the heart in vertebrates shows an evolutionary sequence from two to four chambers. Amphibians have a 3-chambered heart with two atria and a ventricle. Reptiles have a 3-chambered heart with two atria and a ventricle that is incompletely divided into two partial chambers. Birds and mammals have 4-chambered hearts with two atria and two ventricles. A 4-chambered heart allows for separation of deoxygenated and oxygenated blood going to the capillaries of the lungs and all other capillaries, respectively. This increases the efficiency of the circulatory system, which is a necessary adaptation for endothermic birds and mammals that have a greater metabolic demand than the ectothermic amphibians and reptiles.**

10. About 65 million years ago, an asteroid impact may have caused a mass extinction, which led to the demise of dinosaurs and created new opportunities for surviving plants and animals, including mammals. Create a short evolutionary scenario for the next man-made or natural mass extinction event. **Possible scenarios could revolve around a nuclear war, biological/chemical war, global warming, loss of ozone protection from solar radiation, depletion of non-renewable natural resources, or another large asteroid impact.**

PLANT ORGANIZATION: VEGETATIVE ORGANS OF FLOWERING PLANTS

Materials and Equipment

32.1 External Structure of the Flowering Plant

Per student group (table)
- mature corn plant

Per lab room
- living bean and corn plants in flats
- potted dumbcane (*Dieffenbachia*) plants
- dishpan half-filled with water
- potted geranium (*Pelargonium*) plants

32.2 The Root System

Per student
- single-edged razor blade
- coverslip
- buttercup (*Ranunculus*) root, c.s., prepared slide
- microscope slide
- compound microscope

Per student pair
- dH₂O in dropping bottle

Per lab room
- demonstration slide of Casparian strip in endodermal cell walls (*Equisetum*; see *Notes*)
- germinating radish seeds in large petri dishes

32.3 The Shoot System: Stems

Per student
- monocot stem, c.s. (corn, *Zea*)
- woody stem (basswood, *Tilia*), c.s., prepared slide
- herbaceous dicot stem, c.s., (flax, *Linum*, *or* alfalfa, *Medicago*), prepared slide
- woody twigs (hickory, *or* horse chestnut, *or* tree-of-heaven, *Ailanthus*, *or* others)
- metric ruler or meter stick

Per student pair
- cross section of woody branch (tree trunk)
- dissecting microscope

Per lab room
- demonstration slide of lenticel

32.4 The Shoot System: Leaves

Per student
- dicot leaf, c.s. (lilac, *Syringa)* slide
- monot leaf, c.s. (corn, *Zea)* slide

Preparation of Materials and Equipment

32.1 External Structure of the Flowering Plant

Bean and corn plants: Plant in flats of vermiculite approximately 21 days before needed, at least one plant of each per student.

32.2 The Root System

Radish seeds: Germinate on moist filter paper in petri dishes 5 days before needed.

32.3 The Shoot System: Stems

None required.

32.4 The Shoot System: Leaves

None required.

Notes

32.1 External Structure of the Flowering Plant

Mature corn plants should be collected in late summer or early fall. Select well-grown plants with representative prop roots.

32.2 The Root System

Purchase prepared slides of *Equisetum* roots to demonstrate Casparian strips in endodermal walls. When ordering, request that the Casparian strip be in surface view in the plane of section.

32.3 The Shoot System: Stems

Collect woody twigs of hickory (*Carya*), horse-chestnut (*Aesculus*), tree-of-heaven (*Ailanthus*), or other species in winter or before buds break in spring. Select twigs that show at least two years growth.

32.4 The Shoot System: Leaves

Ordering Information

See General Laboratory Supplies list on page vii for basic items

32.1 External Structure of the Flowering Plant

bean and corn seed	Purchase from local garden supply
Pelargonium and *Dieffenbachia* plants	Purchase from local greenhouse

32.2 The Root System

buttercup (*Ranunculus*) root, c.s., prepared slide	Triarch	13-10A	(specify tetrarch)
Zea root, c.s., prepared slide	Triarch	14-10AAA	

32.3 The Shoot System: Stems

alfalfa (*Medicago*) stem, c.s., prepared slide	Triarch	11-18a
basswood (*Tilia*) stem, c.s., prepared slide	Triarch	11-32C
elderberry (*Sambucus*) stem, lenticel, prepared slide	Triarch	11-28B
flax (*Linum*) stem, c.s., prepared slide	Triarch	11-14A

32.4 The Shoot System: Leaves

lilac (*Syringa*) leaf, c.s., prepared slide	Triarch	15-20A
monocot (*Zea*) leaf, c.s., prepared slide	Carolina	30-4054

Answers to In-Text Questions

32.1 External Structure of the Flowering Plant

A. Dicotyledons

12.

_____ node **(green)**   _____ terminal bud **(brown or at least not green)**
_____ internode **(green)**   _____ leaf petiole **(green)**
_____ axillary bud **(green)**   _____ leaf blade **(green)**

What color are the stems of the plants you've examined?
(See above)

What structure in the cytoplasm of the cells making up the stem is responsible for this color? **Chloroplast**
What is the function of this structure? **Photosynthesis**
What, then, is one function of the stem? **Photosynthesis**

13. Compare the leaves of the bean with those of the geranium. Are the geranium leaves simple or compound? (You may wish to refer to some of the figures in Exercise 18, Taxonomy: Classifying and Naming Organisms, if you have difficulty deciding.) **Simple**
Is there a single midvein in the geranium, or are there many large veins? **Many large veins**
List all the features shared by the leaves of beans and geraniums. **All the structures are present in both.**
List any differences you observe in the leaves. **The leaves of beans are compound (except the first-formed foliage leaves), while those of geranium are simple. The shape of the leaves is different – the bean leaflet comes to a point while there is no defined tip on the leaf geranium. Also, there is one large midvein in the bean.**

B. Monocotyledons

Figure 32-4a label: **Root system**
Figure 32-4b labels **(from top to bottom): Leaf sheath; prop root**

3. Trace the adventitious roots back to the corn grain. Where do they originate? **The cotyledonary node**
4. Examine the mature corn plant. Identify the large prop roots at the base of the plant. Where do prop roots arise from? **They come off the stem.**
Would you classify these as adventitious roots? (yes or no) **Yes**
8. Obtain a potted specimen of the dumbcane plant. Observe its external morphology, comparing it with the corn plant. Does the dumbcane have sheathing leaves like corn, or does each leaf have a petiole? **Each leaf has a petiole.**
Are the veins in the leaves parallel, or is netted venation present? **Netted**
Is there a midvein? (yes or no) **Yes**
Is the terminal bud obvious or is it deeply embedded, as in the corn plant? **Obvious**
Are prop roots present on the dumbcane plant? **No**

32.2 The Root System

A. Living Root Tip

5…Do they originate all the way down to the root cap? (yes or no) **No**
6. Examine the root hairs carefully. What happens to their length as you observe them at increasing distance from the root tip? **The longest root hairs are from the root tip.**
The youngest root hairs are the shortest. What does this imply regarding their point of origin and pattern of maturation? **The root hairs originate near the growing point of the root (near the tip).**

B. Dicot Root Anatomy

5…Based on the presence of starch grains, what would you suspect one function of this root might be? **Storage of carbohydrates in the form of starch.**

C. Monocot Root Anatomy

3. Next locate the cortex. Count the number of cell layers and draw the cortex. Do you find any starch grains in the cortex of the corn stem? **No**

32.3 The Shoot System: Stems

A. Dicot Stem: Primary Structure

B. External Features of Woody Dicot Stems

1. Examine a twig of hickory (Carya) or buckeye (Aesculus) that has lost its leaves. Label Figure 32-13 as you study the twig.

> **Figure 32-13 labels (top to bottom):**
> **terminal bud**
> **bud scale**
> **vascular bundle scar**
> **internode**
> **leaf scar**
> **axillary bud**
> **lenticel**

6.…If the most recent growth took place during the last growing season (summer), when was the portion of the twig immediately adjacent to the cut end produced? **Answer varies depending upon the stem.**

TABLE 32-1 Average Annual Terminal Growth in Woody Stems	
Species	**Average Distance between Terminal Bud Scale Scars (cm)**
Carya (or Aesculus)	While the growth will vary, the growth of Carya (or Aesculus) is clearly less than that of Ailanthus.
Ailanthus	While the growth will vary, the growth of Carya (or Aesculus) is clearly less than that of Ailanthus.

8. Now obtain twigs of several other species, including the tree of heaven (*Ailanthus*), and do the same. Would you say the growth rate is similar or quite variable among species that grow in your area? **Answers will likely vary, but students should see some variation in growth rate.**

C. Secondary Growth: Gross Anatomy of a Woody Dicot Stem

5.…How old would you estimate your section to be? **(Answer variable) Years**
7.…The periderm performs the same function as the epidermis before the epidermis ruptured as a result of the stem's increase in girth. What is the function of the periderm? **To protect underlying tissues and gaseous exchange.**

D. Secondary Growth: Microscopic Anatomy of a Woody Dicot Stem

2… How old is this section? **(Answer may vary, but typically one, two, or three years old. In many instances the slide label may indicate age.) Years**

32.4 The Shoot System: Leaves

A. Dicot Leaf Anatomy

6.…Does the spongy mesophyll contain any chloroplasts? (yes or no) **Yes**
What is one function that occurs within the spongy mesophyll? **Photosynthesis**
7.… Is the lower epidermal layer covered by a cuticle? **Yes**
8. Compare the abundance of stomata within the lower epidermis with that in the upper epidermis. Which epidermal surface has more stomata? **The lower surface has more stomata.**

B. Monocot Leaf Anatomy

3. Search on both epidermal layers for stomata. Count them on each layer. Are there more, fewer, or about the same number on the upper epidermis vs. the lower? **About the same**

4. Think about the orientation of the leaf blade on the plant. (If necessary, examine a living or dried corn plant to gain an impression of the orientation.) Is the orientation of the corn leaves the same or different from that of a dicot, such as the bean plant? **Different**.

If you determined it is different, in what way is it different? **Corn leaves grow more vertically than do bean leaves.**

5. Make a hypothesis relating the orientation of the leaf blade and the number of stomata on each surface of a leaf blade. **Leaves that grow in such a way that the blade is oriented horizontally with respect to the ground are likely to have more stomata on their lower surface, relative to leaves that grow vertically with respect to the ground.**

6. ... Is the mesophyll divided into palisade and spongy layers? (yes or no) **No**

Name _____

Section No. _____

PLANT ORGANIZATION: VEGETATIVE ORGANS OF FLOWERING PLANTS

Pre-lab Questions

1. An axillary bud: a. would be found along internodes; b. produces new roots; c. is the structure from which branches and flowers arise; d. is the same as a terminal bud.

2. The midrib of a leaf: a. contains the midvein; b. contains only xylem; c. is part of the spongy mesophyll; d. contains only phloem.

3. A taproot system lacks: a. lateral roots; b. a taproot; c. both of the above; d. none of the above.

4. The study of a plant's structure is: a . physiology; b. morphology; c. taxonomy; d. botany.

5. The endodermis: a. is the outer covering of the root; b. is part of the vascular tissue; c. contains the Casparian strip, which regulates the movement of substances; d. none of the above.

6. The bundle sheath in a monocot leaf: a. is filled with intercellular space; b. is the location of stomata; c. is covered with a cuticle to prevent water loss; d. functions in a manner somewhat similar to the root endodermis.

7. A plant with two seed leaves is: a. a monocotyledon; b. a dicotyledon; c. exemplified by corn; d. a dihybrid.

8. Which structure is not part of the shoot system? a. stems; b. leaves; c. lateral roots; d. axillary buds.

9. Meristems are: a. located at the tips of stems; b. located at the tips of roots; c. regions of active growth; d. all of the above.

10. To determine the age of a woody twig, one counts the number of: a. nodes; b. leaf scars; c. lenticels; d. regions between sets of terminal bud scale scars.

PLANT ORGANIZATION: VEGETATIVE ORGANS OF FLOWERING PLANTS

Answers to Pre-lab Questions
in Lab Manual Order

1. b	6. c		
2. b	7. d		
3. d	8. d		
4. c	9. a		
5. c	10. d		

Answers to Pre-lab Questions
in Instructor's Manual Order

1. c	6. d		
2. a	7. b		
3. d	8. c		
4. b	9. d		
5. c	10. d		

Answers to Post-lab Questions

1. What type of root system do you see on the dandelion at the right? **Taproot system**

2. Describe the location, structure, and importance of the Casparian strip. **Location: the endodermis, the innermost layer of cortex; Structure: a waxy band within the wall of the endodermal cells; Importance: seals the vascular column from the cortex so materials moving in or out of the vascular column must go through cytoplasm and differentially permeable membranes.**

3. On the figure below, identify structures a, b, and c. **a—terminal bud; b—leaf scar; c—lateral bud.**

4. Identify the structures labeled a and b on the figure below. **a—lenticel; b—terminal bud scale scar.**

5. What feature(s) would you use to determine the age of a woody twig? **Count increments between bud scale scars, or, if in cross section, count the annual rings.**

6. Label the diagram using the following terms: bark; heartwood; sapwood; secondary phloem; vascular cambium. **(Left to right:) Bark, secondary phloem, heartwood, sapwood. (Bottom left:) vascular cambium**

7. The photo shows the microscopic appearance of maple wood. Using your knowledge of the woody stem section, identify cell type a and the "line" of cells at b. (Note: The outside of the tree from which this section was taken is toward the bottom of the page.) **a is a vessel member; b is a ray (xylem ray)**

8. A section cut from an ash branch is shown below. a. Identify region a. **Vascular cambium.** b. Which meristem is located at b? **Pith.** c. Within ± 3 years, how old was this branch when cut? **27 ± 3 years.**

9. The following photo shows a section of a leaf from a dicot that is adapted to a dry environment. Its lower epidermis has depressions, and the stomata are located in the cavities. Even though it's different from the leaf you studied in lab, identify the regions labeled a, b, and c. **a is cuticle; b is palisade mesophyll; c is spongy mesophyll**

10. A major problem for land plants is water conservation. Most water is lost through stomata due to evaporation at the surface of the leaf. Many plants, including lilac (the leaf section you examined), orient their leaves perpendicular to the drying force of the sun's rays. What did you observe about the relative abundance of stomata in the lower epidermis versus the upper epidermis? Why do you think this distribution has evolved? **More stomata are found on the lower leaf surface. This distribution subjects the stomata to less heat from the sun and hence fewer evaporative forces. Consequently, less water would be lost even though the stomata are open to allow carbon dioxide to enter the leaf for photosynthesis.**

ANIMAL ORGANIZATION

Materials and Equipment

33.1 Tissues

Per student
- compound microscope
- lens cleaning solution (optional)
- dropper bottle of immersion oil (optional)
- lens paper
- lint free cloth (optional)
-

Prepared slides of the following:
- longitudinal section of tendon
- sections of the three muscle types
- small intestine, c.s., (preferably of ileum)
- cross section of compact bone, ground
- section of the cortex of mammalian kidney
- teased spread of loose (areolar) connective tissue
- smear of the spinal cord of an ox (neurons)
- whole mount of mesentery (simple squamous epithelium), w.m.
- sections of contracted and distended urinary bladders
- section of trachea
- section of esophagus
- section of white adipose tissue
- section of mammalian skin

Per lab room
- 50-mL beaker 3/4 full of water
- two small glass rods
- demonstration slide of intercalated disks in cardiac muscle tissue
- 50-mL beaker 3/4 full of immersion oil

33.2 Analysis of an Organ

Per student
- compound microscope and lens paper
- lens cleaning solution (optional)
- prepared slide of small intestine cross section (preferably the ileum)
- dropper bottle of immersion oil (optional)
- lint free cloth (optional)

33.3 Systems

Per student
- colored pencils—green, yellow, black, red, brown, pink, and blue

Per lab room
- demonstration dissection of a sheep brain
- labeled demonstration dissection of a mouse (optional)

33.4 Observation: Mouse Dissection

Per student group
- freshly euthanized mouse
- dissecting scissors and cotton balls
- squeeze bottle containing 0.9% saline solution
- small plastic bag for disposal of organs and soiled cotton balls

- forceps, blunt probe, and dissecting needle
- dissecting tray and four dissecting pins

Per lab section
- large plastic bag for disposal of the small plastic bags and carcasses at the end of the exercise

Per lab room
- demonstration dissection of nervous system of the mouse
- boxes of different sizes of latex gloves

Preparation of Materials and Equipment

Killing jar for mice: Perform this task in a fume hood. Place absorbent cotton or paper toweling in the bottom of a large, covered jar or dish (e.g., 8 in. culture dish with glass cover). Add ethyl ether as anesthetic and place mice in the covered container for approximately 15 minutes.

Demonstration dissection of a mouse:
1. With a scalpel, make a longitudinal incision through the skin to the mouse's right of the midline of the ventral surface. With a pair of scissors pierce the body wall just below the ribs. Cut along the incision through the rib cage and collar bone. Likewise cut down through the abdominal muscles.

2. Pull the sides of the longitudinal incision apart and look for the diaphragm separating the body cavities of the thorax and abdomen. Use the scissors to make two perpendicular cuts through the body wall just below the diaphragm. Extend these cuts around and to the back of the mouse. Cut the diaphragm away from its attachment to the body wall and separate the organs of the thoracic cavity from their attachment to the ventral body wall.

3. You should at this point be able to fold back four triangular flaps of body wall, opening up the ventral body cavities, the thoracic cavity in the thorax, and the abdominopelvic cavity in the abdomen. To fold back the two upper flaps, you must break the ribs with your hands near their attachment to the vertebral column. Pin the flaps to the dissecting tray. Rinse any coagulated blood from the body cavity with 0.9% saline solution and remove any excess fluid with cotton balls. Keep body cavity moist with saline as needed.

4. In the thoracic cavity, remove thymus. Label: lungs, trachea, esophagus, heart, and bronchus (see Lab Manual Figure 33-24).

5. In the abdominopelvic cavity, locate and label: liver, gallbladder, stomach, spleen, small intestine, mesentery, pancreas, large intestine, rectum, caecum, urinary bladder, kidneys, ureters, urethra, uterus, oviduct, and ovary (if female), or vas deferens, epididymis, seminal vesicle, prostate, and testis (if male; see Lab Manual Figures 33-25 and 33-26).

6. Skin one of the mouse's legs, and separate one skeletal muscle organ by tearing the connective tissue with a dissecting needle. Remove all the skeletal muscles from the upper part of the leg and expose the bone.

| *0.9% saline* (100 mL): | NaCl | 0.9 g |
| | dH$_2$O | 100 mL |

Dissection of the nervous system of the mouse: Obtain a freshly euthanized mouse and make a longitudinal incision extending from the face to the base of the tail. Peel back the skin from the skull and the back and pin it to a dissecting tray.

To expose the spinal cord, remove the muscles dorsal and just lateral to the vertebral column. With a sharp scalpel, shave down the spines and neural arches of the vertebral column until the spinal cord with its connective tissue covering is exposed. Carefully remove the dura mater with fine scissors and forceps.

Spinal nerves can be seen by shaving down neural arches sufficiently at the vertebral forama and removing the dura mater.

To expose the brain, make a longitudinal cut along the mid-dorsal line of the skull with a sharp scalpel, taking care not to cut too deeply. Make two lateral cuts approximately 1/4 in. apart and break off the skull pieces with forceps until the entire brain is exposed. Cut through the occipital bone and carefully remove the bone surrounding the junction of the brain and spinal cord.

Keep the tissues moist with saline solution.

Preparation of sheep brain demonstration: Sheep brains are shipped with a variable amount of attached tissues. Prepare the brain for classroom observation by removing any extra meninges and extraneous tissue.

Notes

33.1 Tissues

Demonstration of intercalated disks in cardiac muscle tissue should be set up using an oil immersion lens. These structures can best be seen on slides specifically made and labeled for this purpose (see *Ordering Information*). General preparations are usually too thickly sectioned for demonstration of intercalated disks.

Glass rods in beakers of dH$_2$O and immersion oil for demonstration of refractive indices should be only slightly taller than the beakers to prevent accidental tipping.

Ordering Information

See General Laboratory Supplies list on page vii for basic items

33.1 Tissues

areolar connective tissue, teased	Triarch	HB3-1
bone, human, c.s., ground thin	Triarch	HB8-4
cardiac muscle, showing intercalated disks	Triarch	HD4-22
esophagus, c.s.	Triarch	HK5-2
ileum, c.s., prepared slide	Triarch	HK7-23
kidney, c.s.	Triarch	HL1-2
muscle, three types	Triarch	HD5-1
simple squamous epithelium, w.m.	Carolina	31-2326
skin, c.s	Triarch	HI1-21
spinal cord, ox, smear	Triarch	HE4-1
tendon, l.s.	Triarch	HB5-1
trachea, c.s	Triarch	HJ2-1
urinary bladder, contracted and distended, c.s.	Triarch	HL3-211
white adipose tissue	Triarch	HB4-1

33.2 Analysis of an Organ

ileum, c.s., prepared slide	Triarch	HK7-23

33.3 Systems

ethyl ether	Fisher	E134-1
living mouse (can be obtained from local pet store)	Ward's	87V 8600
NaCl	Fisher	S671-500
sheep brain, preserved	Ward's	69 V 7101

33.4 Observation: Mouse Dissection

ethyl ether	Fisher	E134-1
living mouse (can be obtained from local pet store)	Ward's	87V 8600
NaCl	Fisher	S671-500

Answers to In-Text Questions

33.1 Tissues

A. Epithelial Tissues

1. …What is the shape of the surface cells? **Polygonal**

5. …Is the shape of the outermost cells squamous, cuboidal, or columnar? **Squamous**
Are there one or many layers of cells in this tissue? **Many layers of cells**
Name this subtype of epithelial tissue. **Stratified squamous epithelium**

B. Connective Tissue

3. …Describe the density and arrangement of the fibers. **There are many collagen fibers arranged in a parallel fashion.**
… How are the fibroblasts oriented relative to the arrangement of the fibers? **Fibroblasts forms are situated between the fibers in parallel arrays.**

4. ….In which fluid is it easier to see the glass rod? **The glass rod is easier to see in the water.**

5. …Which tissue, bone or cartilage, will heal quicker? Explain why you made this choice. **Bone tissue readily heals as oxygen and nutrients are readily available and carbon dioxide and wastes are easily removed.**

33.3 Systems

Systems	Vital Functions
TABLE 33-4 The Organ Systems of Mammals	
Integumentary	**e.g., protection, thermoregulation (e.g., sweating), reception of stimuli from external environment**
Nervous	**point to point (neuronal) control of body functions, integration of body activities, perception of sensations**
Endocrine	**hormonal control of body functions**
Skeletal	**support of body, protection of internal organs, skeletal muscle attachment sites, blood cell production, mineral storage and release**
Muscular	**moves body and its parts, posture, heat generation**
Circulatory	**rapid transport of materials throughout body, maintenance of stability of internal environment**
Lymphatic	**immunity, return of tissue fluid to blood**
Respiratory	**gas exchange between external environment and blood, short-term regulation of acid-base balance**
Digestive	**ingestion of food molecules and water, digestion, absorption, defecation**
Urinary	**urine production, maintenance of stability of internal environment, long-term control of acid-base balance**
Reproductive	**production of eggs and sperm, sex, gestation and birth (female)**

33.4 Observation: Mouse Dissection

A. External Features

9. …If you have a mature female, find the well-developed teats of the *mammary glands*. How many do you count? **There are twelve teats on the ventral body surface.**

D. Abdominopelvic Cavity

6. Stretch out the length of the small intestine and measure it.
Length of small intestine **"fill in number"** cm
Now measure the mouse from the tip of the nose to the base of the tail.
Length of head and body of mouse **"fill in number"** cm
How many times the length of the mouse is its small intestine? **"fill in number"**
Note: The small intestine is about 3.5 times body length.

Name _____

Section No. _____

ANIMAL ORGANIZATION

Pre-lab Questions

1. In which tissue would you look for cells that function in point-to-point communication? a. connective; b. epithelial; c. muscle; d. nervous.

2. The ventral body cavities include a. the thoracic cavity; b. the cranial cavity; c. the abdominopelvic cavity; d. both a and c.

3. _____ are constructed of all four basic tissue types. a. organs; b. systems; c. cells; d. organelles.

4. A collection of similarly specialized cells and any extracellular material they secrete and maintain describes: a. an organ; b. a systems; c. a tissue; d. organelles.

5. The middle layer of the skin: a. is called the dermis; b. is primarily connective tissue; c. contains collagen fibers; d. is all of the above.

6. An epithelial tissue formed by more than one layer of cells and with column-like cells at the surface is called: a. simple squamous; b. stratified squamous; c. simple columnar; d. stratified columnar.

7. The cranial cavity contains a. the lungs and heart; b. the spinal cord; c. the brain; d. both b and c.

8. Organs strung together functionally, and usually structurally, form: a. organs; b. systems; c. tissues; d. organelles.

9. Histology is the study of: a. cells; b. organelles; c. tissues; d. organisms.

10. To which subtype of muscle tissue does a fiber with cross striations and many peripherally located nuclei belong? a. skeletal; b. cardiac; c. smooth; d. none of the above.

ANIMAL ORGANIZATION

Answers to Pre-lab Questions
in Lab Manual Order

1.	c	6.	d
2.	c	7.	a
3.	b	8.	d
4.	a	9.	d
5.	d	10.	d

Answers to Pre-lab Questions
in Instructor's Manual Order

1.	d	6.	d
2.	d	7.	d
3.	a	8.	b
4.	c	9.	c
5.	d	10.	a

Answers to Post-lab Questions

1. In the correct order from smallest to largest, list the levels of organization present in most animals. **Organelles, cells, tissues, organs, systems, organism.**

2. Describe the main structural characteristics of the four basic tissues. a. epithelial tissue—**cover surfaces, line tubular organs, no blood vessels, basement membrane;** b. connective tissue—**fibers and ground substance make up an extensive extracellular matrix;** c. muscle tissue—**shortened fibers during contraction, transverse striations (except for smooth);** d. nervous tissue—**neurons, neuroglia.**

3. Describe the main functions of the four basic tissues. a. epithelial tissue—**protection and transport (absorption, secretion, etc.);** b. connective tissue—**protection, support, storage;** c. muscle tissue— **contraction;** d. nervous tissue—**point-to-point communication.**

4. Identify the following tissues. **a. stratified squamous epithelium; b. simple cuboidal epithelium**

5. Choose any organ. What is its specific function? Describe its functional histology. **E.g., skin, trachea. Refer to text of lab manual for examples.**

6. Briefly describe the ventral body cavities and the major organs they contain. **Ventral body cavity is located toward the belly side of the body, and is subdivided by the diaphragm into the thoracic and abdominopelvic cavity. The thoracic cavity is further divided into two lateral pleural cavities containing the right and left lungs and a medial pericardial cavity containing the heart. The abdominopelvic cavity consists of an upper abdominal cavity (contains stomach, small intestine, liver, etc.) that is continuous with a lower pelvic cavity (contains urinary bladder, etc.).**

7. Briefly describe the dorsal body cavities and the major organs they contain. **The continuous cranial (contains the brain) and spinal cavities (contains spinal cord) compose the dorsal body cavities.**

8. Identify the following structures. **a. trachea; b. esophagus; c. liver; d. urinary bladder.**

9. Bone is a subtype of connective tissue and bones are organs. How are the two related yet different from each other? Can you think of another tissue/organ pair that potentially crates a similar confusing situation? **Bones are organs that comprise the skeletal system. Each bone organ is a composite of the four basic tissue types. Bone tissue is the most common connective tissue subtype found in bone organs. A similar situation exists for skeletal muscle organs and skeletal muscle tissue.**

10. Search the phrase "tissue engineering" on the World Wide Web. List two sites and briefly summarize their content. **Answers will vary.**

EXERCISE 34

DISSECTION OF THE FETAL PIG: INTRODUCTION, EXTERNAL ANATOMY, AND MUSCULAR SYSTEM

Materials and Equipment

34.1 External Anatomy of the Fetal Pig

Per student pair
- dissecting tray or pan
- one preserved fetal pig injected with red and blue latex
- plastic bag for storing fetal pig

Per lab room
- permanent marking pens or pencils
- box of safety goggles
- boxes of different sizes of latex or vinyl gloves
- box of name tags (if not provided by supplier)
- liquid waste disposal bottle

34.2 Muscular System

Per student pair
- dissecting needles and scissors
- dissecting tray or pan
- one preserved fetal pig injected with red and blue latex
- plastic bag to store fetal pig
- four large rubber bands *or* two 60-cm. long pieces of string
- scalpel and forceps
- dissecting pins and blunt probe

Per lab room
- Box of safety goggles
- boxes of different sizes of latex or vinyl gloves

Preparation of Materials and Equipment

None required.

Notes

The recommended pigs are shipped in a formalin-free preservative and so should not present a problem to students with formalin-sensitivity. Nevertheless, we recommend providing plastic gloves and safety goggles to the students.

Waste bottles should be of plastic, not glass. Dispose of liquid preservative waste according to your institution's guidelines.

You may wish to have students purchase their own dissecting kits.

Emphasize to students the need to *cut* their specimens as little as possible. Instead, they should rely on their fingers and blunt probes to separate organs as much as possible while preserving their connections. The dissecting scalpel should be used only to chip away cartilage around the spinal column and cranium, rather than as a general cutting instrument.

Students must dispose of all waste tissue in the large plastic bags provided, and these bags should be discarded and replaced before each laboratory section. Be sure that dissecting trays and instruments are washed at the end of each laboratory period and that trays are stacked to dry. Clean all tissue from the sink and discard in the large plastic bags.

Ordering Information

See General Laboratory Supplies list on page vii for basic items

bone-cutting forceps	Carolina	62-5652		
fetal pig, 9 to 11 in., double injected, bulk pak	Ward's	69 V 5712	Carolina	22-8424
tags, one hundred	Carolina	65-7521		

Answers to In-Text Questions

34.1 External Anatomy of the Fetal Pig

B. Body Regions and Their Features

5. Is an umbilical cord present in the adult pig or human? **No**

DISSECTION OF THE FETAL PIG: INTRODUCTION, EXTERNAL ANATOMY, AND THE MUSCULAR SYSTEM

Pre-lab Questions

1. The *insertion* of a skeletal muscle is: a. attached to the less mobile portion of the skeleton; b. attached to the portion of the skeleton that moves when the muscle contracts; c. never attached to the skeleton; d. its belly.

2. When the directions for a fetal pig dissection refer to the left, they are referring to: a. your left; b. the pig's left; c. the pig's right; d. a and c.

3. The biceps brachii is responsible for flexing the forearm, while the triceps brachii extends the forearm. Muscles with such opposite actions are called: a. cooperative; b. antagonistic; c. involuntary; d. sensory.

4. Pigs have digitigrade locomotion because they walk on: a. their ankles; b. the soles of their feet; c. the tips of their toes, which are modified as hooves; d. their hands and knees.

5. In a fetal pig, *dorsal* and *ventral* refer to: a. the head and tail regions of the body, respectively; b. the tail and the head regions of the body, respectively; c. the upper (back) portion and the lower (underside) portion of the body, respectively; d. the lower (underside) portion and the upper (back) portion of the body, respectively.

6. The origin of a skeletal muscle is: a. attached to the less mobile portion of the skeleton; b. attached to the portion of the skeleton that moves when the muscle contracts; c. never attached to the skeleton; d. its belly.

7. *To dissect* means primarily: a. to cut open; b. to remove all internal organs; c. to expose to view; d. all of the above.

8. A fetus is: a. a newborn pig; b. a newborn human; c. an unborn mammal; d. all of the above.

9. The female *fetal* pig is similar to the male *fetal* pig in that its body: a. has separate openings for the urinary system and the reproductive system; b. has a common opening for the urinary system and the reproductive system; c. has an opening for the urinary system but none for the reproductive system; d. has an opening for the reproductive system but none for the urinary system.

10. The umbilical cord functions to: a. carry waste products in the blood from the fetus to the mother; b. carry waste products in the blood from the mother to the fetus; c. carry oxygen in the blood from the mother to the fetus; d. a and c.

EXERCISE 34

DISSECTION OF THE FETAL PIG: INTRODUCTION, EXTERNAL ANATOMY, AND THE MUSCULAR SYSTEM

Answers to Pre-lab Questions in Lab Manual Order

1. c		6. b	
2. c		7. c	
3. b		8. a	
4. c		9. b	
5. d		10. b	

Answers to Pre-lab Questions in Instructor's Manual Order

1. b		6. a	
2. b		7. c	
3. b		8. c	
4. c		9. b	
5. c		10. d	

Answers to Post-lab Questions

1. Identify these external features of a fetal pig. **a. shoulder; b. hip; c. wrist; d. digit; e. elbow; f. umbilical cord; g. knee; h. ankle.**

2. What is the function of the umbilical cord? **To transport wastes and nutrients in the blood between the mother and the fetus. Specifically, the arteries of the umbilical cord carry blood with metabolic wastes and carbon dioxide from the fetus to the placenta of the mother, and the umbilical vein carries oxygenated blood from the placenta of the mother to the fetus.**

3. Briefly describe how your feet differ from those of the pig. **Humans walk on the soles of the feet, which are supported by the phalanges, metatarsals, and tarsals. Pigs and have hoofs and walk on the tips of the digits or phalanges.**

4. Using external features, briefly describe how you can determine the difference between a male and a female fetal pig. **Male—single urogenital opening just posterior to the umbilical cord and a small pouch or sac, the scrotum, between the hindlimbs. Female—single urogenital opening just ventral to the anus.**

5. Describe in general terms the *origin, insertion*, and *action* of a skeletal muscle organ. **Origin—the end attached to the stationary or less mobile part of the body. Insertion—the end attached to a bone or portion of the skeleton, which moves when the muscle contracts. Action—the movement induced in a limb or other body part when the muscle contracts.**

6. What does the phrase "antagonistic muscles" mean? **Muscles with opposite actions. For example, muscles that move an appendage in opposite directions (biceps and triceps).**

7. Complete the table.

Muscle Group	Skeletal Muscles in Group	General Actions of Group
Hamstrings	biceps femoris	extend thigh at hip and flex shank at the knee
	semimembranosus	
	semitendinosus	
Quadriceps femoris	rectus femoris	flex thigh at hip and extend shank at knee
	vastus medialis	
	vastus lateralis	
	vastus intermedius	

8. The right and left sternocleidomastoid muscles of humans originate on the upper surfaces of breast bone and collar bones, pass along both sides of the neck, and insert just behind the ears on the mastoid processes. Describe the action that occurs if both side contract together. **The action is to flex the head as in lowering the chin to the middle of the chest.**

9. Explain the basic difference between *digitigrade* and a *plantigrade* locomotion. **Plantigrade locomotion is when the entire foot is used for walking. Digitigrade is locomotion where the weight of the body is borne on the tips of the digits, or toes.**

10. Search the World Wide Web for sites that describe human body movements. List two sites and briefly summarize their contents. **Answers will vary.**

DISSECTION OF THE FETAL PIG: DIGESTIVE, RESPIRATORY, AND CIRCULATORY SYSTEMS

Materials and Equipment

35.1 Ventral Body Cavities

Per student pair
- dissecting kit, pan and pins
- piece of string 20 cm long
- one preserved fetal pig injected with red and blue latex
- four large rubber bands *or* two pieces of string, each 60 cm long
- plastic bag for storing fetal pig
- bone shears

Per lab room
- box of safety goggles
- boxes of different sizes of latex or vinyl gloves
- liquid waste disposal bottle

35.2 Digestive Systems

Per student pair
- dissecting kit, pan and pins
- piece of string 20 cm long
- dissecting microscope
- one preserved fetal pig injected with red and blue latex
- four large rubber bands *or* two pieces of string, each 60 cm long
- plastic bag for storing fetal pig
- bone shears
- meter stick (optional)

Per lab room
- box of safety goggles
- boxes of different sizes of latex or vinyl gloves
- liquid waste disposal bottle

35.3 Respiratory Systems

Per student pair
- dissecting kit, pan and pins
- one preserved fetal pig injected with red and blue latex
- four large rubber bands *or* two pieces of string, each 60 cm long
- plastic bag for storing fetal pig

Per lab room
- box of safety goggles
- boxes of different sizes of latex or vinyl gloves
- liquid waste disposal bottle

35.4 Blood Vessels and the Surface Anatomy of the Heart

Per student pair
- dissecting pan, kit and pins
- one preserved fetal pig injected with red and blue latex
- four large rubber bands *or* two pieces of string, each 60 cm long
- plastic bag for storing fetal pig

Per lab room
- box of safety goggles
- boxes of different sizes of latex or vinyl gloves
- liquid waste disposal bottle

35.5 Internal Structure of the Heart

Per student pair
- dissecting kit, pan and pins
- plastic bag for storing fetal pig

Per lab room
- box of safety goggles
- boxes of different sizes of latex or vinyl gloves
- liquid waste disposal bottle

Preparation of Materials and Equipment

None required.

Notes

The recommended pigs are shipped in a formalin-free preservative and so should not present a problem to students with formalin-sensitivity. Nevertheless, we recommend providing plastic gloves and safety goggles to the students.

Waste bottles should be of plastic, not glass. Dispose of liquid preservative waste according to your institution's guidelines.

You may wish to have students purchase their own dissecting kits.

Emphasize to students the need to *cut* their specimens as little as possible. Instead, they should rely on their fingers and blunt probes to separate organs as much as possible while preserving their connections. The dissecting scalpel should be used only to chip away cartilage around the spinal column and cranium, rather than as a general cutting instrument.

Students must dispose of all waste tissue in the large plastic bags provided, and these bags should be discarded and replaced before each laboratory section. Be sure that dissecting trays and instruments are washed at the end of each laboratory period and that trays are stacked to dry. Clean all tissue from the sink and discard in the large plastic bags.

Ordering Information

See General Laboratory Supplies list on page vii for basic items

bone-cutting forceps	Carolina	62-5652		
fetal pig, 9 to 11 in., double injected, bulk pak	Ward's	69 V 5712	Carolina	22-8424
tags, one hundred	Carolina	65-7521		

Answers to In-Text Questions

35.2 Digestive System

A. Mouth

4. ...What is the difference between the two regions?
The hard palate is supported by part of the maxillae and palatine bones. The soft palate has no bony support.
6. ...If you would run your probe posteriorly through the esophagus, where would it emerge?
The tip of the probe emerges in the stomach.

E. Stomach, Small Intestine, Large Intestine or Colon, Rectum, and Anus

2. ... Describe any contents of the stomach.

A fetus's digestive tract contains meconium, which is composed of a variety of bile stained mucus, amniotic fluid, sloughed epithelial cells, and hair.

3. ... What role might the rugae play in digestion?

They increase the surface area of the wall of the stomach for the many glands that secrete pepsinogen and hydrochloric acid.

5. Measure the length with a meter stick and record it: **"about 80 cm"**

6. ...How does the inner surface appear?

The inner surface of the small intestine is covered with projections called villi, which increase the surface area for enzymatic action and absorption.

9. ...How does its internal surfaces compare with that of the small intestine?

There are no villi in the colon.

35.3 Respiratory System

B. Trachea, Bronchial Tubes, and Lungs

4. ...Are the lungs of the fetal pig filled with air? **No**

5. ...Where does this exchange occur in the fetus? **In the placenta**

35.4 Blood Vessels and the Surface Anatomy of the Heart

A. Pulmonary Circuit and Surface Anatomy of the Heart

4. ...Through what structure does the inferior vena cava pass? **The diaphragm**

5. ...Do these arteries contain red or blue latex? **Blue latex**

After birth, do these arteries carry oxygen-rich or oxygen-poor blood? **Oxygen-poor blood**

8. ...Why is it not necessary for large quantities of blood to enter the pulmonary system of a fetus?

The exchange of gasses between the fetus, mother, and external environment is accomplished in the placenta.

C. Systemic Circuit—Major Arteries and Veins Posterior to the Heart

6. ...Is it rich in oxygen or carbon dioxide? **Carbon dioxide**

7. ...What is the relationship between the navel and the umbilical cord?

The navel marks the spot in an adult where the umbilical cord emerged from the fetus.

35.5 Internal Structure of the Heart

6. ...Do the cusps appear similar to the tricuspid valve? **Yes**

7. ...Do they appear similar to those in the right ventricle? **Yes**

8. ...Is the orientation of the aortic semilunar valve the same as that of the semilunar valve between the pulmonary trunk and the right ventricle? **Yes**

10. ...Why is the wall of the left ventricle thicker than that of the right ventricle?

The blood pressure is greater in the systemic circuit. Thus the heart must work harder to push the blood into it. More work means the cardiac muscle in the ventricular wall must contract with greater force. Hence there is more muscle tissue and a thicker wall ventricular wall to contain it.

DISSECTION OF THE FETAL PIG: DIGESTIVE, RESPIRATORY, AND CIRCULATORY SYSTEMS

Pre-lab Questions

1. The two *major* body cavities of a fetal pig are the: a. thoracic and pleural; b. thoracic and pericardial; c. abdominopelvic and thoracic; d. abdominopelvic and pericardial.

2. The digestive system is concerned with: a. blood circulation; b. digestion and the absorption of nutrients; c. reproduction; d. excretion of urine.

3. The microscopic air sacs, or alveoli, are the sites where blood: a. picks up oxygen; b. gives up carbon dioxide; c. gives up oxygen; d. a and b.

4. The hearts of a fetal pig and a human are similar in that they are: a. the primary pump of the circulatory system of the body; b. both 4-chambered; c. composed of cardiac muscle tissue; d. all of the above.

5. A vein is a blood vessel that always carries: a. blood toward the heart; b. blood away from the heart; c. oxygen-rich blood; d. oxygen-poor blood.

6. As a general rule, the small intestine of a pig or human is: a. about 60 cm long; b. about 1.5 m long; c. about as long as the individual is tall (or long, in the case of the pig); d. about five times the height of the individual.

7. In humans, the front of the larynx is commonly referred to as the: a. voice box; b. Adam's apple; c. food pipe; d. both a and b.

8. The diaphragm is a sheetlike skeletal muscle that separates the: a. thoracic and pleural cavities; b. thoracic and pericardial cavities; c. thoracic and abdominopelvic cavities; d. pleural and pericardial cavities.

9. The liver functions to: a. produce bile; b. pump blood; c. form urea; d. a and c.

10. The cardiac, pyloric, anal, and iliocecal sphincters are all part of the: a. digestive tract; b. respiratory tract; c. circulatory system; d. muscular system.

DISSECTION OF THE FETAL PIG: DIGESTIVE, RESPIRATORY, AND CIRCULATORY SYSTEMS

Answers to Pre-lab Questions in Lab Manual Order

1.	c	6.	a
2.	c	7.	d
3.	b	8.	d
4.	d	9.	a
5.	d	10.	d

Answers to Pre-lab Questions in Instructor's Manual Order

1.	c	6.	d
2.	b	7.	d
3.	d	8.	c
4.	d	9.	d
5.	a	10.	a

Answers to Post-lab Questions

1.   Describe the location of the two *major* ventral body cavities. **The thoracic cavity is located between the chest and the upper portion of the back. The abdominopelvic cavity is located inside the lower half of the trunk of the body. The diaphragm separates these two cavities.**

2.   Describe the difference between the digestive system and the digestive tract. **The digestive system is comprised of the digestive tract and associated glands—salivary, liver (and gallbladder), and pancreas. The digestive tract is a tube that runs from mouth to anus.**

3.   List in order the organs through which food, etc., passes in its journey into, through, and out the digestive tract. **oral cavity ∧ pharynx ∧ esophagus ∧ stomach ∧ small intestine ∧ large intestine ∧ anal canal.**

4.   Describe the major similarities and differences in the location, structure, and function of the trachea and esophagus? **Trachea—the windpipe, reinforced by cartilaginous rings, which runs from the glottis to the thoracic cavity where it divides to form the bronchi to the lungs. The trachea carries oxygen and carbon dioxide between the lungs and the nasal passages. Esophagus—part of the alimentary canal between the mouth and the stomach. It is a very muscular organ but has no cartilaginous rings.**

5.   Identify the following structures in the photo on the right. **a. right common carotid artery; b. right subclavian artery; c. right ventricle; d. dorsal aorta; e. celiac artery; f. left renal artery; g. left external iliac artery; h. right umbilical artery.**

6.   What is the main difference between the pulmonary and the systemic circuits of the circulatory system? **The pulmonary system involves blood circulation to the lungs, while systemic circulation is concerned with the flow of blood to the rest of the body.**

7.   What is the foramen ovale? **The foramen ovale is a temporary opening in the wall separating the right and left atria of the heart of a fetus. It allows oxygenated blood (originally from the umbilical vein) from the inferior vena cava to pass directly from the right atrium to the left atrium of the heart and thus bypass the lungs. What is its fate after birth? The foramen ovale closes when the newborn first breathes.**

8.   With regard to blood circulation, what is the difference between an artery and a vein? **An artery carries blood away from the heart while a vein carries blood toward the heart.**

9.   Briefly describe the function of a portal vein system (for example, the hepatic portal vein). **The hepatic portal vein collects blood from the capillaries of the digestive tract and associated organs and transfers it to the capillaries of the liver before it is returned to the inferior vena cava and the heart.**

10. Search the World Wide Web for sites that describe artificial hearts. List two sites and briefly summarize their contents. **Answers will vary.**

DISSECTION OF THE FETAL PIG: UROGENITAL AND NERVOUS SYSTEMS

Materials and Equipment

36.1 Urogenital System

Per student pair
- dissecting kit, pan and pins
- one preserved fetal pig injected with red and blue latex
- four large rubber bands *or* two pieces of string, each 60 cm long
- plastic bag for storing fetal pig

Per lab room
- box of safety goggles
- boxes of different sizes of latex or vinyl gloves
- liquid waste disposal bottle

36.2 Kidney

Per student pair
- dissecting kit, pan and pins
- compound light microscope
- one preserved fetal pig injected with red and blue latex
- four large rubber bands *or* two pieces of string, each 60 cm long
- plastic bag for storing fetal pig
- prepared section of kidney

Per lab room
- box of safety goggles
- boxes of different sizes of latex or vinyl gloves
- liquid waste disposal bottle

36.3 The Nervous System

Per student pair
- dissecting kit, pan and pins
- dissection microscope
- one preserved fetal pig injected with red and blue latex
- four large rubber bands *or* two pieces of string, each 60 cm long
- plastic bag for storing fetal pig

Per lab room
- box of safety goggles
- boxes of different sizes of latex or vinyl gloves
- liquid waste disposal bottle

Preparation of Materials and Equipment

None required.

Notes

The recommended pigs are shipped in a formalin-free preservative and so should not present a problem to students with formalin-sensitivity. Nevertheless, we recommend providing plastic gloves and safety goggles to the students.

Waste bottles should be of plastic, not glass. Dispose of liquid preservative waste according to your institution's guidelines.

You may wish to have students purchase their own dissecting kits.

Emphasize to students the need to *cut* their specimens as little as possible. Instead, they should rely on their fingers and blunt probes to separate organs as much as possible while preserving their connections. The dissecting scalpel should be used only to chip away cartilage around the spinal column and cranium, rather than as a general cutting instrument.

Students must dispose of all waste tissue in the large plastic bags provided, and these bags should be discarded and replaced before each laboratory section. Be sure that dissecting trays and instruments are washed at the end of each laboratory period and that trays are stacked to dry. Clean all tissue from the sink and discard in the large plastic bags.

Ordering Information

See General Laboratory Supplies list on page vii for basic items

fetal pig, 9 to 11 in., double injected, bulk pak	Ward's	69 V 5712	Carolina	22-8424
kidney, c.s., prepared slide	Triarch	HL1-2		
tags, one hundred	Carolina	65-7521		

Answers to In-Text Questions

36.1 Urogenital System

B. Female Reproductive System

2. …How does this compare with the structure of the reproductive system of most male mammals?
The urinary and reproductive tracts of most male mammals share a duct and an opening.

C. Male Reproductive System

4. …Why do you think this is so?
Our posture puts considerable pressure on the floor of the abdominopelvic cavity. Four-footed mammals do not have this problem.

Name _____

Section No. _____

DISSECTION OF THE FETAL PIG: UROGENITAL AND NERVOUS SYSTEMS

Pre-lab Questions

1. When a human male has a vasectomy, the operation involves: a. removal of the male gonads, or testes; b. removal of the urethra; c. the severing of the vas deferens; d. removal of the prostate gland.

2. The ureters drain urine into the: a. renal pelvis; b. cecum; c. urinary bladder; d. small intestine.

3. The brain is surrounded by a set of membranes called the: a. pleural membranes; b. peritoneum; c. pericardial membranes; d. meninges.

4. The testes of a male differ from the ovaries of a female in that the testes: a. develop in the body cavity and migrate to a position outside of the body cavity; b. require a slightly higher temperature than that of the body to produce viable gametes; c. produce zygotes; d. a and b.

5. The urogenital system refers to the: a. urinary and reproductive systems; b. urinary and excretory systems; c. reproductive system; d. external genitalia.

6. The largest part of the brain of a mammal is the: a. cerebrum; b. cerebellum; c. pons; d. medulla oblongata.

7. Semen contains: a. sperm; b. the secretions of sex accessory glands; c. eggs; d. both a and b.

8. The functional unit of the kidney is the: a. renal pelvis; b. ureter; c. cortex; d. nephron.

9. The central nervous system of a mammal includes: a. the brain; b. the spinal cord; c. the brain and spinal cord; d. the brain, spinal cord, and every major nerve in the body.

10. The clitoris of the female and a portion of the penis of the male are homologous structures. This means they have a similar: a. function; b. structure; c. origin; d. origin and structure.

DISSECTION OF THE FETAL PIG: UROGENITAL AND NERVOUS SYSTEMS

Answers to Pre-lab Questions in Lab Manual Order		*Answers to Pre-lab Questions in Instructor's Manual Order*	
1. a	6. d	1. c	6. a
2. c	7. d	2. c	7. d
3. d	8. c	3. d	8. d
4. a	9. d	4. a	9. c
5. c	10. a	5. a	10. d

Answers to Post-lab Questions

1. What is the urogenital system? **A collective term for the urinary system and the reproductive system.**

2. Briefly describe the functions of the kidney, ureters, bladder, and urethra in the adult male pig. **Kidney— removes urea, excess salts and water from the blood and forms urine; balances or controls the concentrations of various ions in the blood (e.g., sodium and chloride). Ureters—carry urine from the kidneys, where it is produced, to the bladder for storage before transport out of the body. Urinary bladder—a storage sac for urine before it leaves the body via the urethra. Urethra—tube through which urine and sperm pass to the outside of the body.**

3. What is the vulva? **The external female genitalia of a mammal.**

4. How does the uterus of female pigs and humans differ? Include the site of embryo implantation in your discussion. **The uterus of the pig consists of three regions—the cervix at the entrance to the uterus, the uterine body, and two uterine horns. Thus the pig has a bicornuate uterus, in which embryo implantation and development occur in the uterine horns. In the human female there are no uterine horns, and the embryo implants and the fetus develops within the body of the simplex uterus.**

5. What is the inguinal canal in males and how does it form during development? **The inguinal canal is the opening in the abdominal cavity through which the testes of a male descend into the scrotum.**

6. Identify the following structures. **a. kidney; b. allantoic bladder; c. penis; d. inguinal canal; e. urethra; f. testis.**

7. Name the functional unit of the kidney. Briefly describe how it operates. **The nephron is the functional unit of the kidney. It carries out its activities through blood filtration, reabsorption, and tubular secretion.**

8. Describe the basic organization of the nervous system of a mammal. **The nervous system is divided into the central nervous system (CNS) and the peripheral nervous system (PNS). The CNS is comprised of the brain and spinal cord. The PNS has nerves, ganglia and associated structures.**

9. List the three meninges in order from the surface of the brain to the inside of the skull. **Pia mater, arachnoid, and dura mater.**

10. Search the World Wide Web for sites that describe kidney transplants an dialysis treatments. List two sites and briefly summarize their contents. **Answers will vary.**

EXERCISE 37

HUMAN SENSATIONS, REFLEXES AND REACTIONS

Materials and Equipment

37.1 Sensations

Per student pair

- compound microscope
- bristle and camel-hair brush
- scientific calculator
- reflex hammer
- tissue paper
- two blunt probes in 250-mL beaker of ice water
- two blunt probes in 250-mL beaker of hot tap water
- prepared slide of mammalian skin stained with hematoxylin and eosin stain
- felt-tip, nonpermanent pen
- ice bag
- 1-L beaker containing ice water
- 1-L beaker of room temperature water
- 1-L beaker containing water at 45°C
- dissecting needle

Per lab room

- demonstration slide of Pacinian corpuscle

37.2 Reflexes

Per student pair

- reflex hammer
- penlight

37.3 Reactions

Per student group (4)

- scientific calculator
- Reaction Time Kit (Carolina Biological Supply Company)
- chair or stool

Preparation of Materials and Equipment

None required.

Notes

37.1 Sensations

Change the hot water in the 250-mL beaker with the blunt probe every 5 to 10 minutes to maintain warm temperature.

37.2 Reflexes

A more expensive alternate reflex hammer, which contains a stainless steel pin and a bristle brush within the handle, is available from Carolina Biological Supply. See catalogue for ordering details.

37.3 Reactions

Note that this exercise as written involves modifications of the instructions given in the Reaction Time Kit from Carolina Biological Supply. Other experiments can be done with this kit from the directions if time allows.

Ordering Information

See General Laboratory Supplies list on page vii for basic items

37.1 Sensations

camel-hair brush	local art supply store	
Pacinian corpuscle, section, human prepared slide	Ward's	93V 3667
reflex hammer	Carolina	69-6435
skin, monkey, section, prepared slide	Carolina	31-4504
water soluble pen	Ward's	15V 1152

37.2 Reflexes

reflex hammer	Carolina	69-6435

37.3 Reactions

Reaction Time Ruler Set	Carolina	69-6410

Answers to In-Text Questions

37.1 Sensations

A. Modality

4. Figure 37-3 Grid for testing skin stimuli and recording modality data.
"Fill in grid results."
7. TABLE 37-1 Positive Identifications to Stimuli Applied to 25 Cells in a 0.25-cm^2 Patch of Skin
"Fill in cells."
9. Does each cell in the grid contain a receptor for all four modalities studied? **No** (yes or no)
10. Can you see a pattern or patterns in the distribution of positive responses marked in Figure 37-3? **In general, the answer should be no.** If yes describe the pattern(s):
11. Are the densities for the receptors for each modality the same? **No**

B. Projection

7. What can you conclude about projection and the receptors on the surface of the hand and forearm?
Holding an ice bag on or tapping the inside of the elbow produces sensations in the hand and forearm. These sensations are due to the brain assigning the stimulation of neuron pathways leading from the receptors back to their location in the skin.

C. Adaptation

Figure 37-4 Front and back views of forearm and hand for recording projection data.
"Note sensations or lack of sensation."
4. What can you conclude about the skin receptors for temperature and their capacity for adaptation?
Skin receptors for temperature undergo adaptation.
What about the ability of other kinds of receptors to adapt? Use your own experiences for smell, touch, and pain to answer this question. (Hints for touch: Can you feel your clothes? How about when you first get dressed after a shower?) **The sensations of smell and touch undergo adaptation, pain does not. You don't really feel your cloths, especially compared to when you first put them on.**

37.2 Reflexes

A. Stretch Reflexes

TABLE 37-2 Sensations Felt When Preadapted Hands Are Placed in Room-Temperature Water
2. Your lab partner taps the patella ligament with a reflex hammer (Figure 37-6). Describe the response.
The lower leg "kicks" or temporarily straightens out (extends).
3. Even with your eyes shut, are you aware of the stimulus and the response? **Yes**
4. Stretch reflexes are *somatic reflexes* because they involve somatic motor neurons and skeletal muscles. Can you willfully inhibit a stretch reflex? **Yes**

B. Pupillary Reflex

1. Shine the penlight into your lab partner's eyes. Does the size of the pupil (the diameter of the opening into the eye that is surrounded by the pigmented iris) get larger or smaller? **Smaller**
2. Now turn off the penlight. Does the size of the pupil get larger or smaller? **Larger**
3. Repeat steps 1 and 2. Which is faster, constriction of the iris (which makes the pupil smaller) or dilation of the iris (which makes the pupil larger)? **Constriction**
4. Are you aware of the pupil's changing diameter? **No**
5. Can you willfully inhibit the pupillary reflex? **No**

C. Complex Reflexes

1. Cup your hand around your neck and swallow. Feel the complex skeletal muscular movements involved in swallowing. Do you consciously control all these muscles? **No**
2. Is it possible to swallow several times in quick succession? **No**
3. Explain this result. It has something to do with the stimulus.
Swallowing is stimulated by the presence of saliva, food, or drink in the throat.
4. What part of swallowing does your conscious mind control, and what part is a reflex?
Your conscious mind may start a swallow by initiating a sequence of tongue muscle contractions that throw saliva into the throat. Further muscle contractions are part of the complex swallowing reflex.

37.3 Reactions

7. **TABLE 37-3** Reaction Time Data
"Fill in cells."
10. The reaction times of most of the ten trials should be similar, but perhaps the first few or one at random may be relatively different from the others. If this is true for your own or your lab partner's data, suggest some reasons for this variability.
Reasons include unfamiliarity with test, being distracted by other activities in the room, and loss of focus toward the end of the ten trials.

Name _____

Section No. _____

HUMAN SENSATIONS, REFLEXES, AND REACTIONS

Pre-lab Questions

1.   A pupillary reflex is: a. somatic; b. autonomic; c. a and b; d. none of the above.

2.   Neurons that carry messages from receptors to the CNS are: a. sensory; b. motor; c. interneurons;
      d. autonomic.

3.   A reaction is: a. a reflex; b. involuntary; c. voluntary; d. a and b.

4.   Neurons that carry messages within the CNS are: a. sensory; b. motor; c. interneurons; d. autonomic.

5.   Skin contains: a. free neuron endings; b. encapsulated neuron endings; c. no nervous tissue; d. both a and b.

6.   Which characteristic of receptors does phantom pain illustrate? a. modality; b. projection; c. adaptation;
      d. proprioception.

7.   A stretch reflex is: a. somatic; b. autonomic; c. a and b; d. none of the above.

8.   A simple reflex arc is made up of a receptor and: a. a sensory neuron; b. a motor neuron; c. an effector;
      d. all of the above.

9.   Knowledge of the position and movement of the various body parts is: a. modality; b. projection;
      c. adaptation; d. proprioception.

10.   Neurons that carry messages from the CNS to effectors are: a. sensory; b. motor; c. interneurons;
      d. both a and b.

EXERCISE 37

HUMAN SENSATIONS, REFLEXES, AND REACTIONS

*Answers to Pre-lab Questions
in Lab Manual Order*

1.	a	6.	b
2.	b	7.	d
3.	c	8.	a
4.	d	9.	b
5.	d	10.	c

*Answers to Pre-lab Questions
in Instructor's Manual Order*

1.	b	6.	b
2.	a	7.	a
3.	c	8.	d
4.	c	9.	d
5.	d	10.	b

Answers to Post-lab Questions

1. Where in the brain does your consciousness reside? **Cerebral cortex.**

2. In your own words, define the following terms: a. *modality*—**the production of a specific sensation upon stimulation of a specific receptor.** b. *projection*—**the assignment of a sensation by the brain back to its source.** c. *adaptation*—**the process that produces a short-term decline in responsiveness of a sensor after repeated stimulation.**

3. Identify the structure indicated in these photos. **a. Meissner's corpuscle; b. Pacinian corpuscle**

4. List the basic steps of a simple reflex arc like the stretch reflex. **First, a sensory neuron carries messages from receptors to the CNS, after which a motor neuron carries messages from the CNS to the effectors (a muscle or gland). Finally, effectors respond to nerve signals by producing movement or chemicals.**

5. How does the patella reflex differ from the pupillary reflex? **Patella reflex is a stretch reflex (somatic). Pupillary reflex is an autonomic reflex.**

6. Indicate whether the following actions are due to reactions or reflexes. a. a baby wetting a diaper. **Reflex.** b. braking a car to avoid an accident. **Reaction.** c. withdrawing your hand from a hot stove surface. **Reflex.** d. sneezing. **Reflex.** e. waving to a friend across the street. **Reaction.**

7. What are the advantages and disadvantages to an organism of receptor adaptation? **Advantages: Allows a greater range of sensitivity to ambient conditions; removes "noise" from the environment. Disadvantages: Is a short-term response and produces a time lapse in adjusting for a set of conditions.**

8. All animals do not perceive the external environment in exactly the same way. List some examples from your own knowledge and readings in the textbook. **Many possible examples. Perception of intensity contrast (i.e., black-and-white vision) versus intensity contrast *and* color vision, sensitivity of bats to ultrasonic wavelengths, sensitivity of bees to ultraviolet light wavelengths, and so on.**

9. To survive, an animal needs all its receptors working and even then cannot fully sense the external environment. What extra receptors do you think would be an advantage to the survival of humans in this modern world? **Again, many possible answers. A quick survey of several somewhat cynical people close by brought these answers: radiation detector, mutagen sensors, and built-in lie detectors, among others.**

10. Why is it advantageous for organisms not to be consciously aware of all the activity in their nervous systems? **It would be impossible to control all the autonomic and somatic sensations and responses.**

EXERCISE 38

STRUCTURE AND FUNCTION OF THE SENSORY ORGANS

Materials and Equipment

38.1 The Eyes and Vision

Per student
- compound light microscope
- prepared slide of cross section of eye with retina and optic nerve

Per student pair
- mirror and penlight
- forceps and scalpel
- preserved sheep eye
- dissecting scissors
- measuring tape
- blunt probe *or* dissecting needle
- two sheets of white paper: one blank and one with dime-sized black dot; black and colored construction paper; a white paper dot cut-out and cut-outs of different colored paper shapes (heart, star, etc.)

Per student group (4)
- eye model

Per lab room
- liquid waste disposal bottle
- boxes of different sizes of latex or vinyl gloves
- Snellen eye examination chart on wall, with taped mark 20 ft away
- astigmatism test chart on wall, with taped mark 10 ft away
- box of safety goggles

38.2 The Ears and Hearing

Per student
- compound light microscope
- prepared slide of cross section of cochlea

Per student pair
- mug or other container overfilled with cotton wool

Per student group (4)
- ear model

38.3 Taste and Smell

Per student
- compound light microscope
- prepared slide of nasal epithelium
- prepared slide of section through tongue showing folliate papillae

Per student group (4)
- box of tissues
- permanent marking pen
- 250-mL Erlenmeyer flask marked "SW" containing 10% sucrose
- 250-mL Erlenmeyer flask marked "SL" containing 5% NaCl
- 250-mL Erlenmeyer flask marked "SR" containing 1% acetic acid
- 250-mL Erlenmeyer flask marked "BT" containing 0.5% quinine sulfate or tonic water
- three dishes with cubes of a different vegetable or fruit in each (ex. apple, onion, and potato)

Per lab room
- box of applicator sticks
- box of paper cups
- container of small disposable beakers
- source of drinking water

Preparation of Materials and Equipment

38.3 Taste and Smell

10% sucrose (1 L):	sucrose or table sugar	100 g
	distilled water	1000 mL
1% acetic acid (1 L):	glacial acetic acid	10 mL
	distilled water	1000 mL
Or	white vinegar (5% acidity)	200 mL
	distilled water	800 mL
5% NaCl (1 L):	NaCl (sodium chloride, or table salt)	50 g
	distilled water	1000 mL
0.5% quinine sulfate (1 L):	quinine sulfate dihydrate	5 g
	distilled water	1000 mL

Notes

None required.

Ordering Information

See General Laboratory Supplies list on page vii for basic items

38.1 The Eyes and Vision

astigmatism test chart, pkg. of three	Carolina	69-4616
measuring tape, measuring, pack of ten	Carolina	70-2629
mirror, eye examination	local variety store	
model of eye	Carolina	56-6944
slide, retina with optic nerve entrance, median l. s.	Ward's	93 V 3783
sheep eye, preserved, pack of twelve	Carolina	22-8760
Snellen eye exam chart, pkg. of three	Carolina	69-4611

38.2 The Ears and Hearing

model of ear	Carolina	56-6963B
prepared slide, cochlea of guinea pig, l.s.	Ward's	93 V 3775

38.3 Taste and Smell

acetic acid, glacial	Fisher	A38-500
Erlenmeyer flask, 250 mL, Pyrex	Fisher	10-040F
NaCl	Fisher	S271-500
prepared slide, olfactory epithelium	Ward's	93 V 3787
prepared slide, tongue, folliate papillae	Ward's	93 W 4458
quinine sulfate dehydrate	Fisher	Q39-25
sucrose	Fisher	S5-500
wood applicator sticks	Carolina	70-6865

Answers to In-Text Questions

38.1 The Eyes and Vision

A. External Eye Structures

1. … From your own experience, suggest an additional function for eyelids and eyelashes.
Eyelids close in response to mechanical stimuli (e.g., dust blown into the eye) and to bright light.
2. Which eyelid moves when you open and close your eyes?
The upper lid opens and closes the eye.
3. Why do your eyes water during a cold?
A stuffy nose closes the nasolacrimal duct. This causes lacrimal fluid to back up onto the surface of the eyeball and to overflow the margin of the eye opening.

C. Dissection of the Sheep Eye

5. …What is the effect of the lens and vitreous body on the image with and without these structures?
The image magnifies and inverts the image of the letter e. In the eye, the retinal image is demagnified, inverted, and real.

D. Vision

TABLE 38-1 Visual Acuity
"Fill in cells."
TABLE 38-2 Astigmatism
"Fill in cells."
TABLE 38-3 Near Point
"Fill in cells."
4. …Describe these changes.
The size of the pupil (the diameter of the opening into the eye that is surrounded by the pigmented iris) gets larger in the dark (iris dilates) and smaller (iris constricts) in bright light.
Which occurs more rapidly, constriction or dilation (opening)? **Constriction**
What advantage might this difference confer in changing light conditions?
It controls the amount of light entering the eye to maximize retinal function, reduces glare and over-darkening of the retinal and perceived image.
5. …How many objects do you see? **Two**
7. …Describe the **afterimage. It is a bright spot against a darker background.**
Repeat this test substituting a top sheet of black construction paper with a white dot on it. Describe the afterimage.
It is a dark spot against a brighter background.
Bits of bright red, blue, green, and yellow paper can also be used in this activity. Repeat the experiment and describe the results.
Afterimages are in the complementary color. For example, staring at a red object against a green background will produce a green afterimage surrounded by a reddish background.

38.2 The Ears and Hearing

B. Sense of Direction of Sound

4. Consider the time of arrival and the relative intensity of the waves at each ear, and suggest two ideas as to how the brain determines the direction of the sound source.
The sound is louder to the near ear and it is delayed to the far ear.
TABLE 38-4 Sense of Sound Direction
"Fill in cells." Typically, the subject 'hits' the caller when their ears are uncovered and misses when one ear is covered.

38.3 Taste and Smell

B. Distribution of Taste Buds on the Tongue

4. Can you taste salt, bitter, sweet, and sour with your nostrils pinched closed? **Yes**

C. Interaction Between Taste and Smell

3. In a strictly biological sense, when your nostrils are blocked by congestion, can you taste and smell as well as when they are open? Explain your answers.
Yes, I can taste (sweet, sour, etc.) equally well whether congestion is present or not. Congestion does block my ability to smell. However when we refer to taste on an everyday basis, we usually mean the combination of taste and smell sensations associated with things processed in the oral cavity.
TABLE 38-5 Identity of Vegetable/Fruit
"Fill in cells." Typically the fruit is tasted (sweet, sour, etc.), but not smelled when the nostrils are closed. Opening the nostrils results in the vegetable/ fruit being both tasted and smelled.

Name _____

Section No. _____

STRUCTURE AND FUNCTION OF THE SENSORY ORGANS

Pre-lab Questions

1. Receptors found in the ear are: a. chemoreceptors; b. mechanoreceptors; c. photoreceptors; d. none of the above.

2. Photoreceptors are found in the: a. lens; b. ciliary body; c. iris; d. retina.

3. The olfactory epithelium is found in the: a. ear; b. nasal cavity; c. eye; d. tongue.

4. The most developed sense in humans is: a. hearing; b. vision; c. taste; d. smell.

5. Taste buds detect: a. light; b. atmospheric sound waves; c. chemicals in food and drink; d. movements of the head.

6. The cornea is part of the: a. sclera; b. choroid; c. retina; d. lens.

7. The space between the lens and iris is: a. the posterior cavity; b. the posterior chamber; c. the anterior chamber; d. none of the above.

8. Ossicles are found in the: a. outer ear; b. middle ear; c. inner ear; d. both a and c.

9. Parts of the choroid form the: a. lens; b. ciliary body; c. iris; d. both b and c.

10. Nearsightedness is also called: a. myopia; b. hyperopia; c. presbyopia; d. none of the above.

STRUCTURE AND FUNCTION OF THE SENSORY ORGANS

Answers to Pre-lab Questions
in Lab Manual Order

1.	a	6.	b	
2.	d	7.	b	
3.	d	8.	c	
4.	a	9.	b	
5.	a	10.	b	

Answers to Pre-lab Questions
in Instructor's Manual Order

1.	b	6.	a	
2.	d	7.	a	
3.	b	8.	b	
4.	b	9.	d	
5.	c	10.	a	

Answers to Post-lab Questions

1. Define the following terms:
    a. *myopia*—**also called nearsightedness; occurs when the vertical axis of the eyeball is shorter than the horizontal axis or when ciliary muscle contracts too strongly. Images of distant objects are focused in front of the retina instead of on it.**
    b. *hyperopia*—**also called farsightedness; occurs when horizontal axis of the eyeball is shorter than the vertical axis, so close images are focused behind the retina, not on it.**
    c. *presbyopia*—**condition where lens becomes more inelastic with age, requiring an object to be held farther and farther from the eye in order to focus on it.**

2. How does uncorrected myopia or hyperopia affect the near point? **Uncorrected myopia brings the near point closer to the lens; uncorrected hyperopia moves the near point farther away from the lens.**

3. What types and subtypes of photoreceptors are present in the retina? Briefly describe their function. **The photoreceptors and the cones and rods. Cones are stimulated by bright light and are responsible for color vision when the three subtypes of cones—red, green, and blue—are stimulated. Rods are more sensitive to lower levels of light and function in dim light conditions.**

4. What is an afterimage? How is it formed? **An afterimage is a negative image formed after looking steadily at an object for a time. The bright portions of the image cause light adaptation of the retina while the dark portions cause dark adaptation. In other words, areas of the retina that are stimulated by light become less sensitive while areas that are exposed only to darkness gain in sensitivity. If you then move your eyes away from the scene and look at a bright white surface, you see exactly the same scene that you had been viewing, but the light areas now appear dark and vice versa.**

5. List the eye structures that light passes through as it travels from outside the body to the retina. **Cornea → aqueous humor → pupil → lens → vitreous humor → retina.**

6. List the ear structures that sound waves and resulting vibrations pass through as they travel from outside the body to the organ of Corti. **Outer ear → tympanic membrane → ossicles → oval window → inner ear → fluid in cochlea.**

7. Why do humans and other animals have two nostrils? **Humans evolved from ancestors with bilateral symmetry, including two nostrils. Consequently, we also have two nostrils. In much the same way that having ears on both sides of our heads are advantageous, two nostrils might have been advantageous to our animal ancestors because they allow better determination of the location from which a chemical emanates in three-dimensional space. Also, two nostrils provide more surface area for olfactory epithelium, and so have more sensory cells for chemoreception.**

8. When your nasal passages are blocked due to a heavy cold, food seems to lose its flavor. For example, pizza tastes like salt. Explain why this is so. **Actually, upon testing, persons with severe colds who say that they've lost their sense of taste have usually been found to have completely normal taste sensations. Recall that the primary taste sensations are sweet, bitter, salty, and sour. Much of what we think of as taste, therefore, is actually smell. When a person has a cold, the nasal passages are blocked and chemoreceptors of the nasal epithelium are similarly blocked, depressing the sense of smell.**

9. In what part of the eye are cataracts located? **A cataract is a gradual clouding of the lens that is associated with aging. The clouding may skew the trajectory of incoming light rays; if the lens becomes totally opaque, light cannot enter the eye at all.**

10. What is the relationship between the fluid in the anterior cavity and the disease glaucoma? **Glaucoma results when excess aqueous humor accumulates in the anterior cavity. This causes collapse of blood vessels to the retina, and vision deteriorates as neurons of the retina and optic nerve die.**

EXERCISE 39

HUMAN SKELETAL AND MUSCULAR SYSTEMS

Materials and Equipment

39.1 Adult Human Skeleton

Per student
- pipe cleaner
- lens cleaning solution
- prepared slide of a synovial joint
- prepared slide of ground compact bone, c.s. (optional)
- compound microscope
- lint-free cloth
- prepared slide of skeletal muscle, c.s.

Per student group (table)
- femur
- articulated human skeleton (optional)
- femur sawed in half lengthwise

Per lab room
- labeled chart and illustrations of the adult human skeleton

39.2 Leverage and Movement

Per student pair
- pair of scissors
- pair of forceps
- textbook and pencil
- toggle switch mounted on a board

39.3 Walking

None required.

Preparation of Materials and Equipment

None required.

Notes

39.1 Adult Human Skeleton

Human skeletons, even those of plastic, are very fragile and very expensive. Emphasize to students that they should touch the skeleton only when necessary, and then only with the pipe cleaners provided.

Because of expense, you may wish to have only one adult human skeleton per lab room. The instructor may wish to schedule activities in this exercise so that only a small group of students will examine the skeleton at any one time.

Ordering Information

See General Laboratory Supplies list on page vii for basic items.

39.1 Adult Human Skeleton

articulated adult human skeleton, with stand, natural bone — Carolina 24-6786

articulated adult human skeleton, with stand, plastic bone, human, c.s., ground thin, prepared slide — Carolina 24-6909 — Ward's 82 V 3010

bone, human, c.s., ground thin, prepared slide — Triarch HB8-4

human femur — Ward's 82 V 3780

human femur, bisected longitudinally

pipe cleaner — Ward's 82 V 1115 — or local variety store

skeletal muscle, c.s., prepared slide — Carolina 31-2058 — or 31-2064

skeleton, labeled color chart — Carolina 57-6615

synovial joint model — Ward's 81 V 3444

synovial joint, prepared slide — Ward's 93 V 3319

39.2 Leverage and Movement

toggle switch — local hardware or electrical supply

39.3 Walking

None required.

Answers to In-Text Questions

39.1 Adult Human Skeleton

A. Identification of Some Bones

There are 206 separate bones in the adult human skeleton. Using the labeled chart and illustrations of the human skeleton, identify the following bones on the articulated human skeleton and label them in Figure 39-1.

"In order from top to bottom the callouts the left side are hyoid, sternum, ribs, carpals, metacarpals, and phalanges (foot). Similarly, those on the right are skull, clavicle, scapula, humerus, ulna, radius, sacrum, coxal bone, coccyx, phalanges (hand), femur, tibia, fibula, tarsals, and metatarsals."

B. Joints

Joint	Adjacent Bones
TABLE 39-1 Bones That Form the Major Synovial Joints	
Wrist	**radius and tarsals**
Elbow	**humerus with ulna and radius**
Shoulder	**humerus and scapula**
Hip	**coxal bone and femur**
Knee	**femur and tibia**
Ankle	**femur with tibia and fibula**

C. Surface Features

2. …Which part of the arm does the projection move with, forearm or upper arm? **Forearm**
While still touching this projection, alternately turn the hand palm down and up. Does the projection move? **No**
Which bone belongs to this projection? **Ulna**

TABLE 39-2 Surface Features and Bones

Surface Feature	Bone
Knuckles	metatarsals
Bump next to the wrist and on the same side of the upper appendage as the little finger	ulna
Smaller bump next to the wrist and on the same side of the upper appendage as the thumb	radius
Bump next to and outside the ankle	fibula
Bump next to and inside the ankle	tibia

D. Structure of a Bone

1. …Which bone does the femur join? **Coxal bone.** To which bone of the skeleton does the other end join? **Tibia**
…Are there small tunnels opening onto the surface of the femur? **Yes**
2. …Which kind of bone tissue looks denser? **Compact bone.**
Comparing pieces of equal size, which kind of bone tissue looks lighter? **Spongy bone**

39.2 Leverage and Movement

A. Classes of Levers

1. …Test your understanding of the three classes of levers by examining the objects listed in the following table and then matching them with the appropriate class of lever.

Lever		Object
Class I.	a	a. scissors
Class II.	b	b. toggle switch or light switch
Class III.	c	c. forceps

B. Analysis of Simple Movements

1. …Which joint is the fulcrum? **Elbow**
…In which case—lifting the pencil or the textbook—was the tension in the biceps brachii the greatest?
The tension was greatest when lifting the textbook.
…Where is the pulling force applied? (insertion, origin, or both the insertion and origin)
Both the insertion and origin.
…What class of lever (I, II, or III) is illustrated by the preceding example? **III**
2. …What class of lever is illustrated by this movement? **I**
…Is the tension in the biceps brachii greater with or without the book? **With the book**
Is the tension in the triceps brachii greater with or without the book? **With the book**
3. …What class of lever does this movement exemplify? **II**

39.3 Walking

1. …What part of the foot (toe or heel) strikes the ground first? **Heel**
What part of your foot leaves the ground last? **Big toe**
Does it leave passively, or does it push off? **Pushes off**
2. …Does the pelvic girdle rotate more during short or long strides? **Long**
…...What happens?
Our hips bump because of lateral displacement.
3. …Do their heads remain at the same level, or do they bob up and down? **Bob up and down**

Name _____

Section No. _____

HUMAN SKELETAL AND MUSCULAR SYSTEMS

Pre-lab Questions

1. There are _____ classes of levers. a. two; b. three; c. four; d. more than four.

2. The end of the skeletal muscle that remains stationary during a movement is the: a. action; b. origin; c. insertion; d. none of the above.

3. The step cycle of walking consists of: a. a stance phase; b. a swing phase; c. a and b; d. none of the above.

4. Tendons connect: a. bones to bones; b. skeletal muscles to bones; c. ligaments to bones; d. skeletal muscles to tendons.

5. In an isometric contraction of a skeletal muscle: a. the tension in the muscle increases; b. movement occurs; c. no movement occurs; d. both a and c occur.

6. The class of lever in which the effort is located between the fulcrum and the load is called: a. class I; b. class II; c. class III; d. class IV.

7. Which bone is part of the axial skeleton? a. clavicle; b. radius; c. coxal bone; d. sternum.

8. Ligaments connect: a. bones to bones; b. skeletal muscles to bones; c. tendons to bones; d. skeletal muscles to tendons.

9. The two kinds of bone tissue are: a. compact and loose; b. compact and spongy; c. dense and spongy; d. loose and dense.

10. In an isotonic contraction of a skeletal muscle: a. the tension in the muscle increases; b. movement occurs; c. no movement occurs; d. both a and c.

HUMAN SKELETAL AND MUSCULAR SYSTEMS

Answers to Pre-lab Questions in Lab Manual Order

1.	a	6.	c
2.	b	7.	b
3.	d	8.	b
4.	b	9.	d
5.	b	10.	c

Answers to Pre-lab Questions in Instructor's Manual Order

1.	b	6.	c
2.	b	7.	d
3.	c	8.	a
4.	b	9.	b
5.	d	10.	b

Answers to Post-lab Questions

1. Match the following bones to their location in the body. **a. iv; b. v; c. iii; d. i; e. ii**

2. Label this photo of a femur that has been sawed in half lengthwise. **See Figure 39-10, page 634.**

3. Identify the bones indicated in this illustration. **a. clavicle; b. sternum; c. humerus; d. rib; e. vertebra; f. radius.**

4. Label the fibrous capsule and synovial membrane of this joint. a. **fibrous capsule;** b. **synovial membrane.**

5. Define the following terms: a. the *insertion* of a skeletal muscle—**the attachment of the end of the muscle that usually moves.** b. the *origin* of a skeletal muscle—**the attachment of the end of the muscle that usually remains stationary.** c. the *action* of a skeletal muscle—**a description of the movement produced.** In your own words describe one step cycle of walking. **The leg swings forward (swing phase), heel strikes ground followed by ball of foot and toes. Weight is shifted onto this foot (stance phase) as the other leg is in its swing phase. Pelvic girdle rotates as ball of the foot pushes off (return to swing phase).**

6. Explain the difference between isometric and isotonic contractions. How are both important to normal body movements? **isometric contraction—muscle increases in tone or tension, but doesn't shorten; isotonic contraction—muscle shortens, but doesn't increase in tone.**

7. Draw and label the structures of a typical skeletal muscle organ. **See figure 39-11, page 635**

8. In your own words, describe one step in the walking cycle. **The leg swings forward (swing phase), heel strikes ground followed by ball of foot and toes. Weight is shifted onto this foot (stance phase) as the other leg is in its swing phase. Pelvic girdle rotates as ball of the foot pushes off (return to swing phase).**

9. The skeletal muscle that flexes (bends) the forearm after pronation (palm down position as in a pull-up) is the brachialis. Its origin is the humerus, and the insertion is the upper front of the ulna. Identify the class of lever involved and explain why you made this choice. **The lever system described above (muscle and its attachments) is III class as the effort exerted by the muscle on its insertion (upper front of ulna) is between the fulcrum (elbow) and the majority of the load (most of the ulna and forearm).**

10. Search the World Wide Web for sites that describe diseases of bones (for example, osteoporosis) and of skeletal muscles (such as muscular dystrophy). List two sites and briefly summarize their contents. **Answers will vary.**

EXERCISE 40

HUMAN BLOOD AND CIRCULATION

Materials and Equipment

40.1 Blood

Per student
- compound microscope
- lens cleaning solution (optional)
- dropper bottle of immersion oil (optional)
- prepared slide of Wright stained smear of human blood
- lens paper
- lint free cloth (optional)

Per student group
- plain capillary tubes
- ruler or hematocrit reader
- microhematocrit centrifuge
- blood kits (optional)

Per lab room
- demonstration slide of eosinophil
- blood waste disposal jar
- dropper bottle of aseptic or simulated blood
- glass slide and wax pencil or plastic blood typing trays
- demonstration slide of basophil
- box of depression or stirring sticks

40.2 Blood Vessels

Per student
- compound microscope
- prepared slide of c.s. of companion artery and vein
- prepared slide of mesentary, w.m.

Per student pair
- fish net
- 3 x 7 cm piece absorbent cotton
- coverslip
- small fish (3 to 4 cm long) in aquarium
- petri dish half
- dissecting needle

Per student group
- squirt bottle of dechlorinated water
- anesthetic ("Biocalm") dissolved in dechlorinated water

Per lab room
- clock with a second hand
- several meter sticks taped vertically to the walls

40.3 The Heart

Per lab bench
- Human heart model

Per lab room
- syringe with acetylcholine solution
- **demonstration** of beating heart of doubly pithed frog kept moist with amphibian Ringer's solution
- syringe with epinephrine solution

Preparation of Materials and Equipment

40.1 Blood

None required.

40.2 Blood Vessels

Dechlorinated water: Allow tap water to stand one day or use a chemical dechlorinator ("Clorout"; see *Ordering Information*) for immediate use.

40.3 The Heart

Doubly pithed frog: Grasp the frog firmly with your subordinate hand, holding the body firmly with your thumb and the snout between your second and third fingers. Bend the head downward slightly and imagine a line across the back of the head extending between the anterior edges of the tympanic membranes. Insert a dissecting needle into the spinal column exactly in the middle of this line, keeping the tip of the needle pointed backward in the neural canal. You should not have to force the needle; muscle tremors should indicate that the spinal cord has been severed. Withdraw the needle partway, keeping the tip in the neural canal and push it forward into the brain. Rotate the needle within the cranium to destroy brain tissue, then withdraw. The frog should be flaccid.

Dissection of pithed frog: Lay the pithed frog on its back in a dissecting pan and make an incision through the skin just to the left of the center. Pin back the skin so that the beating heart is visible. Every minute or two, squirt a pipet full of amphibian Ringer's solution over the body cavity to keep it moist.

    The heart should continue to beat for several hours.

Amphibian Ringer's solution:		
	KCl	0.42 g
	$NaCl$	9.0 g
	$CaCl_2$	0.24 g
	$NaHCO_3$	0.20 g
	dH_2O to make	1 L

    Amphibian Ringer's solution may also be purchased (see *Ordering Information*).

Notes

40.1 Blood

    Instructors may have to search several prepared slides to find examples of Wright-stained eosinophils and basophils. These should be on demonstration at compound microscopes in each lab room.

40.2 Blood Vessels

    Goldfish are commonly used for microscopic observation of tail capillaries. Blind cavefish, albino gouramis, or albino catfish also provide excellent subjects for this exercise. Fish wrapped in wet cotton may be taped to the petri dish; place a small amount of dechlorinated water on the tail and add a glass microscope slide or coverslip to form the wet mount. If the tail isn't moving, a covering may not be necessary. The entire petri dish is placed on the microscope stage for observation. You may wish to add a chemical slime replacer ("Stress Coat") to the aquarium to replace the natural skin secretion, which may have been interrupted by handling after the fish are returned.

40.3 The Heart

    Draw acetylcholine and epinephrine solutions (purchased as 1:10,000 concentration (see *Ordering Information*) into appropriately labeled 1-mL syringes. Record the normal heartbeats of the frog heart moistened with Ringer's solution. Add three drops of the substance to be tested and re-record the heartbeats. Wash the heart with Ringer's solution and allow time to restabilize before applying another substance.

Ordering Information

See General Laboratory Supplies list on page vii for basic items

40.1 Blood

antisera for human blood, ABO, Rh	Ward's	36 W 6901
capillary tube sealant	Ward's	15 V 2040
capillary tubes	Ward's	15 V 2099
human blood smear, Wright stained, prepared slide	Triarch	HC1-40
microhematocrit centrifuge	Ward's	15 V 1000
Refill kit for simulated blood typing kit	Ward's	36 W 0034
simulated ABO Rh blood typing kit	Ward's	36 V 0019

40.2 Blood Vessels

absorbent cotton	Carolina	71-2635
artery and vein, c.s., prepared slide	Triarch	HG2-11
Biocalm	Ward's	39W 3609
Clorout	Carolina	67-1990
fantail goldfish	Carolina	14-5292
fish net	Carolina	67-1950
Stress Coat	Carolina	67-1924

40.3 The Heart

acetylcholine, 1:10,000	Carolina	84-1613
adrenalin (epinephrine), 1:10,000	Carolina	84-2091
calcium chloride	Fisher	C79-500
frog Ringer's solution	Ward's	37 W 5100
leopard frog, large	Carolina	14-6390
potassium chloride	Fisher	P217-500
sodium bicarbonate	Fisher	S233-500
sodium chloride	Fisher	S271-500
tuberculin syringe, 1 mL, disposable	Fisher	14-829-9

Answers to In-Text Questions

40.1 Blood

A. Formed Elements (Cells and Platelets) of Blood

1. ...What part of the cell, nucleus or cytoplasm, is stained blue/purple? **Nucleus**

B. Hematocrit

3. ...Determine the percent packed red blood cell volume using a ruler (Figure 40-5) or mechanical measuring device and record it: **"Fill in value"**%

C. Blood Typing

…Individuals with which blood type (sometimes called the *universal donor*) can theoretically give blood to all other blood types? **O**

…Explain why this is so. **Red blood cells from type O donors do not have antigens on their surface, and therefore do not agglutinate in the presence of anti-A and anti-B in the host's plasma.**

Individuals with which blood type (sometimes called the *universal recipient*) can theoretically receive blood from any other type? **AB**

…Explain why this is so. **Hosts with type AB blood do not have antibodies in their plasma, and therefore transfused red blood cells with A or B antigen on their surfaces can't be agglutinated.**

4. …Record the blood type. **"Fill in blood type."**

40.2 Blood Vessels

A. Arteries

…Would you expect blood flow to be more rapid in arteries or veins? **Arteries**

Explain your answer. (*Hint:* look at the pressure differences between arteries, capillaries, and veins in Table 40-5). **Blood flow in arteries is faster because the pressure difference between them and arterioles and capillaries is greater than that between capillaries and veins. Also, the lumen of arteries is narrower than that of veins.**

4. …Compared to your resting heart rate, does your heart rate increase, decrease, or remain the same? **Decreases**

5. …After running in place, does your heart rate increase, decrease, or remain the same? **Increase** Explain these results. **During exercise the rate at which blood is circulated through the body increases. This is accomplished by increasing heart rate and the amount of blood pushed out of the heart with each beat.**

TABLE 40-6 Heart Rate under Different Conditions

"Fill in cells." Numbers should follow the above pattern.

B. Capillaries

1. Can you see red blood cells inside them? **Yes**

4. …Can you see red blood cells moving through them? **Yes** (yes or no) What other vessels can you identify? **There are arterioles and venules, larger vessels also may be seen.**

Is the blood flowing at the same speed in all of the capillaries? **No** (yes or no)

Describe blood flow in the fish's tail.

Muscular arteries deliver blood to arterioles. It then flows into capillaries, which branch from arterioles. After exchange of nutrients, wastes, gasses, etc., capillaries join together and blood flows into larger and larger veins.

C. Veins

2. Describe and explain any changes that take place.

The veins collapse as blood flows out them due to gravity.

TABLE 40-7 Measurement of Venous Blood Pressure

"Fill in cells with observed and calculated numbers."

4. …How does the venous pressure compare to arterial pressures?

Venous pressure is lower than that of arteries.

5. …Does the vein fill up with blood again? **No** (yes or no) Now remove the finger and observe what happens. Try this again, but press blood in the opposite direction. Discuss your observations.

Valves only allow blood to flow in veins toward the heart. When blood is squeezed out toward the heart it can't flow back into the segment. Whereas blood flows rapidly back into the segment when pushed out away from the heart.

40.3 The Heart

B. Demonstration of Frog Heart Function

1. …Is the heart beating? **Yes**

2. …Does the entire heart muscle contract simultaneously or do some parts contract before others? **Some parts contract before others.**

Is there a pattern in the way each contraction sweeps across the heart or is it totally random as to when a particular part contracts? **There is a pattern in the way each contraction sweeps across the heart.**

If you observe carefully, you can see the order in which the chambers contract. Record your observations.

The atria contract prior to the ventricles.

TABLE 40-8 Effect of Acetylcholine and Epinephrine on the Heart Rate of a Frog

"Fill in cells with observed data."

Figure 40-15 Bar graph for plotting heart rate data.

"Plot data from Table 40-15."

7. Describe the effects of acetylcholine and epinephrine on the heart rate.

Acetylcholine slows down and epinephrine speeds up heart rate.

HUMAN BLOOD AND CIRCULATION

Pre-lab Questions

1.   How many chambers does the frog heart have? a. one; b. two; c. three; d. four.

2.   The most common leukocyte in the blood is: a. a lymphocyte; b. an eosinophil; c. a basophil; d. a neutrophil.

3.   The cellular fragments in the blood that function in blood clotting are: a. erythrocytes; b. leukocytes; c. platelets; d. none of the above.

4.   Blood vessels that connect networks of capillary beds are: a. arteries; b. veins; c. portal veins; d. both b and c.

5.   The primary pacemaker of the heart is the: a. bicuspid valve; b. tricuspid valve; c. aorta; d. sinoatrial node.

6.   From which chamber of the heart does the right ventricle receive blood? a. right atrium; b. left atrium; c. left ventricle; d. none of the above.

7.   Red blood cells are: a. erythrocytes; b. leukocytes; c. platelets; d. all of the above.

8.   Blood vessels that return blood from capillaries back to the heart are: a. arteries; b. veins; c. portal veins; d. arterioles.

9.   Blood contains: a. dissolved gases; b. dissolved nutrients; c. dissolved hormones; d. all of the above.

10.   The number of circuits in the circulatory systems of humans is: a. one; b. two; c. three; d. four.

EXERCISE 40

HUMAN BLOOD AND CIRCULATION

Answers to Post-lab Questions

1. Name and give the staining characteristics and functions of the three leukocytes with specific granules.
   a. **Neutrophils have neutral staining specific granules with typical blood stains. Functions include leaving blood vessels early in an inflammation to become phagocytes.**
   b. **Eosinophils have pink staining specific granules with typical blood stains. Functions include phagocytosis of antigen-antibody complexes.**
   c. **Basophils have blue/purple staining specific granules with typical blood stains. Functions include containing histamine and heparin.**

2. Describe the shape, content, and function of an erythrocyte. **An erythrocyte is a biconcave disc without a nucleus, about 2 x 7 μm in size. It is essentially a bag of hemoglobin (for O_2 transport) and enzymes, including carbonic anhydrase, which is important in CO_2 transport.**

3. Why can't you give type A blood to a type B patient? **The erythrocytes of type A blood have A-antigens on their surfaces. The plasma of type B blood has naturally occurring anti-A antibodies, which will cause agglutination of the transfused type A erythrocytes.**

4. Describe how to take someone's hematocrit. **a. Fill a heparinized capillary tube to the mark with blood and seal it with clay. b. Place the sealed capillary tube in a microhematocrit centrifuge and spin. c. Calculate or determine the percent packed red blood cell volume using a ruler (height of packed red blood cells/height of blood column x 100) or mechanical measuring device.**

5. Identify the indicated blood vessel. **Small muscular artery**

6. Pretend you are an erythrocyte in the right atrium of the heart. Describe one trip through the human circulatory system, ending back where you started. **Right atrium → right ventricle → pulmonary circuit → left atrium → systemic circuit → right atrium (a more complex answer is possible).**

7. Explain how the heart of a doubly pithed frog can continue to contract in an organized manner after the nervous system is destroyed. **The heart has a pacemaker (sinoatrial node) and its own conduction system, which can operate independently of the nervous system.**

8. How is heart rate controlled by the nervous system in an intact organism? **Neurons around the sinoatrial node release acetylcholine, which slows the heart rate, and norepinephrine, which speeds it up.**

9. Considering its relationship with other systems of the body, what is the importance of the circulatory system? **From an evolutionary viewpoint, this adaptation was necessary for the evolution of large organisms with specialized cells, tissues, and organs. The quick and efficient transport of substances from one place to another via the circulatory system means cells located far apart are actually in close functional contact.**

10. Search the World Wide Web for sites about arteriosclerosis. List two sites and briefly summarize their contents. **Answers will vary.**

HUMAN RESPIRATION

Materials and Equipment

41.1 Breathing

Per student pair
- two pieces of paper, each approx. 14 x 21.5 cm.

Per student pair
- metric tape measure
- large caliper with linear scale, such as a Collyer pelvimeter

Per student group
- functional model of lung
- models of the organs and structures of the respiratory system
- prepared slide of mammalian lung

Per lab room
- clock with second hand on wall
- frogs in terrarium or video of breathing frog

41.2 Spirometry

Per student group
- noseclip (optional)
- disposable mouthpieces for spirometer
- simple spirometer or lung volume bags

41.3 Control of Respiration

Per student pair
- small mirror
- clock with second hand
- place to exercise

41.4 Experiment: Physiology of Exercise

Per student
- calculator

Per lab room
- television or monitor
- videocassette "Experiment: Biology, The Physiology of Exercise"
- videocassette player

Preparation of Materials and Equipment

None required.

Notes

Instructor should demonstrate proper use of spirometer or lung volume bag to calculate lung volumes. Emphasize that each student must use a sterile mouthpiece and should only exhale into the apparatus, never inhale from it.

Students should be seated in a straight high-backed chair with their backs straight. Lung volumes may change in the course of an experiment if the student changes position and thus alters the size of the chest cavity or if the subject undergoes even mild exercise.

Students should breathe normally for the first four breaths before exhaling into a spirometer or lung bag. It is especially important that the fourth breath (just before the deep inhalation) is a normal, quiet expiration.

Watch carefully for signs of hyperventilation and faintness when performing the deep breathing, lung volume determination, and control of respiration portions of this exercise. Students should stop immediately if they feel faint.

Instructors may wish to videotape a frog breathing normally for class viewing. No commercial source for such a film was known at the time of publication of this manual.

Ordering Information

See General Laboratory Supplies list on page vii for basic items

41.1 Breathing

Collyer pelvimeter	U.S.E Surgical	30-005	
frogs, leopard, living	Carolina	14-6400	
functional model of lung	Carolina	69-2636	
mammalian lung, inflatable	Ward's	14 V 8329	
mammalian lung, prepared slide	Ward's	93 V 4891	or composite, w.m. Wards 93 V 6922
metric tape measure	Carolina	70-2629	
models of organ systems	Ward's	81 V 3560	
paper	local supply		

41.2 Spirometry

lung volume bags	Carolina	69-2645
noseclip	A-M Systems	166000
replacement mouthpieces, disposable (for lung volume bags)	Carolina	69-2647
small mirror	local supply	
spirometer mouthpieces, replacements (for portable dry spirometer)	Carolina	69-2671
spirometer, portable dry	Carolina	69-2670

41.3 Control of Respiration

Small mirror from local supply.

41.4 Experiment: Physiology of Exercise

Videocassette "Experiment: Biology, The Physiology of Exercise"—Films for the Humanities and Sciences, Inc.

Answers to In-Text Questions

41.1 Breathing

B. Ventilation

2. Pull down the rubber diaphragm. Describe what happens to the balloons.

The balloons inflate as air is drawn into them.

As you pull down the rubber diaphragm, does the volume of the space in the container increase or decrease? **Increase**

As the volume changes, does the pressure in the container increase or decrease? **Decrease**

As the balloons inflate, does the volume of air in the balloons increase or decrease? **Increase**

Why do the balloons inflate?

The balloons inflate because pulling the rubber diaphragm down increases the volume of the transparent chamber. As the amount of air in this chamber is constant, its pressure decreases. Air pressure in the balloons, which are open to the outside, is now higher than that of the transparent chamber causing them to expand.

3. Push up on the rubber diaphragm. Describe what happens to the balloons and why it takes place.

The balloons deflate as air is pushed out of them. This occurs because pushing up on the rubber diaphragm decreases the volume of the transparent chamber, increasing its air pressure. Pressure in the balloons is now relatively lower, causing them to collapse.

5. Pucker up your lips and inhale. As you inhale, place one piece of paper directly over your lips. What occurs?

The paper sticks to the lips, held in place by the suction force.

6. …What difference did the water make?

The two pieces of paper adhere to each other.

7. …Count and record how many times the frog lowers and raises the floor of the mouth (one breath) in 3 minutes. **"Fill in observed number."** breaths/3 minutes

Divide by three to calculate the average respiratory rate and record it: **"Fill in calculated number."**

C. Breathing Movements

1. …What do you feel during each inspiration?

The abdominal muscles relax.

each expiration?

The abdominal muscles contract.

2. …What do you feel during each inspiration?

The chest rises.

each expiration?

The chest falls.

D. Measurements of the Thorax

TABLE 41-2 Chest Measurements (cm)

"Fill in cells with observed values."

3. …Interpret the data in Table 41-2 and in your own words describe changes in the size of the thorax during

a. a restful inhalation **There may be slight increases in the C_{xp} and A/PD.**

b. a passive exhalation **There may be slight decreases in the C_{xp} and A/PD.**

c. a forced inhalation **There should be large increases in the C_{xp} and A/PD.**

d. a force exhalation **There should be large decreases in the C_{xp} and A/PD.**

Does the size of the thorax change significantly during a restful inhalation or a passive exhalation? **No** (yes or no)

How does the shape of the thorax change during a forced inhalation?

During a forced inhalation the thorax increases in size by raising the rib cage forward (anteriorly) with a greater displacement along its lower (inferior) margin.

How does the shape of the thorax change during a subsequent forced exhalation?

During a forced exhalation, the thorax decreases in size by the rib cage falling or being pulled back to its position prior to inhalation.

41.2 Spirometry

1. ...Repeat this procedure two more times (trials 2 and 3) and calculate the total and average tidal volume at rest. **"Fill in observed and calculated values."**

TABLE 41-3 Vital Capacity and Lung Volumes at Rest (mL)

"Fill in cells with calculated values."

2. Determine the volume of air you can forcibly exhale after a restful inhalation (average of three trials). **"Fill in observed and calculated values."**

3. Determine the volume of air you can forcibly exhale after a forceful inhalation (average of three trials). **"Fill in observed and calculated values."**

4. Calculate the FEV at rest by subtracting step 1's result from step 2's result. **"Fill in calculated value."**

5. Calculate the FIV at rest by subtracting step 2's result from step 3's result. **"Fill in calculated value."**

6. Does **vital capacity** change as tidal volume increases or decreases? **No**

7. Measure and record your height in centimeters. **"Fill in observed value."**

...Is there a relationship between vital capacity and height? If so, describe it mathematically using a graphing calculator or with words.

There is a positive linear relationship (y=mx+b) between height and vital capacity.

41.3 Control of Respiration

2. ...Record the number of breaths: **"Fill in observed number of breaths in 3 minutes"** breaths

4. ...As times goes on, does it become easier or more difficult to continue rapid deep breathing? **More difficult**

Immediately have your lab partner count and record the number of breaths you take in the next 3 minutes: **"Fill in observed number of breaths."**

6. ...Does hyperventilation increase, decrease, or have no effect on the CO_2 concentration of the blood? **Decrease**

7. ...Immediately after sitting down, again have your lab partner count how many breaths you take in 3 minutes and record it: **"Fill in observed number of breaths."**

...Does running in place increase or decrease the CO_2 concentration of the blood? **Increase (actually blood gases don't change as much as might be expected).** What causes the CO_2 concentration to change while you are running in place? **While running in place the metabolic rate increases. Increased respiration means more CO_2 is released in the skeletal muscle and related tissues of the body.**

9. Use Table 41-4 to summarize your results: **Hyperventilation decreases respiratory rate and increases the time we could hold our breaths. Exercise produces the opposite results.**

TABLE 41-4 Respiratory Data

Prediction 1: If respiration removes CO_2 from the body, then hyperventilation will lower levels in the blood, decrease respiration rate, and increase breath holding time.

Prediction 2: If exercise increases body CO_2 production, then it will tend to increase blood CO_2, increase respiration rate, and decrease breath holding time.

"Fill in cells with observed and calculated values."

Conclusions: The predictions are accepted.

41.4 Experiment: Physiology of Exercise

3. Independent variable **severity of exercise**

Dependent variables **heat rate, systolic pressure, respiratory rate, and tidal volume**

Controlled variables **same subject, same environmental conditions, adequate rest period, etc.**

4. Plot these results in the following graphs:

"Plot data from Table 41-5."

TABLE 41-5 Physiology of Exercise				
Prediction: If the metabolic rate due to exercise is increasing, then all of these dependent variables will increase.				
Intensity of exercise	Heart rate (beats/min)	Systolic pressure (mm Hg)	Respiratory rate (Breaths/min.)	Tidal volume (L)
0 km/hr (rest)	6.6 X 10	120	1.3 X 10	0.6
10 km/hr	8 X 10	145	1.4 X 10	1.8
15 km/hr	1.1 X 100	155	1.7 X 10	2.3
20 km/hr	1.4 X 100	190	2.0 X 10	2.7
25 km/hr	1.8 X 100	195	2.7 X 10	3.0
Conclusion:				

5. …At 10 km/hr, did respiratory rate increase? **No (or slightly)** (yes or no) Did tidal volume increase? **Yes** (yes or no)

6. During which period of work did the respiratory rate first increase? **15** km/hr

7. Calculate the amount of air exhaled per minute during the most strenuous exercise period (25 km/hr). **81** L/min.

Name _____

Section No. _____

HUMAN RESPIRATION

Pre-lab Questions

1. An instrument that measures lung volumes is a: a. caliper; b. spirometer; c. barometer; d. stethoscope.

2. Human ventilation is: a. negative pressure inhalation; b. positive pressure inhalation; c. negative pressure exhalation; d. both b and c.

3. Which of the following muscles may contract during inspiration? a. external intercostals; b. internal intercostals; c. abdominal; d. both b and c.

4. An untied inflated balloon flies because: a. the pressure is higher inside than outside the balloon; b. the pressure is lower inside than outside the balloon; c. air flows down its pressure gradient; d. both a and c occur.

5. Respiration is controlled by: a. chemoreceptors; b. stretch receptors; c. centers in the brain stem; d. all of the above.

6. Which muscles may contract during a more forceful expiration? a. external intercostals; b. diaphragm; c. abdominal; d. both b and c.

7. Which of the following muscles contract during a restful expiration? a. external intercostals; b. internal intercostals; c. diaphragm; d. none of the above.

8. Frog ventilation is: a. negative pressure inhalation; b. positive pressure inhalation; c. positive pressure exhalation; d. both b and c.

9. Vital capacity is always equal to: a. tidal volume; b. forced inhalation volume; c. forced exhalation volume; d. a + b + c.

10. The most important stimulus in the control of respiration is the concentration in the blood and other body fluids of: a. oxygen (O_2); b. carbon dioxide (CO_2); c. hydrogen ions (H^+); d. nitrogen (N_2).

HUMAN RESPIRATION

1.	a	6.	d
2.	d	7.	d
3.	c	8.	b
4.	d	9.	d
5.	a	10.	b

1.	b	6.	c
2.	a	7.	d
3.	a	8.	d
4.	d	9.	d
5.	d	10.	b

Answers to Post-lab Questions

1. Which skeletal muscles are contracted during: a. restful inhalation—**Primarily the diaphragm.** b. forced inhalation—**Primarily the diaphragm and external intercostal muscles.** c. restful exhalation—**None.** d. forced exhalation—**Primarily the internal intercostals and abdominals.**

2. How does the size of the thorax change during: a. inhalation—**Increases.** b. exhalation—**Decreases.**

3. How does the potential volume of the pleural sacs change during: a. inhalation—**Increases.** b. exhalation—**Decreases.**

4. Define these terms: a. *negative pressure inhalation*—**The suction caused by the negative pressure created in the lungs by the contraction of the muscles of inspiration. The air flows because pressure is higher outside than inside the lungs.** b. *positive pressure exhalation*—**The size of the thorax and pleural sacs decreases, pressure in the lungs increases and air flows out of the body down its concentration gradient.**

5. How does breathing in a human differ from that of a frog? **Frog inspiration is positive pressure inhalation versus negative pressure inhalation for humans; also, humans have diaphragms and frogs don't.**

6. Explain the relationship between vital capacity, tidal volume, forced inhalation volume, and forced exhalation volume. **Tidal volume (TV) is the volume of air inhaled or exhaled during breathing. It normally varies from a minimum at rest to a maximum during strenuous exercise. Forced inhalation volume (FIV) is the volume of air you can voluntarily inhale after inhalation of the tidal volume. Forced exhalation volume (FEV) is the volume of air you can voluntarily exhale after an exhalation of the tidal volume. IRV and ERV both decrease as TV increases. Vital capacity always equals the sum of TV, FIV, and FEV.**

7. What substance is the most important stimulus in the control of respiration? **Carbon dioxide (CO_2).** How is its production linked to changes in metabolic rate, such as occur during exercise? **Exercise increases the level of CO_2 in the body as well as decreases the level of oxygen. Rising levels of CO_2 stimulate increases in the depth and rate of breathing, resulting in moving more CO_2 out of the body and more oxygen (O_2) into the body.**

8. Give an explanation for the fact that athletes' resting heart rates are usually slower than the average rate for healthy humans. **Exercise improves the efficiency of the respiratory and circulatory system. One of the effects is to increase the volume of blood pumped out of the heart with each contraction (stroke volume). Thus fewer heartbeats are needed to push the same amount of blood through the arteries and capillaries of the lungs and the rest of the body.**

9. Explain why hyperventilation can prolong the time you can hold your breath. Can this be dangerous (for example, hyperventilation followed by swimming under water)? **Hyperventilation decreases the level of CO_2 in blood. Yes, it can be dangerous, especially if exercising, because O_2 can be depleted before rising CO_2 forces a breath to be taken, therefore causing you to pass out.**

10. Search the World Wide Web for sites about emphysema. List two sites below and briefly summarize their contents. **Answers will vary.**

EXERCISE 42

ANIMAL DEVELOPMENT: GAMETOGENESIS AND FERTILIZATION

Materials and Equipment

42.1 Gametes

Per student
- compound microscope
- lens cleaning solution (optional)
- microscope slide and coverslip
- dissecting needle
- dropper bottle of immersion oil (optional)
- prepared slide of whole mount of bull sperm
- lens paper
- lint free cloth (optional)
- one piece plastic dropping pipet

Per student pair
- unfertilized hen's egg
- dissecting tray or pan
- two camel-hair brushes
- paper towels
- Syracuse dish
- dissecting microscope

Per lab group (table)
- model of a frog ovum (optional)

Per lab room
- phase contrast compound light microscope (optional)

42.2 Gametogenesis

Per student
- compound microscope
- prepared slide of adult mammalian testis (iron hematoxylin stain)
- prepared slide of adult mammalian ovary with corpus luteum
- prepared slide of adult mammalian ovary with mature follicles

42.3 Sperm Penetration and Fertilization in the Frog

Per student pair
- Syracuse dish
- dissecting microscope
- two camel-hair brushes

Per lab group (table)
- model of frog zygote (optional)

Per lab section
- live frog zygotes in pond water
- film or videotape of sperm penetration and fertilization in frog (optional)
- pond water

Preparation of Materials and Equipment

42.1 Gametes

Frog sperm: Living sperm can only be obtained by pithing a mature male leopard frog and removing the testis. (These are fairly large, yellowish, oval organs posterior to the kidneys on the dorsal surface of the peritoneal cavity.) Crush the testis thoroughly in 10 mL pond water or break the testis up by forcing the testis through a syringe with an 18-gauge needle. Mature testes are easily crushed, while those of immature males are white and very difficult to break up. Wait 5 to 15 minutes for full sperm activity, which may be determined by examination with a compound microscope.

Frog ova: Normal ovulation can be induced in female leopard frogs by injecting pituitary hormones into the peritoneal cavity. Leopard frogs may be purchased at any time of the year (see *Ordering Information*), but the amount of pituitary extract required to induce ovulation will vary with the time of year. Less extract will be needed the closer to the time of natural ovulation (March and April for northern Rana pipiens), but for best results each female frog should be injected with six whole pituitary glands. Pituitaries from female frogs are more effective, but those from male frogs may be used by doubling the number required (i.e., twelve male pituitaries are equivalent to six female pituitaries).

To obtain fresh pituitaries, first pith the frog, destroying only the spinal cord. Cut off the upper jaw and head, using heavy scissors and cutting from the corner of the mouth diagonally as far posterior as possible behind the eyes and tympanic membrane. The brain and part of the medulla should be intact. Insert the point of fine dissecting scissors into the back of the cranial cavity from the ventral side of the head (the roof of the mouth) at the foramen magnum (posterior opening of the cranial cavity leading to the spinal cord). Cut through the bone anteriorly and outward from the midline of the skull, keeping as far outward as possible to avoid injury to the pituitary. After both sides have been cut, the floor of the cranial cavity should be lifted with forceps as a small flap of bone. The pituitary will usually be found in this flap of bone, or it may be lying on the ventral surface of the brain. It is a small (1 to 2 mm) pink body often surrounded by white connective tissue, which should be removed by very gently rolling the gland on a damp paper towel. Be careful not to rupture the gland, and place it in a small vial or finger bowl with 1 mL of 10% Holtfreter's solution, aged tap water, or pond water.

Draw all pituitaries collected into a syringe with a small amount of water or Holtfreter's. Put a No. 22 needle on the syringe and inject the pituitaries through the lower abdominal wall of a female frog, directing the needle somewhat anteriorly. Be sure that the glands do not adhere to the sides of the syringe.

Place the injected female in a quiet, dim, undisturbed area. Ovulation will occur in approximately 72 hours after injection in October, November, and December. During January and February, ovulation occurs in 48 hours, and after 24 to 36 hours in March and April.

When the eggs are ready for release, the abdomen will become swollen. Firm but gentle pressure on the sides should cause release of a few eggs. To strip all or part of the egg, grasp the female firmly in the palm of one hand while holding the legs with the other hand. Push posteriorly on the abdomen with a firm but gentle milking motion to force the eggs from the uterus. Maintain gentle pressure once egg laying begins and form a spiral pattern of eggs into a clean, dry petri dish so that the eggs do not accumulate in piles.

The eggs may be scraped from the petri dish with a flat, non-metal object such as a flexible ruler and placed in pond water for class. Eggs that are to be fertilized should be allowed to remain adhering to the petri dish, but should be barely covered with pond water.

Eggs can be held for 2 to 3 days at most at 56 to 58°F, with viability decreasing over time.

A large female frog will produce at least 2000 eggs.

(Adapted from: K. W. Perkins, R. L. Franks, and R. H. Whitten. 1981. *Reptiles and Amphibians: Care and Culture*. Carolina Biological Supply Company, Burlington, NC/Gladstone, OR.)

Holtfreter's solution (100 mL):		
	NaCl	0.35 g
	KCl	0.005 g
	$CaCl_2$	0.01 g
	$NaHCO_3$	0.02 g
	glass distilled or deionized water	100.0 mL

Dilute this full-strength solution 1 part:9 parts glass-distilled water for use with eggs and zygotes up to the first 24 hours. Holtfreter's solution may also be purchased (see *Ordering Information*).

42.2 Gametogenesis

None required.

42.3 Sperm Penetration and Fertilization in the Frog

Frog zygotes: Fertilize eggs by gently pipetting fresh sperm suspension over the eggs in the petri dish. Allow to stand for about 5 minutes, then add 50 mL pond water. After about 20 minutes, pour off this water and add enough fresh water to barely cover the eggs. The eggs may then be gently scraped from the petri dish and transferred to culture bowls. Using scissors, cut the mass of eggs into groups of about 10 eggs each, with about 25 to 30 eggs per dish of 50 mL of pond water.

Fertilized eggs will rotate after one hour (at about the time of the first cleavage) so that the black animal hemisphere is uppermost.

Notes

Do not use tap water, which may contain harmful ions and chemicals, or distilled water, which does not contain necessary salts, for culturing frog eggs. Instead use 10% Holtfreter's solution (for the first 24 hours only), water from ponds known to support amphibian life, or purchased pond water.

Frogs for breeding and/or freeze-dried pituitary extract may be purchased from Carolina Biological Supply in various combinations, including pre-injected females (ready to spawn upon receipt). Consult the Carolina Biological Sciences catalogue for the most appropriate materials for your needs and specific shipping information.

Generally, fresh pituitaries will more reliably stimulate spawning of a larger number of viable eggs than will freeze-dried glands or extract.

Much valuable information can be gleaned from the handbook Reptiles and Amphibians: Care and Culture, published by Carolina Biological Supply. This handbook is supplied with orders for frogs, but additional copies can also be purchased (see *Ordering Information*).

Ordering Information

See General Laboratory Supplies list on page vii for basic items

42.1 Gametes

CaCl$_2$	Fisher	C79-500
disposable pipets	Fisher	13-711-5A
female leopard frog	Carolina	14-6350
frog development models	Ward's	81 W 0302
KCl	Fisher	P217-500
male leopard frog	Carolina	L 1495M
NaCl	Fisher	S271-500
NaHCO$_3$	Fisher	S233-500
pond water	Carolina	16-3380
Reptiles and Amphibians: Care and Culture	Carolina	45-4801
sterile hypodermic needles, 18 ga.	Ward's	14 W 2309
sterile hypodermic needles, 22 ga.	Ward's	14 W 2304
Syracuse dish	Carolina	74-2320
unfertilized hen's egg	local grocery store	
Holtfreter's standard solution, 100%*		

* Holtfreter's standard solution can be made using the instructions outlined under *Preparation of Materials and Equipment*.

42.2 Gametogenesis

mammalian ovary, section, with corpus luteum	Triarch	HN1-23
mammalian ovary, section, with mature follicles	Triarch	HN1-22
mammalian testis, section (iron hematoxylin stain)	Triarch	HM1-2

42.3 Sperm Penetration and Fertilization in the Frog

$CaCl_2$	Fisher	C79-500
camel-hair brush	local art supply store	
Female leopard frog	Carolina	14-6350
Frog Anatomy 1. Life Cycle, filmstrip	Ward's	67W 6500
frog development models	Ward's	81 W 0302
KCl	Fisher	P217-500
male leopard frog	Carolina	14-6356
NaCl	Fisher	S271-500
$NaHCO_3$	Fisher	S233-500
pond water	Carolina	16-3380
Reptiles and Amphibians: Care and Culture Free from	Carolina	
sterile hypodermic needles, 18 ga.	Ward's	14 W 2309
sterile hypodermic needles, 22 ga.	Ward's	14 W 2304
Syracuse dish	Carolina	74-2320

Holtfreter's standard solution, 100% *

Frog Life Cycle, still-frame video—see Carolina catalogue for ordering and/or rental information

* Holtfreter's standard solution can be made using the instructions outlined under *Preparation of Materials and Equipment*.

Answers to In-Text Questions

…What two Mendelian principles largely account for this?

The two Mendelian principles that largely account for this are segregation and independent assortment.

…Why?

Having individuals with range of characteristics maximizes the chance that the some will survive in a changing and unpredictable environment to reproduce and pass their genes on to the next generation.

42.1 Gametes

A. Sperm

2. …The acrosome contains enzymes that aid in the penetration of the egg. Considering its cell size, why does a sperm have a lot of mitochondria?

Sperm have a lot of mitochondria because of large amount of ATP needed to sustain motility.

3. …Describe what you see.

Sperm move by rotating their tails in a spiral motion through the water. This produces waves of force in a backward direction, propelling the sperm straight.

B. Ova

2. *Frog egg.*

(a) …Which surface (light-side or dark-side) of the ovum floats up in the pond water? **Dark-side**

(b) …Why does a frog ovum have less yolk than a bird ovum?

Frog eggs incubate at the environmental temperature (lower metabolic rate, no incubation as in bird eggs) and relative developmental time in the egg is shorter.

Suggest one or more possible functions for the black pigment in the animal pole. (*Hint:* One function is the same as that for the pigment in your skin that increases when exposed to sunlight.)

The black pigment protects the developing embryo from the ultra violet portion of sunlight.

3. …Why do most mammalian ova have very little yolk?

Mammalian embryos develop in the uterus and nutrition is delivered from the maternal blood supply, and later through the placenta.

42.3 Sperm Penetration and Fertilization in the Frog

…Why is external fertilization generally limited to aquatic animals?

Sperm could not swim to egg and gametes exposed to a terrestrial environment would dry out.

1. …Which surface of the zygote (light- or dark-side) floats up in the pond water? **Dark-side**

Name _____

Section No. _____

ANIMAL DEVELOPMENT: GAMETOGENESIS AND FERTILIZATION

Pre-lab Questions

1. One primary oocyte will form: a. one ovum; b. four ova; c. up to three polar bodies; d. a and c.

2. Most mammals have: a. internal fertilization; b. external fertilization; c. internal development; d. a and c.

3. Which process results in a zygote? a. meiosis; b. mitosis; c. fertilization; d. none of the above.

4. The formation of gametes in the gonads is called: a. gametogenesis; b. spermatogenesis; c. oogenesis; d. none of the above.

5. Ova are: a. male gametes; b. female gametes; c. specialized for motility; d. a and c.

6. Which structure is found in a section of the testis? a. secondary spermatocytes; b. sperm; c. Sertoli cells; d. all of the above.

7. Most animals reproduce by: a. asexual means; b. sexual means; c. both of these means; d. none of these means.

8. Oocytes are found in an ovary in: a. seminiferous tubules; b. follicles; c. corpora lutea; d. none of the above.

9. Sperm: a. are male gametes; b. are female gametes; c. contain yolk; d. are produced in the ovaries.

10. Most animals: a. are monoecious; b. are dioecious; c. have two sexes; d. b and c.

ANIMAL DEVELOPMENT: GAMETOGENESIS AND FERTILIZATION

Answers to Pre-lab Questions in Lab Manual Order

1.	b	6.	d
2.	d	7.	d
3.	a	8.	b
4.	b	9.	d
5.	a	10.	c

Answers to Pre-lab Questions in Instructor's Manual Order

1.	d	6.	d
2.	d	7.	b
3.	c	8.	b
4.	a	9.	a
5.	b	10.	d

Answers to Post-lab Questions

1. Define and characterize the following: a. *gametes*—**Mature haploid products of meiosis in gonads, sperm produced in males and ova in females, which function as sexual reproductive cells.** b. *gonads*—**Reproductive organs in which gametes are produced.** c. *gametogenesis*—**The production of gametes, oogenesis in females and spermatogenesis in males.**

2. Describe the similarities and differences between sperm and ova. **Sperm are small and motile. Ova are large, nonmotile, and contribute most cytoplasm to zygote. Similarities are that both are haploid products of gametogenesis.**

3. Compare chicken, frog, and mammalian ova as to size and the amount of yolk present.

Ova	Size	Amount of Yolk
Chicken	3 cm	large
Frog	2 mm	moderate
Mammal	0.2 mm	little

4. Why do you think four sperm cells are produced as a result of gametogenesis, but only one ovum? **Only one ovum is produced because the ovum has many biological molecules necessary for early development. Also, vastly greater numbers of mature sperm are usually produced.**

5. Why is meiosis a necessary part of gametogenesis? **To produce haploid gametes.**

6. Are oogonia present in adult human females? **No.** Explain your answer. **At birth, all of the primary oocytes are present in the follicles. No other oocytes will be formed.**

7. Read about the gray crescent in your textbook. How does its location relate to the site of sperm penetration? **The gray crescent forms *after* fertilization and *opposite* the point of penetration.**

8. What substances are contained in the acrosome of a sperm? What is the function of these substances during sperm penetration? **The acrosome contains lytic enzymes, which function in egg penetration.**

9. As various newspaper articles, books, and movies suggest, the cloning of human beings—producing new individuals from activated somatic cells, perhaps followed by uterine implant—is a distinct possibility. Can you suggest any biological advantages or disadvantages to having the earth populated with clones of a few of the best examples of our species? **Possible advantage would be opportunity to prolong the potential of gifted individuals. It would reduce variation within the human population, however, with potentially dire evolutionary consequences. Also, the selection of the "best" individuals would be subjective and no doubt a matter of intense controversy.**

10. Search the World Wide Web for sites about identical twins. List two sites and briefly summarize their contents. **Answers will vary.**

ANIMAL DEVELOPMENT: CLEAVAGE, GASTRULATION, AND LATE DEVELOPMENT

Materials and Equipment

43.1 Cleavage

Per student
- compound microscope
- lens cleaning solution (optional)
- dropper bottle of immersion oil (optional)
- prepared slide of whole mount of sea star development through gastrulation
- lens paper
- lint free cloth (optional)

Per student pair
- two Syracuse dishes
- two blue camel-hair brushes (optional)
- dissecting microscope
- two red camel-hair brushes

Per lab section
- frog embryos in pond water, 1 hour after fertilization (optional)

Per lab room
- dH$_2$O tap or carboy
- models of early human development
- preserved specimens of 2-, 4-, and 8-cell stages, morulae (32-cell) and blastulae of frog
- models of early frog development
- pond water (optional)

43.2 Gastrulation

Per student
- compound microscope
- prepared slides of whole mounts of chicken embryos at 18 and 24 hours of incubation
- prepared slide of whole mount of sea star development through gastrulation

Per student pair
- two Syracuse dishes
- two red camel-hair brushes
- fertile hen's eggs incubated for 18 and 24 hours (optional)
- dissecting microscope
- two blue camel-hair brushes (optional)

Per student group (bench or table)
- models of human gastrulation

Per lab section
- pond water
- frog embryos in pond water 21 hours after fertilization (optional)
- frog embryos in pond water 36 hours after fertilization (optional)

Per lab room
- dH$_2$O carboy or tap
- preserved specimens of early and late frog gastrulae
- models of early and late frog gastrulae

43.3 Extraembryonic Membranes

Per student group (4)
- dissecting microscope
- fertile hen's egg incubated for 5 days (optional)

Per student group(bench or table)
- models of human intrauterine development
- preserved pig fetus and placenta with injected vessels

43.4 Organ Formation

Per student
- compound microscope
- prepared slides of whole mounts of chicken embryos at 48 and 72 hours incubation

Per student group (4)
- dissecting microscope
- fertile chicken egg incubated for 48 and 72 hours or longer (optional)

Preparation of Materials and Equipment

43.1 Cleavage

Camel-hair brushes: Handles of camel-hair brushes can be colored by dipping them in paint or with a band of colored tape. Emphasize to students to not handle living embryos with brushes that have been dipped into formalin-containing solutions.

Frog embryos: Obtain frog sperm and ova as described in exercise 36, part 1. Eggs are fertilized as described in exercise 36, part 3. Ova should be fertilized approximately 1 hour before needed in class, with successfully fertilized eggs rotating just before the first division so that the black animal hemisphere is uppermost.

Embryos can also be incubated at temperatures of approximately 18°C. At this temperature, development will be slowed as follows: 2 cells, 1 hour; 4 cells, 4.5 hours; 8 cells, 5.7 hours; 32 cells, 7.5 hours; late blastula, 21 hours; mid-gastrula, 34 hours. (Adapted from: K. W. Perkins, R. L. Franks and R. H. Whitten. 1981. *Reptiles and Amphibians: Care and Culture.* Carolina Biological Supply Company, Burlington, NC/Gladstone, OR.)

43.2 Gastrulation

Frog embryos: Fertilize embryos approximately 21 hours and 36 hours before needed in laboratory if held at room temperature.

Chicken embryos: Obtain fertilized hen's eggs (see *Notes* and *Ordering Information*) and place in incubator 18 and 24 hours before laboratory. (Add 2 hours to these times if eggs have been held in a refrigerator.) Incubator should maintain temperatures of 37.5 to 38°C closely or development may proceed abnormally. An incubator may be purchased (see *Ordering Information*), or a still air incubator may be constructed if small numbers of eggs will be needed. Two sources of plans for incubator construction are: 4-H Manual 99, *Embryology*, available from the Cooperative Extension Service, Extension Bulletin Room, Room 83, P&AS Building, Clemson University, Clemson, SC, 29631; Pamphlet L81a, *How to Make a Still Air Incubator*, Cooperative Extension Service, Cornell University, Ithaca, NY, 14853.

The humidity within the incubator must be kept high by maintaining pans of water or wet sponges in the incubator. Rotate each egg 1/4 turn at least once a day so that development will proceed normally.

Students should hold the eggs in the orientation in which they were last incubated (mark an "X" on the top side of the shell with pencil to indicate which side should remain up) so that the embryo will be uppermost. Carefully crack the eggs into culture dishes to examine the embryos with dissection microscopes.

43.3 Extraembryonic Membranes

Chicken embryos: Fertile chicken eggs may be incubated as described above for 5 days before laboratory, or an alternative *ex ovo* culture technique may be used. This plastic-wrap culture method allows continuous observation of an embryo after the third day of incubation, and thus is useful for demonstrating development of the extraembryonic membranes and circulatory system.

The culture chamber is composed of: a 3-in. length of 3-in. diameter plastic drainpipe; a 6 to 8 in. square of Handiwrap plastic wrap; a 1-in. length of the 3-in. diameter plastic drainpipe with a longitudinal cut to allow the pipe to spring open slightly, and the top of a 100-mm petri dish. Assemble the chamber as follows: Wash the pieces of pipe and petri dish lid and sterilize by soaking in a solution of 10% commercial bleach in water. Place the plastic wrap over the 3-inch length of drainpipe and allow the wrap to sag down about halfway into the pipe. The 1-in. split ring is placed over the wrap on the outside of the longer pipe, clamping the plastic wrap in place. Allow the split ring to extend a couple of millimeters above the rim of the Handiwrap to improve gas exchange.

Use fertile eggs that have already been incubated in the shell for 3 days before beginning this culture process. (Survival is low if embryos are cultured by this method before 3 days of incubation.) Swab each egg with 70% ethanol to limit contamination and allow the eggs to rest in position several minutes so that the embryos will be uppermost. Crack the eggs gently, and carefully release the contents into the Handiwrap depression. Place the petri dish lid on top of the culture chamber and incubate in a 37.5 to 38°C incubator with high humidity.

The embryos can be removed from the incubator and examined periodically, though they should be disturbed as little as possible and should remain out of the incubator for only short periods. The major obstacle with this method lies in successfully cracking the eggs without rupturing the yolks. About half of those embryos placed intact into culture will survive for 7 days, with approximately 15 % surviving to 14 days (17 days total incubation including the initial 3 days). Embryos will not survive much further, perhaps because of damage to or abnormal development of the amnion or yolk sac, imperfect gas exchange, or calcium deficiencies.

Students should work in pairs to prepare the embryos for observation with a dissection microscope. One student should firmly grasp as much of the edges of the plastic wrap as possible with both hands while a second student removes the split ring clamp. The egg-filled plastic wrap can then be gently lowered into a culture dish for examination, after which it is discarded.

(Adapted from: S. R. Scadding. 1985. *How to Culture Chicken Embryos in Plastic Wrap Suspension.* The American Biology Teacher 47(2):107–108.)

43.4 Organ Formation

Chicken embryos: Incubate fertile hen's eggs for 43 and 72 hours before class (remember to add 2 hours if eggs have been refrigerated) in a 37.5 to 38°C incubator with high humidity. Instructors may wish to use the plastic wrap culture method above to demonstrate development at various stages after 72 hours of incubation.

Notes

43.1 Cleavage

Instructors may wish to place preserved specimens of frog embryos in labeled, covered petri dishes if easily accessible screw-top vials are unavailable.

43.2 Gastrulation

Fertile chicken eggs may be purchased from Carolina Biological Supply (see *Ordering Information*) or from health food stores, commercial hatcheries, or the Poultry Science department of a university. Check with your preferred source early to ensure that eggs will be delivered in time. Fertile eggs may be stored in a refrigerator for several days to a week before beginning incubation.

43.3 Extraembryonic Membranes

Use Handiwrap brand plastic wrap for the *ex ovo* culture method. Other brands may have different gas permeabilities.

Ordering Information

See General Laboratory Supplies list on page vii for basic items

43.1 Cleavage

early blastulae	Carolina	P1530GF*
early human development models	Carolina	56-3122
frog development models	Ward's	81 W 0302
frog embryos, preserved 2-cell	Carolina	P1530BF*
frog embryos, preserved 4-cell	Carolina	P1530CF*
frog embryos, preserved 32-cell	Carolina	P1530FF*
frog embryos, preserved 8-cell	Carolina	P1530DF*
starfish development, w.m., all stages through bipinnaria	Triarch	ZJ 1-4
Syracuse dish	Carolina	74-2320

* Call Carolina Biological Supply to place order (minimum purchase of 50).

43.2 Gastrulation

chicken embryo, w.m., 18 hours	Triarch	EE2-1
chicken embryo, w.m., 24 hours	Triarch	EE4-1
early human development model	Carolina	56-3122
fertile chicken eggs	Carolina	13-9290
frog development models	Ward's	81 W 0302
frog embryos, preserved early gastrulae	Carolina	P1530K*
frog embryos, preserved late gastrulae	Carolina	P1530NF*
incubator, still air	Carolina	70-1191
starfish development, w.m., all stages through bipinnaria	Triarch	ZJ 1-4
Syracuse dish	Carolina	74-2320

* Call Carolina Biological Supply to place order (minimum purchase of 50).

43.3 Extraembryonic Membranes

drainpipe, plastic, 3-in. diam.	local hardware or plumbing supply	
fertile chicken eggs	Carolina	13-9290
Handiwrap	local grocery	
human development model	Carolina	56-3122
incubator, still air	Carolina	70-1191
pig uterus with fetus and placenta, injected, freeze-dried	Ward's	69 V 7261

43.4 Organ Formation

chicken embryo, w.m., prepared slide 40 to 43 hours	Triarch	EE7-1A
chicken embryo, w.m., prepared slide, 72 hours	Triarch	EE11-1
fertile chicken eggs	Carolina	13-9290
incubator, still air	Carolina	70-1194

Answers to In-Text Questions

43.1 Cleavage

A. Cleavage in the Sea Star

"Draw sea star developmental stages."
…What is the orientation (parallel or perpendicular) relative to each other of the first two cleavage planes?
Perpendicular What is the orientation (parallel or perpendicular) of the third cleavage plane compared to the first cleavage plane? **Perpendicular**

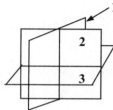

B. Cleavage in the Frog

3. Why? (*Hint:* What is present in the vegetal pole that would hinder cleavage?)
Yolk interferes with cleavage.

43.2 Gastrulation

C. Gastrulation in the Chicken

4. …Count the number of pairs of somites present in your embryo. Record this number: **Approximately 4**

43.4 Organ Formation

1. Has the number of somites increased compared with those of the chicken embryo incubated for 24 hours? **Yes**

Name _____

Section No. _____

ANIMAL DEVELOPMENT: CLEAVAGE, GASTRULATION, AND LATE DEVELOPMENT

Pre-lab Questions

1.   The entrance into the cavity formed during gastrulation in the sea star and frog is called the: a. archenteron; b. blastocoel; c. blastocyst; d. blastopore.

2.   The three primary germ layers are formed during: a. fertilization; b. cleavage; c. organ formation; d. gastrulation.

3.   Cleavage is complete and unequal in the: a. sea star; b. frog; c. chicken; d. human.

4.   The cavity within a blastula is called the: a. archenteron; b. blastocoel; c. blastocyst; d. blastopore.

5.   Muscle tissues, connective tissues, and the epithelia lining the urinary and reproductive systems arise from: a. mesoderm; b. endoderm; c. ectoderm; d. two of the above.

6.   How many extraembryonic membranes are there? a. one; b. two; c. three; d. four.

7.   The majority of mammals derive most of their nourishment during development from: a. the yolk sac; b. the placenta; c. the fluid in the amniotic cavity; d. none of the above.

8.   In which species do all of the cells derived from the zygote contribute to the body of the embryo? a. frog; b. chicken; c. human; d. both b and c.

9.   Choose the correct chronological order in a-d for the first five stages of development listed below: 1. fertilization, 2. cleavage, 3. organ formation, 4. gametogenesis, 5. gastrulation: a. 1,2,3,4,5; b. 1,4,2,5,3; c. 2,1,4,5,3; d. 4,1,2,5,3

10.   The blastocyst consists of the: a. inner cell mass; b. trophoblast; c. placenta; d. both a and b.

ANIMAL DEVELOPMENT: CLEAVAGE, GASTRULATION AND LATE DEVELOPMENT

*Answers to Pre-lab Questions
in Lab Manual Order*

1.	d	6.	d
2.	d	7.	d
3.	a	8.	a
4.	b	9.	d
5.	b	10.	b

*Answers to Pre-lab Questions
in Instructor's Manual Order*

1.	d	6.	d
2.	d	7.	b
3.	b	8.	a
4.	b	9.	d
5.	a	10.	d

Answers to Post-lab Questions

1. Define and describe how it differs from typical cell division. *cleavage*—**Rapid, successive divisions in an animal zygote that result in an increase in cell numbers without an increase in size. There is no period of cell growth between the mitotic divisions as there would be in typical cell division.**

2. Identify the following sea star developmental stages. **a. 16-cell stage; b. 4-cell stage; c. 2-cell stage; d. gastrula.**

3. How do the amount and distribution of yolk in animal zygotes affect cleavage? **With little yolk, cleavage can be complete. With moderate amounts of yolk, the animal pole will divide before the vegetal. With large amounts of yolk, cleavage will be incomplete and will occur in the animal pole.**

4. In what ways is gastrulation in humans more like that of the chicken than that of the sea star? **Gastrulation occurs through a primitive streak as in the chicken, rather than through a blastopore as in the sea star.**

5. List the primary germ layers formed by gastrulation. What tissues will they form in the adult? **Ectoderm gives rise to nervous tissues, epidermis and its derivatives. Mesoderm gives rise to muscle and connective tissues and the epithelia of the excretory and reproductive systems. Endoderm gives rise to the epithelial lining of most of the digestive and respiratory tracts and associated glands.**

6. List the extraembryonic membranes of a chicken embryo and give their function. **The amnion forms the fluid-filled cavity in which the developing embryo is suspended. The yolk sac serves as the digestive organ of the developing embryo and as a respiratory organ. The chorion is the outermost membrane around the embryo. The allantois functions as a respiratory organ and in accumulation of excretory wastes.**

7. Briefly describe the formation of the placenta in mammals. What are its functions? **The placenta is formed in the third week of development from the allantois—a connecting stalk of chorionic tissue between the embryo and the mother—and the trophoblast. The placenta mediates oxygen, nutrient, and waste interchanges between the embryo and the mother.**

8. Define organ formation. At what point does an embryo become a fetus? **During organ formation, the four basic tissue types formed associate and form the organs of the body. Once the organs and basic body shape of an embryo are established, the embryo is called a fetus.**

9. Most body cells have a full set of chromosomes and identical genes. Yet there are many different kinds of body cells (for example, cells of the epidermis, blood cells, skeletal muscle fibers, and neurons). Look up the definition of *cell differentiation* in your textbook and in your own words, describe how cells become specialized. **Cell differentiation is the process by which cells become specialized. During this process genes are turned "on and off" so that the differences between types of mature cells are due to the expression of somewhat different sets of genes.**

10. These days, the progress of intrauterine development is usually followed by sonograms and the genes of a fetus may be checked by amniocentesis. Search the World Wide Web for sites about these procedures. List one site for each and briefly summarize its contents. **Answers will vary.**

THE NATURAL ARSENAL: AN EXPERIMENTAL STUDY OF THE RELATIONSHIPS BETWEEN PLANTS AND ANIMALS

Materials and Equipment

44.1 Experimental Design and 44.2 Bioassay Procedures

A. Preparation of Plant Extract

Per student group
- 25-mL graduated cylinder
- 50-mL beakers
- spatula
- plant material of your choice (See *Preparation of Materials and Equipment*)
- two 20-mL beakers
- small mortar and pestle
- glass stirring rod

Per lab room
- weighing papers or boats
- several electronic balances calibrated to weigh in 0.1-g increments
- liquid nitrogen (optional)

B. Artemia Bioassay

Per student group
- glass microscope slides
- compound microscope
- acetic acid in dropping bottle
- dissecting needle
- fine-pointed water-resistant marker or wax pencil
- wide-mouth plastic graduated transfer pipets
- plant extract(s) in brine prepared in part A
- coverslip
- razor blade or scalpel
- trypan blue stain in dropping bottle

Per lab room
- live *Artemia* in aquarium or beaker
- paper towels
- plant extracts

For instructor prepared materials
- Instant Ocean or synthetic sea salt
- aquarium with air stone and pump

C. Fast Plant™ Bioassay

Per student group (4)
- fine-pointed water-resistant marker
- four paper-towel wicks
- 15-cm plastic ruler
- disposable pipets and bulb
- plant extract(s) prepared in water in part A
- four microcentrifuge tubes with caps
- Forceps
- dH₂O in dropping bottle
- eight Wisconsin Fast Plants™ seeds

44.3 Analysis of Results

None required.

Preparation of Materials and Equipment

44.1 Experimental Design and 44.2 Bioassay Procedures

A. Preparation of Plant Extract

Instructors should have plant material available for the students to choose from for the experimental design and bioassays to follow. Suggested materials: fresh rosemary, fresh oregano, horseradish root, lemon grass stems and/or leaves, dandelion leaves, dried mustard seeds, black peppercorns, ground coffee beans.

While plant material can be ground fresh or dried, freezing with liquid nitrogen greatly improves the ease and speed of the plant extract preparation.

B. Artemia Bioassay

Artemia medium:	Instant ocean or synthetic sea salt	255 gm
	dH$_2$O	3200 mL

Maintain *Artemia* in aquarium with air stones to provide oxygen.

0.4% trypan blue stock solution:	95% ethanol	50 mL
	trypan blue powder	0.4 gm

Shake well until the solution appears uniform. Then Add 95 mL dH$_2$O and shake again until completely dissolved.

Trypan blue for class use:	0.4% trypan blue stock solution	5 mL
	Synthetic sea salt/Instant Ocean solution	20 mL

Acetic acid:	commercial vinegar may be used.

C. Fast Plant^{TM} Bioassay

Preparation of film canister: Many film processing outlets or camera stores discard great numbers of empty film canisters. Ask them to save the film containers for you. Punch four 7-mm diameter holes in lid of 35-mm film canister with a drill press. Alternatively, heat a small Pyrex test tube and melt holes in lid.

Wicks: Cut wicks from white household paper towels or rough filter paper. Wicks should be triangular, approximately 3.5 cm in length, and 1 cm across base.

Seeds: RCBr (rapid-cycling *Brassica rapa*) seeds are extremely small. Supply adhesive tape to your students and direct them to attach the seeds to the tape to prevent seed loss.

Extra seeds may be stored for a few years if refrigerated in a sealed container with a small amount of silica gel desiccant or powdered milk to absorb moisture.

Students' bioassay canisters should be placed where they will be undisturbed and where temperatures can be maintained between 21°C and 27°C for optimal germination within 24 hours. Germination will not occur if temperature is below 15°C.

Ordering Information

See General Laboratory Supplies list on page vii for basic items

44.2 Bioassay Procedures

A. Preparation of Plant Extract

mortar	Fisher	12-961AA
pestle	Fisher	12-961-5AA
weighing dishes	Fisher	02-202B
plant material of your choice	collected locally or purchased at grocery store	

B. Artemia Bioassay

acetic acid	Carolina	84-1313	or purchase vinegar
Artemia	Carolina	14-2230	
trypan blue, 0.4% solution	Fisher	ICN1691049	
trypan blue, powder	Fisher	AC18935-0250	

C. Fast Plant^{TM} Bioassay

35-mm film canister	local film processing center	
microcentrifuge tubes with caps	Carolina	19-9684
RCBr (Wisconsin Fast Plants^{TM}) seeds(200)	Carolina	15-8805

Answers to In-Text Questions

44.1 Experimental Design

The hypothesis we will test is
Answers vary
Our experimental design is
Answers will vary, but should include appropriate replication and controls.
What will be your control treatment(s)? What is the purpose of a control treatment?
Purpose of control is to separate treatment effects from effects due to other factors.
How will you provide replication to improve the reliability of your results?
Students should consider number of seeds or individual brine shrimp samples, as well as amoebocytes counted.
Write a prediction for your experiment.
Answers vary
List the possible general outcomes of your experiment. What does each tell you about your prediction and hypothesis?
For *Artemia* bioassay, students could see no killed cells (extract has little cytotoxicity), many killed cells (extract has high cytotoxicity), or both living and killed cells (extract shows some cytotoxic activity). Similar for Fast Plant^{TM} germination bioassay.

Remaining questions will have variable answers depending on student procedure and results.

Name _____

Section No. _____

THE NATURAL ARSENAL: AN EXPERIMENTAL STUDY OF THE
RELATIONSHIPS BETWEEN PLANTS AND ANIMALS

Pre-lab Questions

1. *Artemia* and Fast Plant™ bioassays can be used to identify: a. cytotoxins; b. herbicides; c. plant growth stimulators; d. all of the above.

2. The dH$_2$O-only treatment in the Fast Plant™ bioassay provides: a. control; b. moisture for seed germination; c. dilution of potential cytotoxins; d. none of the above.

3. Dead *Artemia* cells that have been treated with trypan blue appear: a. colorless; b. blue; c. red; d. indistinguishable from living treated cells.

4. Trypan blue is: a. taken up by living cells; b. taken up by dead cells; c. taken up by both living and dead cells; d. used to identify plant cells.

5. Plant defenses against herbivore grazing include: a. thorns; b. plant secondary compounds; c. motility; d. both a and b.

6. *Artemia,* brine shrimp,: a. are aquatic organisms; b. live in salty ecosystems; c. are filter-feeding primary consumers; d. are all of the above.

7. Bioassays: a. are performed in a test tube using killed cells; b. expose a population of living organisms to a test substance; c. are used for chemotherapy; d. are none of the above.

8. Chemicals that are poisonous to specific cell types are said to be: a. hazardous; b. cytotoxic; c. allelochemicals; d. bioactive.

9. Allelochemicals are active in preventing: a. herbivore feeding; b. germination of plant competitors; c. infection by pathogens; d. all of the above.

10. Plant secondary compounds are chemicals that: a. have no known metabolic function in the plant; b. are required for enzyme function; c. are generally carbohydrates or proteins; d. are important in cell division.

THE NATURAL ARSENAL: AN EXPERIMENTAL STUDY
OF THE RELATIONSHIPS BETWEEN PLANTS AND ANIMALS

Answers to Pre-lab Questions
in Lab Manual Order

1.	a	6.	d
2.	d	7.	b
3.	b	8.	b
4.	b	9.	a
5.	d	10.	d

Answers to Pre-lab Questions
in Instructor's Manual Order

1.	d	6.	d
2.	a	7.	b
3.	b	8.	b
4.	b	9.	d
5.	d	10.	a

Answers to Post-lab Questions

1. Why have plants evolved secondary compounds? **Secondary compounds serve as defense mechanisms against animal consumers, plant competitors, and pathogenic microorganisms.**

2. Describe how a pharmaceutical company might use a bioassay to identify potential drugs in rainforest plants. **Prepare an extraction solution from the plants, and conduct a bioassay on potential pathogens or tissue culture cell lines to determine the toxic effects of those extracts.**

3. Would a chemical that is cytotoxic to brine shrimp cells necessarily have the same effect on Fast Plant™ cells? Explain. **No. Plant cells and animal cells have different structures (e.g. cell walls) that may change the way the cell responds to the chemical. The cells may also have different metabolic capabilities to metabolize the chemical.**

4. How can replication be increased in the *Artemia* bioassay to improve reliability of results? **Increase the number of brine shrimp used in the experiment, or increase the total number of cells that are counted.**

5. What was the purpose of the *Artemia* slide prepared with droplets of: a. brine and trypan blue only? **Serves as a negative control. This will determine the number of dead cells in a normal brine shrimp that has not been exposed to a test chemical.** b. brine, trypan blue, and acetic acid? **Serves as a positive control. Allows the experimenter to observe the effect of a known toxic substance.**

6. If seed germination took place in 100% of plants at the 1.0 mg/mL concentration, and no germination was observed at the 0.1 mg/mL concentration, how would you modify a second experiment to determine the actual effective concentration? **Use a narrower range of concentrations for the experimental conditions.**

7. If you found no cytotoxic effects with your plant extract, does this prove the extract is not cytotoxic? **No.** Explain. **It only shows that the extract is not toxic at those concentrations and under those specific experimental conditions.**

8. If you found no cytotoxic effects with your plant extract, does this prove that the plant species from which the extract was made has no cytotoxic allelochemicals? **No.** Explain. **It only indicates that the water soluble extract was not cytotoxic at the given concentrations of the experiment.**

9. How might you alter the two bioassay procedures to provide more information? a. *Artemia* bioassay: **Prepare the extract using organic solvents instead of water, increase the number of replications, and change the concentration variables are all possible solutions.** b. Fast Plant™ bioassay: **See above suggestions, and also look at extracts prepared from other plant parts such as the roots.**

10. What other kinds of tests could you perform to provide more information about possible cytotoxicity of a plant extract? **Test the toxicity of the extract on a different organism, such as *Daphnia*.**

EXERCISE 45

ECOLOGY: LIVING ORGANISMS IN THEIR ENVIRONMENT

Materials and Equipment

45.1 Food Webs

None required.

45.2 Flow of Energy Through an Ecosystem

None required.

45.3 Survivorship

Per student
- 15-cm ruler

Per lab bench
- bucket containing 50 dice
- soap bubble solution and wand
- stopwatch or digital watch

Per lab room
- one to two survivorship frames
- overhead transparency of figures 45-2 and 45-3 from Laboratory Manual
- "Sharpie" or similar marking pens: red, blue, black, and green
- overhead projector and screen

45.4 Plotting Survivorship Curves and 45.5 Interpreting the Survivorship Curves

None required.

Preparation of Materials and Equipment

45.1 Food Webs

None required.

45.2 Flow of Energy Through an Ecosystem

None required.

45.3 Survivorship

B. Soap Bubble Survivorship

A wooden frame with attached bubble wand should be constructed to determine survivorship of Population 3 (see illustration next page for specifications.) Students will attempt to maneuver bubbles through the upper opening in the frame above the paper or cardboard.

Ordering Information

See General Laboratory Supplies list on page vii for basic items

45.3 Survivorship

10-mm dowel and 2.5 x 5 cm stock	local hardware store or lumber yard
dice	local variety store
soap bubble solution and wand	local toy or variety store

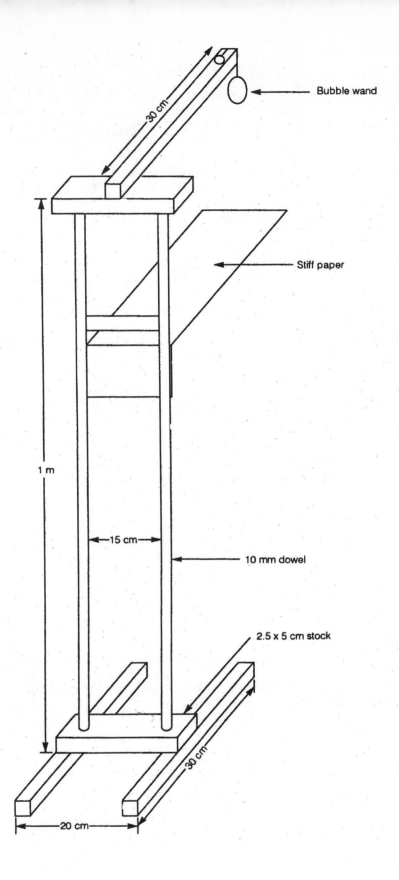

Bubble wand

30 cm

Stiff paper

1 m

15 cm

10 mm dowel

2.5 x 5 cm stock

30 cm

20 cm

325

Answers to In-Text Questions

45.1 Food Webs

How would you classify yourself with respect to your feeding strategy and trophic level?
Humans are consumers. Most students are omnivores feeding at primary, secondary, and tertiary consumer levels. A strict vegan would intend to be a primary consumer. In reality, consumption of insect parts that contaminate grains and other foodstuffs results in vegans actually being secondary consumers.

In the blanks provided, list the *most specific* trophic level from the descriptions earlier.
- Human (black raspberries, hickory nuts, deer, rabbits) **Omnivore**
- Black raspberry (sun) **Producer**
- Deer (black raspberries) **Primary consumer (herbivore)**
- Bear (black raspberries, deer) **Omnivore**
- Coyote (deer, rabbits, black raspberries) **Omnivore**
- Caterpillar (living hickory leaves) **Primary consumer**
- Bacterial species 1 (living black raspberry leaves) **Primary consumer (parasite)**
- Bacterial species 2 (dead skin cells of deer) **Decomposer**
- Bacterial species 3 (dead hickory trees, dead black raspberries, dead humans, dead black bears, dead deer) **Decomposer**
- Weasels (young rabbits) **Secondary consumer**
- Mosquito (blood of living humans, deer, and bears) **Omnivore (parasite)**
- Hickory tree (sun) **Producer**
- Fungal species 1 (living black raspberry stems) **Primary consumer (parasite)**
- Fungal species 2 (dead black raspberries) **Decomposer**
- Rabbit (black raspberries) **Primary consumer**

Suppose a new parasite species that kills black raspberry plants is introduced from another part of the world into this forest community. Speculate on the consequences of loss of black raspberries for the rabbit population.
Given the conditions specified (that rabbits feed exclusively on black raspberries), the rabbit population would decrease greatly due to lack of food.

How might the elimination of black raspberries affect the coyote populations?
Coyotes feed on both black raspberries and rabbits and would lose those food sources. They would then have only deer to feed on. Coyote populations would be expected to decline.

The weasel population?
Weasels feed only on young rabbits and so would lose their food source. Their population would decrease.

What if pesticide spraying unintentionally kills both fungal species? What effect might these species losses have on both the raspberry and rabbit populations?
Fungal species 1 is a parasite of raspberries—its loss will improve the health of the raspberries and benefit the rabbit populations; both would be expected to increase. Fungal species 2 is a decomposer. Its loss would decrease nutrient cycling in the long term and might slightly decrease health of both populations (however, there are other decomposers remaining in this ecosystem).

45.2 Flow of Energy Through an Ecosystem

What percentage of the energy contained in plant foods has been captured by the secondary consumer that feeds on an herbivore (primary consumer)?
10% x 10% = 1%

A tertiary consumer eats the first (herbivore-eating) secondary consumer. Assuming a similar flow of energy, how much of the sun's *original* energy does this secondary consumer gain?
10% x 1% = 0.1%

Suppose an omnivore can obtain all the nutritional requirements necessary for life by eating either plant material or animal material. From an energetics standpoint, which route will allow the omnivore to capture the greater amount of the sun's energy?
Eating plant material allows more efficient capture of the solar energy falling on an ecosystem. The energy captured from eating consumers has been processed through one or more additional trophic levels, with corresponding losses in useful energy.

What other routes would enable this organism to obtain equal amounts of the sun's energy?
Several possibilities include eating more nutritionally dense foods (those providing more calories per gram).

45.3 Survivorship

A. *Dice Survivorship*

How does adding another cause of death affect the survivorship rate?
Usually, the survivorship rate will be lower.

Do you think this activity models human survivorship well? Why or why not?
Not particularly, because of care and medical technologies that allow humans to survive diseases that may be more lethal in the absence of such behavioral and technological measures.

B. *Soap Bubble Survivorship*

Remaining answers vary depending on student data.

Name _____

Section No. _____

ECOLOGY: LIVING ORGANISMS IN THEIR ENVIRONMENT

Pre-lab Questions

1. Which term best describes a human being? a. omnivore; b. herbivore; c. carnivore; d. parasite.

2. A survivorship curve shows the: a. number of individuals surviving to a particular age; b. cause of death of an individual; c. place an organism exists in its environment; d. organism's trophic level.

3. A population includes: a. all organisms of the same species in one place at a given moment; b. the organisms and their physical environment; c. the physical environment in which an organism exists; d. all organisms within the environment at a given moment.

4. An herbivore: a. eats plant material; b. eats primary producers; c. would be exemplified by a deer; d. all of the above.

5. A decomposer: a. is exemplified by a fungus; b. is the same as a parasite; c. feeds on living organic material; d. feeds on primary consumers only.

6. An ecosystem: a. includes populations but not habitats; b. is the same as a community ; c. consists of a community and the physical and chemical environment; d. is none of the above.

7. Which organism is *not* a consumer? a. killer whale; b. human; c. bean plant; d. fungus.

8. The place that an organism resides is its: a. community; b. habitat; c. population; d. all of the above.

9. The trophic level that an organism belongs to : a. is determined by what it uses as an energy source; b. determines the population it belongs to; c. can be thought of as its feeding level; d. is both a and c.

10. The Greek word *oikos* means: a. environment; b. habitat; c. house; d. community.

ECOLOGY: LIVING ORGANISMS IN THEIR ENVIRONMENT

*Answers to Pre-lab Questions
in Lab Manual Order*

1.	c	6.	d
2.	a	7.	a
3.	b	8.	d
4.	c	9.	a
5.	c	10.	a

*Answers to Pre-lab Questions
in Instructor's Manual Order*

1.	a	6.	c
2.	a	7.	c
3.	a	8.	b
4.	d	9.	d
5.	a	10.	c

Answers to Post-lab Questions

1. Define the terms *herbivore, carnivore, omnivore.* **Herbivore—an animal eating only plant material; Carnivore—an animal-eating animal; Omnivore—an animal able to feed on organisms at different trophic levels, i.e., utilizing both plants and animals.**

2. Define the terms *primary producer, primary consumer, secondary consumer.* **Primary producer—a photoautotrophic organism; Primary consumer—an organism that eats primary producers; Secondary consumer—an organism that feeds upon primary consumers.**

3. Characterize yourself, using the terms listed in questions 1 and 2. **Most individuals are omnivores, and primary and secondary consumers. Some few very strict vegetarians might be herbivores and primary consumers only.**

4. Examine the food web you constructed in Table 45-1. Suppose a severe outbreak of rabies occurs in the coyote population, resulting in the death of the entire population. Draw a rough graph that describes the impact of the loss of this predator on the rabbit, deer, and raspberry populations over time and explain your reasoning. **Death of all coyotes in the system would lead to cyclical fluctuations in the populations of herbivores and plants as follows: Death of the predators (coyotes) would allow more deer and rabbits to survive. These higher herbivore populations would lead to lower populations of raspberries, which means less food would eventually be available for the deer and rabbits. The resulting lower populations of herbivores would allow the raspberry levels to build up to sustain more deer and rabbits, leading to the cyclical fluctuations.**

5. You have probably read newspaper articles describing the so-called ozone "hole" over Antarctica and other areas of the planet, as well as health-care cautions that destruction of the earth's protective ozone layer will allow harmful ultraviolet (UV) light to reach the surface. Already, a significant increase in skin cancer is being noticed, a disease known to be caused by excessive exposure to UV light (including that produced by tanning lights). Perhaps not so well known is the damage UV light causes to the photosynthetic machinery of green plants and protists. Explain what would happen over time to the populations of organisms of your food web (Table 45-1) if ozone depletion becomes massive. **Over time, populations of producers and perhaps some decomposers could decrease because of UV damage, knocking out the base of the food chain and causing reductions in populations in higher trophic levels.**

6. You may have heard the advice to "eat low on the food chain." Explain how choosing a soybean-protein "burger" rather than a beef burger for lunch is energy-efficient with respect to energy flow and utilization in trophic levels. **There is more available energy in the soybean protein than in a beef burger prepared from an animal higher on the food chain if one considers the total amount of sunlight energy initially captured by the plants. Each trophic level results in a decreased amount of available energy.**

7. Would you expect a population in which most members survive for a long time to produce few or many offspring? Which would be most advantageous to the population as a whole? **Evolutionarily, it might be most advantageous to produce as many offspring as possible. Ecologically, it would be most advantageous to limit the number of offspring produced.**

8. Suppose a human population exhibits a Type III survival curve. What would you expect to happen to the curve over time if a dramatic improvement in medical technology takes place? **The curve would change, gradually developing into Type I.**

9. Returning to the survivorship model you created using dice: You found that the chance of dying from heart disease is one-sixth for each die, indicating that survivorship is essentially the same for each age group. Relate what happened in your model with a realistic projection showing at what ages most humans die of heart disease. **The dice populations have uniform "mortality" and survivorship at all ages, but in the human population, mortality from heart disease is very low for younger age groups and increases rapidly after middle age. Survivorship, then, is high in young to middle-aged age groups of humans, but drops markedly with increasing age as more individuals die from heart disease.**

10. Ecologist Aldo Leopold, the father of American conservation, said, "The last word in ignorance is the man who says of an animal or plant: 'What good is it?'…If the biota, in the course of aeons, has built something we like but do not understand, then who but a fool would discard seeming useless parts? To keep every cog and wheel is the first precaution of intelligent tinkering." These are strong words indeed. How do they relate to what you've explored in this exercise? **Each student should give some thought to their response. Clearly there should be some recognition given to the extremely important niches occupied by the less charismatic, less visible members of the biota such as the ants, who biologist E.O. Wilson refers to as "the little creatures that run the world." One would hope that students would indicate some understanding of the importance of maintaining a full complement of biodiversity to maintain healthy food web relationships as well as other crucial functions.**

EXERCISE 46

HUMAN IMPACT ON THE ENVIRONMENT: STREAM ECOLOGY

Materials and Equipment

46.1 Streamside Evaluation and Sampling

A. Observations

Per student group
- clear jar or beaker
- map or aerial photo of watershed area (optional)

B. Physical and Chemical Sampling

Per student
- disposable plastic gloves (optional)

Per student group (4)
- nail clippers or scissors
- plastic beaker
- stopwatch or watch with second hand
- plastic sample bottles

Per lab room
- thermometer
- Hach Dissolved Oxygen Kit
- Hach Phosphate Kit
- dH$_2$O tap or carboy
- portable pH meter or pH indicator paper
- Hach Nitrate Kit
- Hach Chloride Kit

C. Biological Sampling

Per student
- forceps or tweezers
- hip boots or other footwear that can get wet

Per student group (4)
- kickseine
- sterile water sample collection bottles
- sample collecting jar
- squeeze bottle of 70% ethanol
- white enamel pan

Per lab room
- Presence /absence ampoule
- two Whirl-Pak™ bags
- nail clipper
- 100-mL plastic beaker
- PathoScreen powder pillow

46.2 Laboratory Analysis—Evaluating Biological Tests and Samples

A. Total Coliform Bacteria

See *Materials and Equipment* for Part C. Biological Sampling above.

B. PathoScreen for Waterborne Pathogens

See *Materials and Equipment* for Part C. Biological Sampling above.

C. Macroinvertebrates

Per student group
- forceps or tweezers
- petri dish and white paper *or* white enamel pan
- dissection microscope *or* magnifying glass

46.3 Analysis of Results

None required.

Preparation of Materials and Equipment

46.1 Streamside Evaluation and Sampling

70% ethanol (950 mL):		
	95% ethanol	700 mL
	distilled water	250 mL

Kickseine: Purchase (see *Ordering Information*) or construct as follows:
> 3 ft. x 6 ft. nylon screening (1/16 in. mesh)
> four strips of heavy canvas (6 in. x 36 in.)
> two broom handles or wooden dowels, 6 ft. long
> finishing nails, thread, sewing machine, hammer, and iron and ironing board.

1. Fold nylon screen in half to make 3' x 3' square.
2. Fold edges of canvas strips under 1/2 in.; press with an iron and then fold strip in half.
3. Sew two of the canvas strips over the edge of the top and bottom of the screening to make a fray-proof edge.
4. Sew the remaining two canvas strips over the side edges of the screening to make casings for the broom handles or dowels on the left and right sides.
5. Insert the broom handles or dowels into the casings. Nail finishing nails through casing into broom handles or dowels, with nails at top and bottom of casing and approximately 4 in. apart along the length of the casing.

46.2 Laboratory Analysis—Evaluating Biological Tests and Samples

None required.

46.3 Analysis of Results

None required.

Notes

Selection of a good stream sampling site is important for the success of this exercise. Choose locations with shallow riffles and with safe access for the students. Secure permission for access from private landowners, if necessary.

In order to save class time, we recommend that the instructor perform all the water tests at the sample sites to determine prior to the laboratory session which nitrate (low-range or mid-range) or phosphate (low-, mid-, or high-range) tests students should perform.

The chemical tests used in this exercise are those that measure nutrients primarily, and will be most useful in areas where significant nutrient input to the stream is likely to occur. Such areas include near golf courses, conventional agricultural fields, or sewage treatment plant outflows. Additional chemical tests are available from Hach Company and other vendors that might measure substances present as a result of industrial activities and storm water runoff, such as copper, phenols, and detergents. You can customize the parameters tested for in this exercise for your particular stream conditions by choosing additional test kits.

State natural resource department or water resource agency field workers might be able to help you locate suitable sampling sites. Consult your local phone directory, government section.

Aerial photos—current and historical—are often available from local planning and zoning offices, as well as U.S. Department of Agriculture Soil Conservation Service offices.

The Izaak Walton League of America (1401 Wilson Blvd., Level B, Arlington, VA 22209) has a wealth of information regarding stream ecology and monitoring through their "Save Our Streams" program.

Plastic or other unbreakable sampling and measuring containers are recommended to avoid breakage at the field site.

Ordering Information

See General Laboratory Supplies list on page vii for basic items

46.1 Streamside Evaluation and Sampling

B. Physical and Chemical Sampling

Hach Basic School Package (includes test kits for DO, phosphorous, nitrate, chloride, and a thermometer)	Hach	24821-00
nail clippers	local drug store	
pH tester, electronic	Fisher	S65285
polypropylene mason jar bottles with caps, 128 oz. (3.8 L)	Fisher	11-815-13D
polypropylene mason jar bottles with caps, 32 oz.	Fisher	11-815-13B

C. Biological Testing

Presence / Absence ampoule		
hip boots	local sporting supply store	
nail clippers	local drug store	
PathoScreen powder pillow	Hach	2610696
plastic screening, 1/16 in. mesh	local hardware or building supply	
polymethylpentene jar (for samples), 8 oz., with caps	Fisher	11-823-31
polypropylene mason jar bottles with caps, 32 oz.	Fisher	11-815-13B
"Save Our Streams" kickseine net	Nichols Net & Twine Co., Inc.	
Whirl-Pak™ bags	Environmental Monitoring Systems	

46.2 Laboratory Analysis

C. Macroinvertebrates

dual plastic magnifier, 3X and 6X	Carolina	60-2276

Answers to In-Text Questions

What human activities can you name that might be affecting your study stream?
Answer varies, but common examples include: roads, houses, and other suburban/urban development; agriculture; forestry; atmospheric deposition of airborne pollutants like acid rain; mercury; dams; and sewage or other point source discharges.

What activities might have affected your study stream in the past that are unlikely to occur today?
Answer varies, but common examples include: some of those above (agriculture, forestry activities, etc.) as well as direct discharge of untreated industrial effluents.

46.3 Analysis of Results

Are your observations, chemical measurements, and biological observations consistent?
Answer varies with student data.

If your results aren't clear-cut, speculate on why this might be so.
Answer varies. This is a good place to point out to students that the chemical tests are a "snapshot" of water quality at the time of sampling, while the macroinvertebrates provide information about long-term overall quality since some macroinvertebrates may live for 2 to 3 years in the stream.

What might you do to increase the consistency and reliability of your results?
Becoming experienced in the procedures would improve consistency and reliability, as would sampling more points with more replication.

Which of your observed or measured factors indicate(s) higher quality water?
Answer varies.

Which of your observed or measured factors indicate(s) lower water quality?
Answer varies.

Why might you find a low SQI value, even if the chemical and physical parameters you measured are within limits for "good" water quality?
Other factors, such as toxins and high biochemical oxygen demand or frequent high turbidity, may reduce water quality. Also, some of the parameters measured, such as plant nutrients, often enter streams in pulses rather than continuously, and you may have missed an important pulse of these pollutants.

If you found indications of organic or nutrient pollution, what might be some of the sources for this pollution in your stream's watershed?
Answer varies, but possibilities include: sewage treatment plants, leaking septic systems, agricultural operations and feedlots, areas of intensively managed turf, and industrial facilities like food-processing plants or paper mills.

Do you think most of the pollutants in your stream result from point source or non-point source pollutants?
Answer varies, depending on your stream. However, nationwide non-point source pollutants are most prevalent and problematic.

How could the negative impacts on your stream be reduced or eliminated?
Answer varies, but students could discuss methods to reduce soil erosion and nutrient runoff from construction sites, agriculture, or forestry operations.

HUMAN IMPACT ON THE ENVIRONMENT: STREAM ECOLOGY

Pre-lab Questions

1. A riffle is: a. the land area surrounding a stream; b. an area of still, deep water; c. the living component of a stream; d. a fast-moving, shallow stream area.

2. Non-point source pollutants include: a. fertilizers from lawns; b. pesticides from farm fields; c. soil erosion from construction sites; d. all of the above.

3. pH is: a. a measure of phosphorous concentration; b. a measure of hydrogen ion concentration ; c. measured by counting the number of different kinds of aquatic insects; d. measured on a scale from 1 to 100.

4. Which pollutant would most likely be the source of coliform bacteria in a stream? a. fertilizers from a golf course; b. discharge from a factory; c. forestry activities; d. sewage or animal wastes.

5. Group 1 aquatic macroinvertebrates: a. require high-quality, unpolluted water; b. require polluted water; c. are tolerant of a wide range of water quality conditions; d. include leeches.

6. Which of these is *not* a type of water pollutant?: a. dissolved oxygen; b. toxic chemicals ; c. organic wastes; d. sediment.

7. A yellow to orange-red coating on a stream bottom indicates: a. high dissolved oxygen; b. possible soil erosion or mine drainage; c. low nitrate concentration; d. high chloride content.

8. Dissolved oxygen content in stream water is affected by: a. organic matter in the water; b. overgrowth of algae; c. water nutrient levels; d. all of the above.

9. Most of the aquatic macroinvertebrates in a stream are: a. clams; b. insect larvae; c. worms; d. arthropods such as crayfish.

10. Nitrates: a. are suspended sediments; b. measure hydrogen ion concentrations; c. are required for animal respiration; d. contain nitrogen, a necessary plant nutrient.

HUMAN IMPACT ON THE ENVIRONMENT: STREAM ECOLOGY

Answers to Pre-lab Questions
in Lab Manual Order

1.	d	6.	d
2.	a	7.	d
3.	d	8.	b
4.	b	9.	a
5.	b	10.	d

Answers to Pre-lab Questions
in Instructor's Manual Order

1.	d	6.	a
2.	d	7.	b
3.	b	8.	d
4.	d	9.	b
5.	a	10.	d

Answers to Post-lab Questions

1. What is a watershed? **The land area that drains into a stream, whether directly or by draining into feeder streams and groundwater that flows into the stream.** What are some of the major human activities occurring in the watershed of the stream you sampled? **Many possibilities, including housing, industry, urban, agriculture, grazing, forestry, or wild lands.**

2. Distinguish between point and non-point sources of pollution. Provide several examples of each. **Point sources of pollution are those with a specific place where a pollutant enters the environment, such as factory smokestacks or sewer outflows. Non-point sources are those where the pollutant enters the environment from many poorly-defined sources covering diffuse areas, such as golf courses, lawns, or farm fields.**

3. Why is it important for sewage treatment plants to remove nitrates and phosphates from sewage? **Nitrates and phosphates are plant nutrients. When wastewater treatment plants dump their effluent into streams, rivers, and lakes, they are in effect massively fertilizing the water unless those nutrients have been removed from the effluent. Adding nitrates and phosphates to the water causes eutrophication and algal blooms, resulting in dissolved oxygen deficits that can kill aquatic animals.**

4. How might an algal bloom (population explosion of microscopic aquatic plants) affect fish in a pool? **Algae are plants that produce oxygen from photosynthesis and consume oxygen for cellular respiration. Animals also require oxygen for cellular respiration. At the start of a bloom, algae produce an abundance of oxygen that could benefit the fish temporarily. However, as the bloom explodes sunlight is blocked, killing plants growing on the bottom of the pool, and thereby decreasing habitat and food for young fish and removing that source of dissolved oxygen. Also, eventually the algae die. Their decomposition then is an aerobic (oxygen-requiring) process that further removes dissolved oxygen from the water, possibly leading to fish mortality.**

5. Trout are fish that require relatively low-temperature water. Suppose a shaded trout stream has its overhanging streamside trees removed. Explain the possible effects of this action on the trout population over the course of a summer. **As summer progresses the water retains more heat. Heated water holds less dissolved oxygen. Therefore, the previously shaded area will become less desirable as trout habitat. The population would likely decrease in that area.**

6. Here are the results of physical and chemical sampling of one stream. What do these results tell you about the suitability of this stream as fish habitat? What are likely causes for each of these values? **A pH value of 5.2 would indicate acidic conditions, unsuitable as fish habitat. Possible sources of this acid would be acid mine drainage, acid precipitation, or an acidic source such as a swamp or bog. A phosphate level of 0.15 mg/L is higher than the standard. A likely source of phosphate contamination may be fertilizer run-off or an influx of other organic material. The dissolved oxygen of this stream is also low. This would indicate high levels of organic material in the water. Generally, these results indicate a stream that is not a suitable fish habitat.**

7. Here are the data from a stream's aquatic macroinvertebrate sample. Calculate the Stream Quality Index value of this stream. What does this sample indicate about the water quality?

    4 taxa of Group 1 organisms X group value 3 = 12
    3 taxa of Group 2 organisms X group value 2 = 6
    2 taxa of Group 3 organisms X group value 1 = 2
    12 + 6 + 2 = Stream Quality Index value = 20, which indicates "Good" water quality.

8. Referring to the stream in question 7, suppose you also know there are very few individuals of the Group 1 taxa present while midge fly larvae are extremely abundant. Does this information alter your assessment of the water quality of the stream? Why or why not? **This condition could indicate the presence of over enrichment of organic matter.**

9. List several ways that sediment pollution could be decreased in your community. **A few methods to decrease sediment pollution include: instituting methods to decrease storm water runoff at construction sites; minimizing the amount of bare soil exposed at construction sites, in agricultural fields, and at logging sites; minimizing soil disturbance on hills and slopes; and zoning restrictions on construction at erodible sites.**

10. List several obstacles to improving stream quality in your community. **Common obstacles include: tradition and acceptance of longstanding practices; zoning laws that allow construction or other activities in sensitive areas; changing detrimental practices might be expensive or time-consuming, and thus provide a financial disincentive; and lack of recognition or belief that improving stream quality is a worthy goal, etc.**

ANIMAL BEHAVIOR

Materials and Equipment

47.1 Instinctive Behavior

Per student pair
- mealworm beetle
- wooden or plastic blocks
- plastic tray

Per lab room
- snails in algae-coated fresh water aquarium
- cover for the left half of the aquarium

47.2 Frog Behavior

Per student group
- frog
- plastic tray and latex gloves
- small rectangular plastic tank filled with room temperature water

47.3 Tropical Fish Behavior

Per lab room
- aquarium with five species of tropical fish species
- sign that displays picture, name and code for each species represented

47.4 Phototaxis Experiment

Per student group
- petri dish and penlight
- planaria
- fresh stream water or aerated pond/spring water

Preparation of Materials and Equipment

47.1 Instinctive Behavior

Be sure to establish aquaria in advance of the lab in order to have sufficient algae growth.

47.2 Frog Behavior

None required.

47.3 Tropical Fish Behavior

None required.

47.4 Phototaxis Experiment

None required.

Ordering Information

See General Laboratory Supplies list on page vii for basic items

47.1 Instinctive Behavior

aquarium	Carolina	67-0144	or purchase at local pet supply
mealworm beetle	Carolina	14-4346	or purchased at local supply
snails	Carolina	14-1141	or purchase at local pet supply

47.2 Frog Behavior

frog	Carolina	14-6530	or 14-6390

47.3 Tropical Fish Behavior

five different species of tropical fish	or purchase at local pet supply		
aquarium	Carolina	67-0144	or purchase at local pet supply

47.4 Phototaxis Behavior

fresh stream water	collect locally	
planaria, living	Carolina	13-2950

Answers to In-Text Questions

47.1 Instinctive Behavior

…List up to five other major environmental stimuli that animals may respond to:
E.g.
1. temperature
2. sound waves
3. chemicals
4. tissue damage (i.e., pain provoking stimuli)
5. electrical fields

A. Response to Gravity

1. Describe the feeding behavior of snails in an algae-coated freshwater aquarium.
They use a rasping tongue-like structure (radula) to scrape whatever surface they find themselves crossing that has a coat of algae.
4. Are most of the snails oriented with their heads directed downward (positive geotaxis) or upward (negative geotaxis)? **Upward**

B. Response to Light

5. Are snails phototactic? **Yes** If so, is their response negative or positive? **Negative**
TABLE 47-1 Orientation of Snails in a Freshwater Aquarium
Orientation/Number/Percentage
"Fill in cells, total the number, and calculate percentages."
TABLE 47-2 Snail Counts in the Light and Dark Halves of an Aquarium
Side/Condition/Initial Count/Final Count/Number Gained (+) or Lost (-)
"Fill in cells and calculate the number of snails gained and lost respectively from the light and dark sides of the tank."

C. Response to Touch

3. Describe its reaction to touching (walking into) an obstacle.

It hesitates and tries another direction.

4. Is your beetle thigmotactic? **Yes** If so, is the response negative or positive? **Negative**

6. Does your beetle show any possible dominance for turning to the right or left?

All outcomes are possible.

TABLE 47-3 Response of Beetle to Touch

Observations/Right/Left

"Fill in the cells for a total of 10 observations and total how many times the beetle turned right and left."

47.2 Frog Behavior

1. …Once it sits still, describe the typical frog **posture**—the position of the body and its parts.

A frog squats on all four legs with its body angled so that the head is higher than the back, which slopes down posteriorly. The front legs support its anterior half, which is held off the surface. The back legs are fully flexed.

2. Place the frog on its back and let go. Describe its response.

Frogs usually turn back over and assume a typical frog posture.

Speculate as to the stimulus that initiates this righting response.

Gravity acting on the frog's sensors for balance and equilibrium stimulates the righting response.

3. …Describe in some detail its response.

The frog usually swims near the surface of the water by alternately flexing and extending the legs in unison with each other.

4. Describe in some detail its response.

The frog usually withdraws the stimulated toe by flexing the leg. At the same time, sometimes the opposite leg is first extended and then withdrawn.

5. …Discuss your observations, come to a group consensus, and summarize them here.

Usually students state that much of this behavior is learned and requires conscious decisions on the part of the frog.

8. …If so, explain.

The usual student response is that more human behavior may be instinctive, that less human behavior may be learned, and that less human behavior may require a conscious decision.

TABLE 47-4 Frog Behavior

Without a Forebrain/Without a Brain/Without a CNS

Response/Prediction Result/Prediction Result/Prediction/Result

"Fill in cells."

Typically frogs without a forebrain right themselves, swim, and withdraw their leg.

Typically frogs without a brain withdraw their leg.

Typically frogs without a CNS do none of these responses.

47.3 Tropical Fish Behavior

4. Describe your chosen species' behavior under these conditions.

Response depends on species observed. Many websites exist that describe the behavior of freshwater tropical fish species.

TABLE 47-5 Fish Present in Aquarium

Common Name/Species Name/Code/Number of Individuals

TABLE 47-6 Behavioral Observations of _____

Behavior/Frequency/Same Species/Another Species/Nonliving

"Fill in cells." Contact your local freshwater tropical fish shop for five species that are available, thrive under the same environmental conditions, and exhibit a variety of behaviors (e.g., swim in upper water column, swim in mid water column, are bottom dwellers, hide in plants, are aggressive).

47.4 Phototaxis Experiment

6. …Are your results consistent with their results?

Typically, the group results are consistent with each other.

7. …Base your answer on the results of this experiment.

Look under stones, overlying banks and other shaded areas.

TABLE 47-7 Presence or Absence, and Direction of Phototaxis in Planarians

Predictions: If the planarians are negatively phototactic then they will turn or move away from the light.

Trial/Light Directed at Front of Head/Light Directed at Side of Head/Light Directed at Tail

"Fill in cells."

Most Common Response: **Fill in which response was most commonly observed. The planarian typically turns or moves away from the light in all situations.**

Conclusion: The prediction is accepted and the hypothesis that planarians are negatively phototactic supported.

Name _____

Section No. _____

ANIMAL BEHAVIOR

Pre-lab Questions

1. An individual who avoids light is exhibiting: a. negative phototaxis; b. positive geotaxis; c. negative thigmotaxis; d. positive thigmotaxis.

2. Braking your car after you observe a child's ball rolling into the street from between parked vehicles: a. is instinctive; b. requires a conscious decision; c. is a reflex; d. both a and b.

3. All behavior: a. has a genetic component; b. involves learning; c. requires a conscious decision; d. both a and c.

4. Learned behavior: a. has a learning component; b. has a genetic component; c. has no genetic component; d. has both a and b.

5. Behavior that is entirely controlled by genes and has no learning component is: a. learned; b. habituated; c. instinctive; d. classically conditioned.

6. Fish can exhibit behaviors that are directed to: a. members of the same species; b. members of different species; c. nonliving constituents of the environment; d. all of these choices.

7. Schooling is: a. a feeding behavior; b. fin nipping; c. fish swimming in synchrony; d. a mating behavior.

8. An individual who avoids the pull of gravity is exhibiting: a. negative phototaxis; b. positive geotaxis; c. negative geotaxis; d. positive thigmotaxis.

9. An individual who responds to walking into an obstruction by pushing into it harder is exhibiting: a. negative phototaxis; b. positive geotaxis; c. negative thigmotaxis; d. positive thigmotaxis.

10. An individual who is attracted to light is exhibiting: a. negative phototaxis; b. positive phototaxis; c. negative thigmotaxis; d. positive thigmotaxis.

ANIMAL BEHAVIOR

*Answers to Pre-lab Questions
in Lab Manual Order*

1. c	6. b
2. d	7. d
3. a	8. c
4. b	9. c
5. a	10. d

*Answers to Pre-lab Questions
in Instructor's Manual Order*

1. a	6. d
2. b	7. c
3. a	8. c
4. d	9. d
5. c	10. b

Answers to Post-lab Questions

1. Compare the contributions of genes and learning to instinctive behavior and learned behavior. **As part of development our genes preprogram instinctive behavior. Together with the basic structure and function of our bodies they form a base that allows us to gather and process information about the external environment. As we learn, we add new behavior to this base.**

2. Does all learned behavior require a conscious decision before responding to a stimulus? Explain why or why not. **No, conditioned reflexes do not require a conscious decision to initiate a response.**

3. Matching (use each answer only once)

     v   a. negative geotaxis   i. avoidance of light
     ii   b. positive geotaxis   ii. attracted to gravity
     i   c. negative phototaxis   iii. attracted to light
     iii   d. positive phototaxis   iv. avoidance of touch
     iv   e. negative thigmotaxis   v. avoidance of gravity
     vi   f. positive thigmotaxis   vi. attracted to touch

4. Does a frog need a consciousness to behave like a frog? Explain. **No. A frog without a forebrain (conscious mind) can still sit, right itself, and swim like a frog. This is because much of the basic behavior of a vertebrate animal is instinctive. Forebrain-dead patients in hospitals likewise posses behavior that we recognize as distinctly human.**

5. Although a tropical fish aquarium is at best an approximation of a natural habitat, what constituents does the aquarium share with the natural habitat that are important to understanding the behavior of a particular species? **Members of different species, members of the same species, and non-living constituents of the environment.**

6. What would you call an aquatic organism's avoidance of high concentrations of a chemical in the water? **Negative chemotaxis**

7. Look up the fight-flight response in your textbook. Describe what it is and how it is still an advantageous part of human behavior. **"Fight-flight" response refers to the reflexual "mass discharge" activation of the sympathetic division of the visceral motor pathways in response to stimuli indicating a threat or similar situation in the external environment. The release of epinephrine (adrenaline), etc., maximizes the body's ability to fight off or flee from the threat. For prehistoric humans, the sudden appearance of a saber-toothed tiger may have been the threat; for us, it could be an out-of-control vehicle heading our way.**

8. You probably have had one, if not several, pet mammals—dogs, cats, and so on. Based on your interactions with them, hypothesize as to whether they can think like humans. If you believe that they can think, how and why might their thoughts be different from ours? (Hint: Consider the differences between the language of humans and other mammals.) **Animals are obviously not as intelligent as humans and can't make conscious decisions to act in response to stimuli that require complex learning, for example, writing down the answer to a math problem. They also have no written or spoken language, but like us they do communicate non-verbally. The real questions are: Do they have conscious minds? Do they posses emotions in a human sense? Are their minds capable of combining several experiences to generate a new idea or to come up with a novel solution to a new problem? All of these questions are hard to demonstrate experimentally. Students should be able to describe fairly easily observations that suggest the former two, and may attempt to establish the latter. This creates the opportunity to discuss the dangers of anthropomorphism, while keeping an open mind to the possibilities.**

9. Search the World Wide Web for sites about animal thinking. List two sites and briefly summarize their contents. **Answers will vary.**

10. Search the World Wide Web for sites that include animal cams. List and briefly summarize the contents of two sites that you would recommend. **Answers will vary.**

GROWTH OF RCBr (WISCONSIN FAST PLANTS™)

Rapid-cycling *Brassica rapa* (RCBr's) were developed as model organisms for laboratory research and classroom study by researchers at the University of Wisconsin. The plants, relatives of the mustard, are particularly useful in the classroom because their rapid development (flowering less than two weeks after planting) and small size allows growth at high densities under artificial lights. Additionally, several genetic variants are available, which may be useful for inheritance studies.

This appendix is intended to provide you with a brief summary of conditions necessary for optimal growth of RCBr plants in the classroom. Instructors who desire more detail, as well as outlines and worksheets for additional classroom exercises, should consult the "Wisconsin Fast Plants Growing Instructions," published by Carolina Biological Supply, (see *Ordering Information*). Some information in this appendix was adapted from that source.

LIFE CYCLE

RCBr plants grow very rapidly. At 1 day after planting, the radicle has emerged; hypocotyl emerges at 2 days; the first true leaves develop by Day 5; flower buds form on Day 9, with the first flower opening on Day 13; seed is set by Day 28. Plants are allowed to dry from Day 36, and seeds may be harvested on about Day 40. Newly harvested seeds may be planted immediately to begin a new generation of plants.

GROWTH MATERIALS

The basic growing unit as purchased from Carolina Biological Supply is a reusable styrofoam four-cell "quad" designed for one plant per cell. Seeds are sown in potting mix containing slow-release fertilizer, and a wick from the bottom of each cell acts to absorb moisture from a capillary water mat over a reservoir. The quads are thus watered automatically, and water is added only to the reservoir.

Alternatively, RCBr's can be grown in discarded film canisters, as described in the preparation notes for Exercise 25, Seed Plants II: Angiosperms, An Investigative Study of the Life Cycle of Flowering Plants.

Another possibility is to grow RCBr's in APS growing trays, which are multiple-celled containers capable of growing dense populations of RCBr's in a minimum of space. The APS-40 ("Accelerated Propagation System") is a polystyrene 40-celled, open-bottomed tray with capillary matting and reservoir

included. It is available from Gardener's Supply (see *Ordering Information*).

Use of anti-algal squares in the reservoirs of the quad watering system and the APS system is recommended.

You may wish to support the stems of the growing plants with small wooden stakes if not using the note card divider pictured in the laboratory manual, Exercise 25 Seed Plants II: Angiosperms, figure 25-18, page 386.

Sterilize all materials in 10% bleach solution (10 mL bleach in 90 mL H_2O for 100 mL) for 1 hour before reusing them. Rinse thoroughly and allow to dry completely before reusing.

LIGHTING

Proper lighting is critical to rapid growth of the RCBr plants. The plants will complete their life cycle in 40 days only with **continuous** high-intensity lighting. Provide lighting from a bank of six, 4-foot cool-white fluorescent bulbs (40 watts). Height of the lights should be adjustable so that lights can remain 5 to 8 cm above the tops of the plants as they grow. Alternatively, the lights can be set at about 40 cm above the bench top, and the reservoirs raised so that the plants are 5 to 8 cm below the bulbs. Gradually lower the reservoirs as the plants grow.

If fewer than six bulbs are available, or if the light source is further than 5-8 cm from the growing tips, the plants will become somewhat etiolated, and the life cycle will be extended several days.

A light fixture kit with pre-cut and pre-drilled lumber is available from Carolina (15-8998). Also, detailed plans for building a light bank are provided in the Wisconsin Fast Plants™ Growing Instructions.

TEMPERATURE

Maintain a temperature of 21° to 27°C. Plant development may be delayed if temperature is lower. Seed germination may be prevented if temperature is lower than 15°C.

WATERING

It is critical that newly planted quads or containers of RCBr seeds be watered gently from above for the first three days after seeding in order to ensure adequate moisture for germination. After that time, sufficient water will be wicked from the capillary matting below.

SEED STORAGE

Extra RCBr seeds may be stored for one to two years if refrigerated in a sealed container containing a small amount of silica gel desiccant or powdered milk to absorb moisture. Replace powdered milk and silica gel periodically.

Do not plan to continuously grow and store seed for many generations for class use, as increasing variability in length of growing cycle and other plant characteristics will occur after a few generations.

PEST CONTROL

While insects should not be a problem in a classroom, the most common insect pest that afflicts RCBr plants are aphids, which are blown in through open windows or brought into the room on clothing. Rubbing the soft-bodied aphids off the plants is an effective control in light infestations. Insecticidal soap sprays are also effective as long as the spray contacts all of the insects. A third method will demonstrate the effects of nicotine on insects: Place a large empty **metal** trashcan inside a large plastic bag. Place infested quads in the bottom of the can, light a cigarette and place it about 7.5 cm from the quads, and close the plastic liner. The burning cigarette will release nicotine, a potent insecticide, and will fumigate the plants. After 1 to 2 hours, remove the quads and return them to their capillary matting.

Ordering Information

Wisconsin Fast Plants™ Growing Instructions	Carolina	15-8952
Wisconsin Fast Plants™ Watering System	Carolina	15-8974
watering tray	Carolina	15-8975
watering mats (two)	Carolina	15-8977
quad wicks (seventy)	Carolina	15-8978
Potting mix—1 L (or from local garden supply)	Carolina	15-8965
Quads, unit of sixteen	Carolina	15-8960
fertilizer, slow release	Carolina	15-8970
plant support stakes (sixteen)	Carolina	15-8984
dried bees, 30 g.	Carolina	15-8985
lighting system	Carolina	15-8998
rapid-cycling *Brassica rapa* seeds, fifty	Carolina	15-8804
APS-40	Gardener's	3-214
Anti-algal squares	Garden Supply	

GENETICS PROBLEMS

Monohybrid Problems with Complete Dominance

1a. b
1b. bb
1c. BB
1d. Bb
1e. 3 Black : 1 Brown

2.   cow: Hh   bull: hh

3a. 3:1
3b. Rr, Rr
3c. Rr
3d. 1 RR : 2 Rr : 1 rr
3e. 3 Red : 1 Purple

Monohybrid Problems with Incomplete Dominance

4a. 100% R^1R^2
4b. 100% pink
4c. red, pink, and white
4d. 1 R^1R^1 : 2 R^1R^2 : 1 R^2R^2

Monohybrid Problems Illustrating Codominance

5a. genotype ratio: 1 RR' : 1 R'R'   phenotype ratio: 1 roan : 1 white
5b. white offspring: RR' x R'R'; R'R' x R'R'; RR' x RR'   roan offspring: RR x R'R'; RR x RR'; RR' x R'R'

Monohybrid, Sex-linked Problems

6a. female is XX; male is XY
6b. X
6c. X or Y
6d. male

7a. X^nY
7b. 0
7c. 0

8a. 50%
8b. X^NX^n x X^nY could result in daughter with genotype of X^nX^n and she would be colorblind.

Dihybrid Problems

9a. PpDD; PpDd
9b. ppdd
9c. One p allele had to come from both father and mother; and the D allele had to come from father.

10a. 1 ppDd : 1 ppdd
10b. 1 blue-eyed, dimple-chinned : 1 blue-eyed, non-dimpled chin

11a. genotype: YyRr   phenotype: yellow seed color, round seed shape
11b. 9 yellow, round : 3 green, round : 3 yellow, wrinkled : 1 green, wrinkled

Multiple Alleles

12a. No. $I^A I^B$ x $I^A I^B \rightarrow I^A I^A$, $I^B I^B$, or $I^A I^B$, and will not yield ii.

12b. O-yes: $I^A i$ x ii $\rightarrow$ ii; A-yes: $I^A i$ x $I^A i \rightarrow$ ii; B-yes: $I^A i$ x $I^B i \rightarrow$ ii; AB-no: $I^A i$ x $I^A I^B$

Chi-Square Analysis

13a. Rr x rr $\rightarrow$ 65 red (Rr) and 49 white (rr). Expected a 1:1 phenotypic ratio of 57 red : 57 white.

13b.

Phenotype	Genotype	O	E	(O - E)	$(O - E)^2$	$(O - E)^2 / E$
Red	Rr	65	57	8	64	64/57=1.12
White	rr	49	57	-8	64	64/57=1.12
Total		114	114	0		2.24

$X^2 = 2.24$. Since 2.24 < 3.841 (from table 13-3, 1 degree of freedom), deviation is probably due to chance.

14a. RrGg x rrGg $\rightarrow$ 3 red-eyed, gray-bodied : 1 red-eyed, ebony : 3 white-eyed, gray-bodied : 1 white-eyed, ebony

14b.

Phenotype	Genotype	O	E	(O - E)	$(O - E)^2$	$(O - E)^2 / E$
red eyes, gray	R_G_	38	36	2	4	0.11
red eyes, ebony	R_gg	12	12	0	0	0
white eyes, gray	rrG_	31	36	-5	25	0.69
white eyes, ebony	rrgg	15	12	3	9	0.75
Total		96	96	0		1.55

$X^2 = 1.55$.

14 c. Since 1.55 < 7.815 (from table 13-3, with 3 degrees of freedom), observed results "fit" the expected, and variation is probably due to chance.

Carolina Biological Supply Company
2700 York Road
Burlington, NC 27215
Tel: 800-334-5551, Fax: 800-222-7112
www.carolina.com

CellServ/College Division
Foundation for Advanced Education in the Sciences, Inc.
One Cloister Court, Bethesda, MD 20814-1460
Tel: 301-496-8290, Fax: 301-402-6292
www.cellservkits.com

Environmental Monitoring Systems
3864 Leeds Avenue
Charleston, SC 29405
Tel: 800-293-3003, Fax: 866-724-5702
www.emssales.net

Films for the Humanities & Sciences, Inc.
P.O. Box 2053
Princeton, NJ 08543-2053
Tel: 800-257-5126, Fax: 609-671-0266
www.films.com

Fisher Scientific
711 Forbes Avenue
Pittsburgh, PA 15219
Tel: 800-766-7000, Fax: 800-926-1166
www.fishersci.com

Forestry Suppliers, Inc.
205 W. Rankin St.
P.O. Box 8397
Jackson, MS 39284-8397
Tel: 800-647-5368, Fax: 800-543-4203
www.forestry-suppliers.com

Gardener's Supply
128 Intervale Road
Burlington, VT 05401-2804
Tel: 888-833-1412
www.gardeners.com

Girard Nurseries
6839 N. Ridge East
P.O. Box 428, Geneva, OH 44041
Tel: 440-466-2881
(for *Pinus edulis* seed)
www.girardnurseries.com

Hach Company
P. O. Box 389
Loveland, CO 80539-0389
Tel: 800-227-4224, Fax: 970-669-2932
www.hach.com

Kemtech
P.O. Box 5826
Whittier, CA 90607
Tel: 800-472-1658, Fax: 800-215-5552
www.kemtech-america.com

New England Biolabs, Inc.
240 County Road
Ipswich, MA 01938-2723
Tel: 978-927-5054, Fax: 978-921-1350
www.neb.com

Rosco Laboratories, Inc.
52 Harbor View,
Stamford, CT 06902
Tel: 800-767-2669, Fax: 203-708-8919
www.rosco.com/us/index.asp

Sigma Chemical Company
P.O. Box 14508
St. Louis, MO 63178-9916
Tel: 800-325-3010, Fax: 800-325-5025
www.sigmaaldrich.com

Triarch Incorporated
P.O. Box 98
Ripon, WI 54971-0098
Tel: 800-848-0810, Fax: 888-848-0810
www.triarchmicroslides.com

VWR Scientific
1310 Goshen Parkway
West Chester, PA 19380
Tel: 800-932-5000, Fax: 866-329-2897
www.vwrsp.com

Ward's Natural Science.
5100 West Henrietta Road
P.O. Box 92912
Rochester, NY 14692-9012
Tel: 800-962-2660, Fax: 716-334-6174
www.wardsci.com